GCSE PHYSICS for CCEA

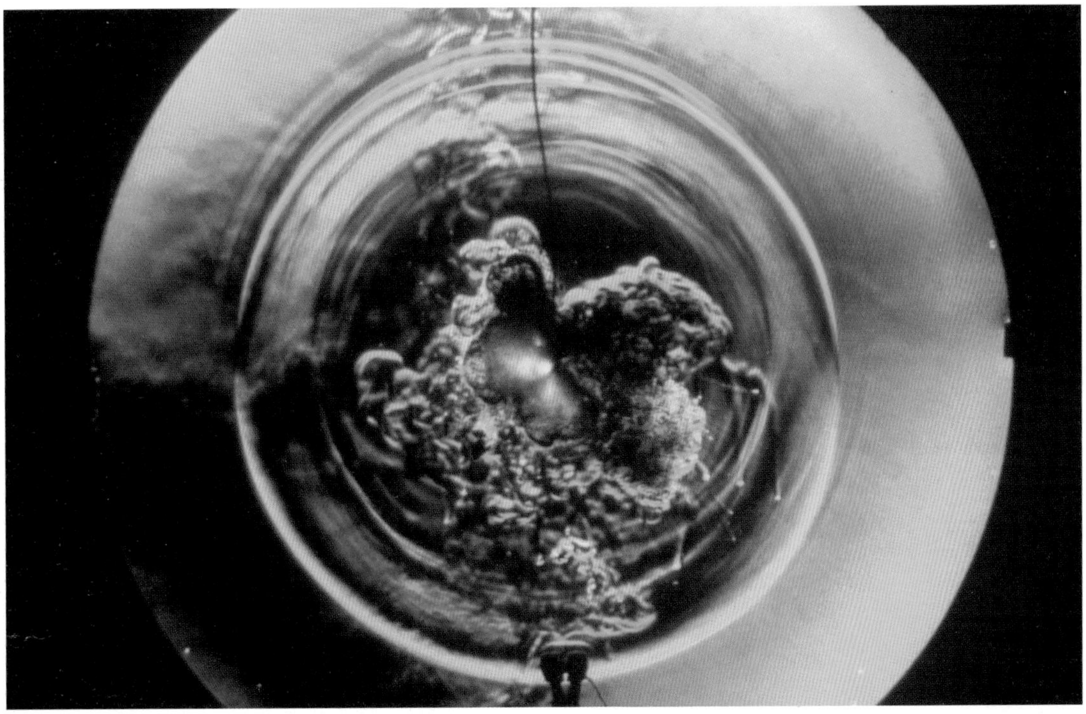

Frank McCauley
Roy White

HODDER EDUCATION
AN HACHETTE UK COMPANY

Photo acknowledgements

The publishers would like to thank the following individuals, institutions and companies for permission to reproduce photographs in this book. Every effort has been made to trace ownership of copyright. The publishers would be happy to make arrangements with any copyright holder whom it has not been possible to contact:

Andrew Lambert (115, 124 all); Associated Press/Saurabh Das (104 top, 150); Corbis Firefly Productions (133 bottom right)/Joe McBride (41)/Kevin R Morris (59 left)/Robin Adshead; The Military Picture Library (18); De Walt (147); Empics (54); Hodder (133 bottom left); Life File (133 top two, 142 bottom); NASA (185); National Grid (152); PA Photos (42)/AFP Elex De La Rosa (112 middle)/David Davies (78); Rex (59 right); Science Photo Library (154)/Alex Bartel (142 top)/BSIP, Cavallini James (103)/Chris Butler (77)/Chris Knapton (113)/Cordelia Molloy (104 bottom)/David Parker (112 top)/Detlev Van Ravenswaay (76 right)/European Space Agency (76 left)/Eye of Science (167)/Hank Morgan (166 bottom) Kaj R Svensson (76 middle)/Kent Wood (112 bottom)/Mark Burnett (26)/Martin F Chillmaid (133 bottom middle)/Martin Dohrn (166 top)/NASA (186 top)/Space Telescope Science Institute, NASA (186 bottom)/Tony and Daphne Hallas (18)/Zephyr (90).

Orders: please contact Bookpoint Ltd, 130 Milton Park, Abingdon, Oxon OX14 4SB.
Telephone: (44) 01235 827720. Fax: (44) 01235 400454. Lines are open from 9.00–5.00, Monday to Saturday, with a 24-hour message answering service. You can order through our website www.hoddereducation.co.uk.

British Library Cataloguing in Publication Data
A catalogue record for this title is available from the British Library

ISBN-13: 978 0 340 85899 8

First Published 2003
Impression number 10 9
Year 2009

Cover photo from Science Photo Library

Typeset by Tech-Set Limited, Gateshead, Tyne and Wear

Printed in Italy for Hodder Education, an Hachette UK Company,
338 Euston Road, London NW1 3BH

Contents

Preface

The GCSE Science for CCEA series comprises of three books: *GCSE Biology for CCEA*, *GCSE Chemistry for CCEA*, and *GCSE Physics for CCEA*, which together cover all aspects of the material needed for students following the CCEA GCSE specifications in:

- Science: Double Award (Modular)
- Science: Double Award (Non-Modular)
- Science: Biology
- Science: Chemistry
- Science: Physics

GCSE Physics for CCEA covers all the material relating to the physics component of the CCEA Science Double Award (Modular and Non-Modular), together with the additional material required for the CCEA Science: Physics specification.

Frank McCauley and Roy White are both physics teachers and examiners with CCEA.

Identifying Specification and Tier

The material required for each specification and tier is clearly identified using the following colour code:

Material required for foundation tier students following either the Science Double Award (Modular and Non-Modular) or the Science: Physics specifications is identified by a blue line running down the left-hand side of the text.

Material required for higher tier students following either the Science Double Award (Modular and Non-Modular) or the Science: Physics specifications is identified by text with a blue tinted background.

Material required for foundation tier students following the Science: Physics specification is identified by a yellow line running down the left-hand side of the text.

Material required for higher tier students following the Science: Physics specification is identified by text with a yellow tinted background.

Scientific Investigation

During your course you will be required to carry out a number of scientific investigations. You will need to provide a written report which focuses on the following three skills:

1 Planning – Here you will need to write about what you intend to do. You will need to think clearly about what you are planning to investigate and what apparatus you will need. You will also need to use your scientific knowledge and understanding to plan a procedure, identifying key factors that will need to be either varied, controlled or considered. In addition you will need to make a prediction about what you think your investigation will demonstrate and to justify your prediction. Finally you will need to outline a strategy for dealing with your results.

2 Obtaining evidence – Here you will need to demonstrate that you can collect and record evidence in an accurate and systematic way. Your teacher will want to be sure that you are working safely and that you have checked and repeated your work where necessary. To gain the highest possible marks you will need to demonstrate that you can carry out the work skilfully, and can obtain and record an appropriate range of reliable evidence.

3 Interpreting and evaluating – In this skill area you need to use diagrams, charts or graphs as the basis for explaining the evidence that you have collected. You will be expected to use numerical methods, such as averaging, where necessary. Your teacher will want to be sure that you can draw a valid conclusion, which is consistent with your evidence, and that draws on your knowledge and understanding. In addition you will need to explain the extent to which your conclusion supports the prediction you made in your plan. Finally you will need to consider the reliability of your evidence and whether your procedure could have been improved. Is there enough evidence to support your conclusion? Are there any strange results, and if so can you explain how they arose?

Chapter 1

Energy

Learning objectives

By the end of this chapter you should know:

- The difference between energy forms and energy resources
- How to define the Law of Conservation of Energy
- How to describe energy transfers in terms of energy flow diagrams
- The main energy resources used by mankind
- The energy issues associated with electricity production
- How to calculate the work done by a force
- How to calculate power using an equation
- How to measure personal power
- How to calculate the efficiency with which energy is transferred
- How to calculate kinetic and gravitational potential energy
- The three main ways in which heat is transferred
- That most solids, liquids and gases expand when heated and some practical applications of expansion

Energy forms

It is important to understand the difference between **energy forms** and **energy resources**. Energy forms are the different ways in which energy can appear, such as heat energy, light energy and chemical energy. Energy resources are the different ways of supplying a particular energy form. Table 1 summarises some of the main energy forms.

Table 1

Energy form	Definition	Examples of resources
Chemical	The energy stored within a substance which is released on burning.	coal, oil, natural gas, peat (turf), wood, food
Gravitational potential	The energy a body contains as a result of its height above the ground.	stored energy in the dam (reservoir) of a hydroelectric power station
Kinetic	The energy of a moving object.	wind, waves, tides
Nuclear	The energy which is stored in the nucleus of an atom.	uranium, plutonium

Other common energy forms are heat, light, sound, magnetic energy and strain potential energy – the energy a body has when it has been stretched or squeezed out of shape and will return to its original shape when the force is removed, such as a wind-up toy.

One of the fundamental laws of physics is the **Law of Conservation of Energy**. This states that:

Energy can neither be created nor destroyed, but it can change its form.

We can show energy changes in an **energy flow diagram**.

What energy changes take place when we strike a match?

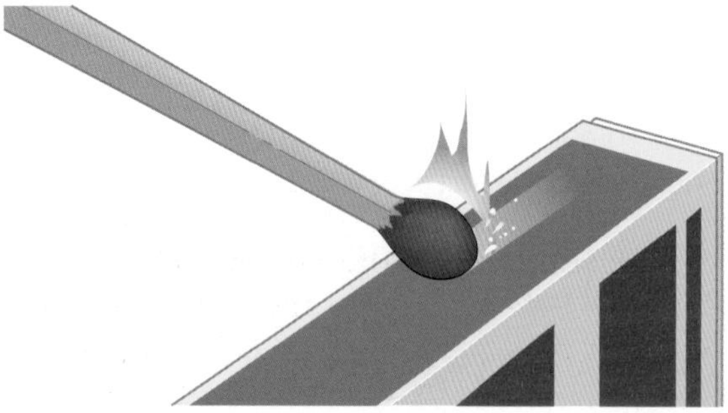

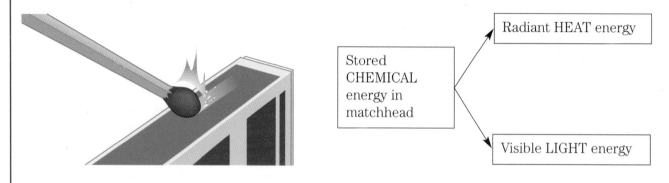

Stored CHEMICAL energy in matchhead → Radiant HEAT energy

Stored CHEMICAL energy in matchhead → Visible LIGHT energy

What energy changes take place when a boy stretches a catapult?

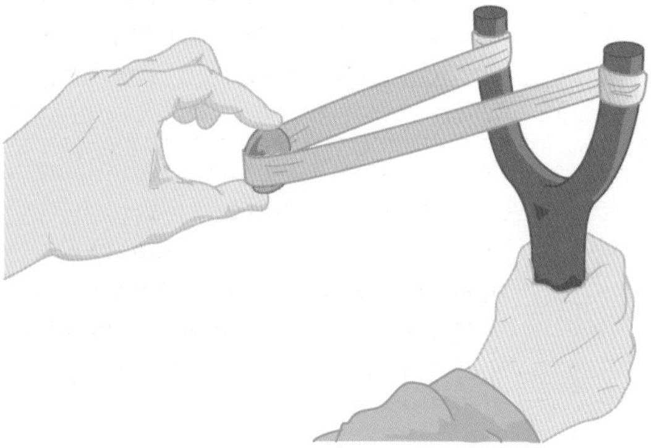

CHEMICAL energy in the boy's body from food → KINETIC energy in stretching the elastic cord

KINETIC energy in stretching the elastic cord → Wasted HEAT energy in the elastic cord

KINETIC energy in stretching the elastic cord → Useful STRAIN POTENTIAL ENERGY in the elastic cord

What energy changes take place when we ring an electric bell?

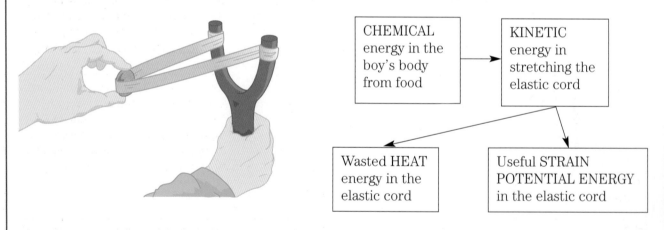

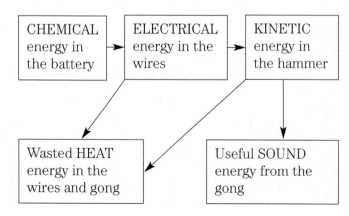

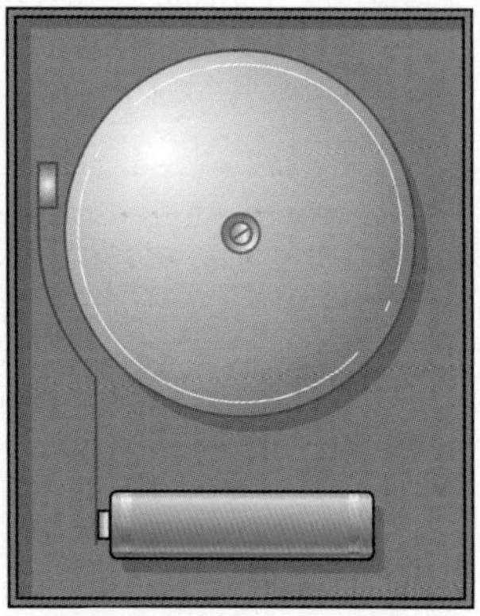

CHEMICAL energy in the battery → ELECTRICAL energy in the wires → KINETIC energy in the hammer

ELECTRICAL energy in the wires → Wasted HEAT energy in the wires and gong

KINETIC energy in the hammer → Wasted HEAT energy in the wires and gong

KINETIC energy in the hammer → Useful SOUND energy from the gong

Energy resources

Energy resources can be classified in several different ways. One way is to split them into renewable and non-renewable resources. **Renewable resources** are those that are replaced by nature in less than a human lifetime. **Non-renewable resources** are those that are used faster than they can be replaced by nature. The government has said that 10% of our energy need must come from renewable resources by 2010.

Renewable resource	Comment
Solar cells 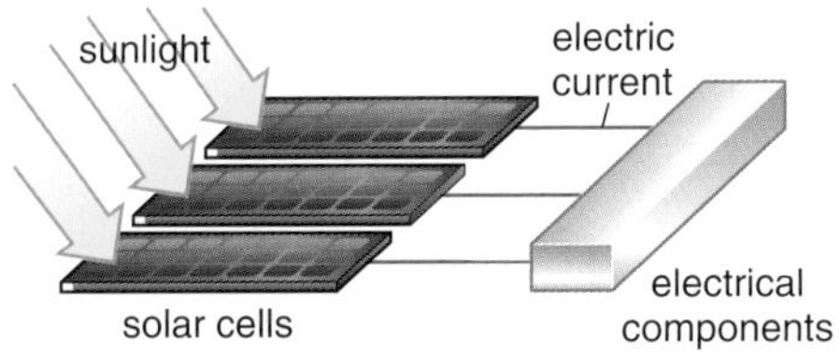 	Solar cells convert sunlight **(solar energy)** directly into electricity. Solar cells are joined together into arrays.
Hydroelectric power stations 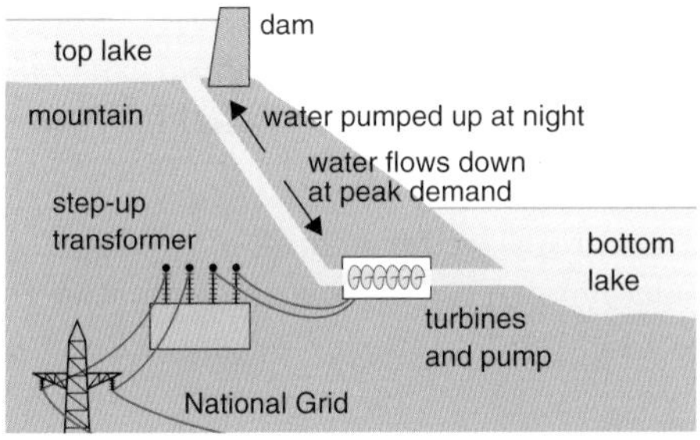 	Because of its height from the ground, water in a dam (reservoir) contains **gravitational potential energy**. The water is allowed to fall from the dam through a pipe and gains **kinetic energy** as it falls. The fast-flowing water falls on a **turbine**, which then drives a **generator**. The output from the generator is **electrical energy**. Some **hydroelectric power stations** use **pumped storage** reservoirs. At times of low demand, such as in the early hours of the morning, the power station buys cheap electricity and uses it to pump water up to a high reservoir. During the day, when demand is high, they sell the electricity they produce at a higher price.
Tidal barrages 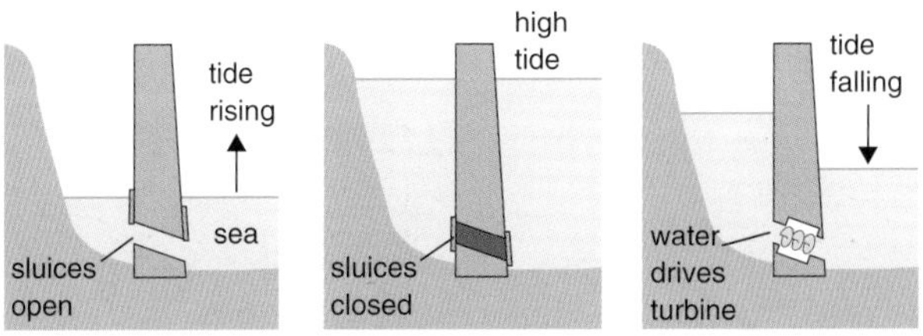 	A **tidal barrage** is created when a dam is built across a river estuary. As the tide rises and falls every 12 hours, provided the water levels on each side of the dam are not equal, water will flow through a gate in the dam. The moving water drives a turbine, which is made to turn a generator. The output from the generator is electrical energy.
Wave machines 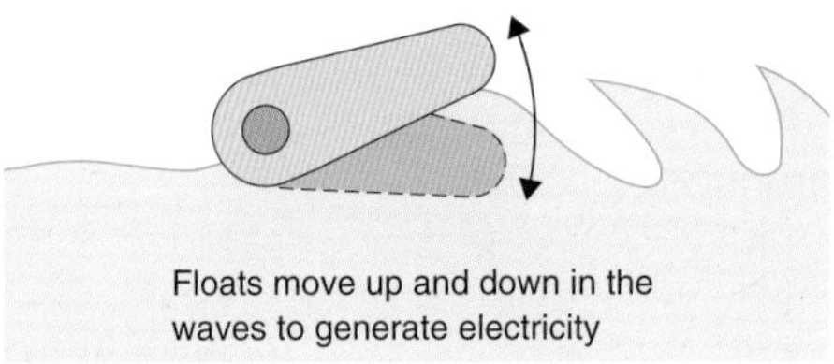 	Waves are produced largely by the action of the wind on the surface of water. The **wave machine** floats on the surface of the water and the up and down motion of the water forces air to drive a turbine and so produces electricity.
Wind turbines 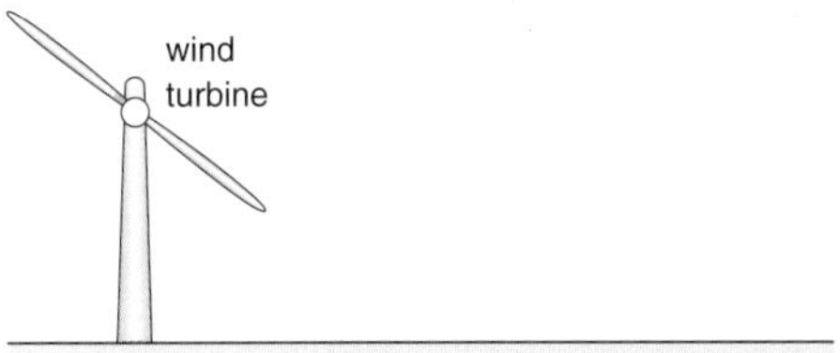 	As the wind blows, the large blade turns and this drives a turbine. The turbine drives a generator, which in turn produces electricity. Large numbers of turbines are often grouped together to form a **wind farm**.

<table>
<tr><th>Renewable resource</th><th>Comment</th></tr>
<tr><td>Geothermal energy
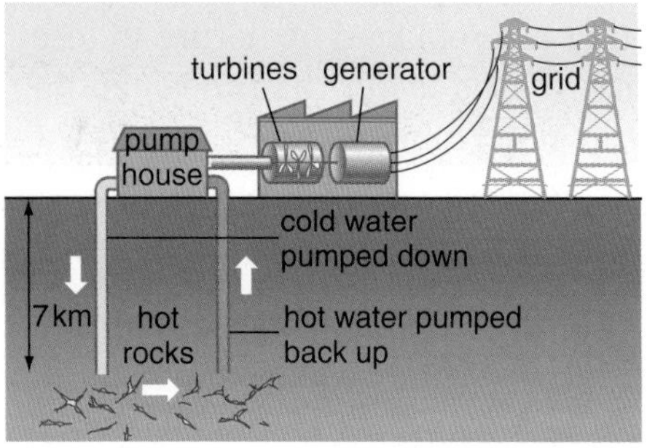</td><td>Geothermal power stations use heat from the hot rocks deep inside the Earth. Cold water is passed down a pipe to the rocks. The water is heated by these rocks and the hot water is then pumped to the surface. Geothermal energy is often used to save fossil fuels in power stations or in district heating schemes.</td></tr>
<tr><td>Biomass
</td><td>Fast-growing trees, like willow, are grown on poor-quality land (or land set-aside from food production) and the timber is harvested around every three years. The wood is dried and turned into woodchips which are then burned in power stations to produce electricity or sold for solid fuel heating.

Other forms of biomass include oilseed rape. The oil from the seeds is converted into biodiesel for road transport.

In Brazil, biomass crops are fermented to produce alcohol. The alcohol can be used as an alternative to petrol as a way of extending the life of scarce fossil fuels.</td></tr>
</table>

<table>
<tr><th>Non-renewable resource</th><th>Comment</th></tr>
<tr><td>Fossil fuels – coal, oil, natural gas
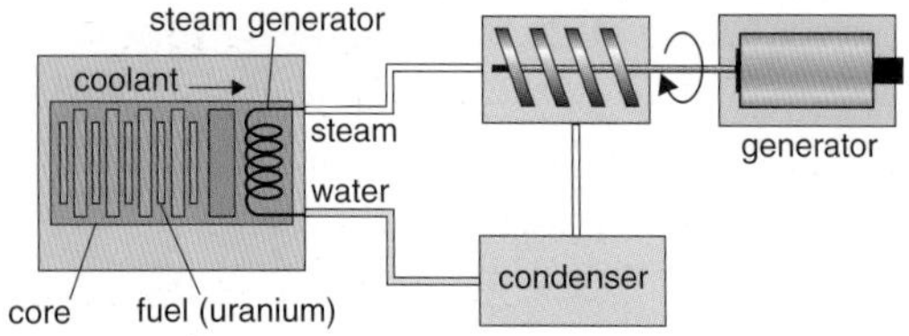</td><td>The fuel is burned in a power station to produce steam which drives a turbine. The turbine turns a generator to produce electricity.</td></tr>
<tr><td>Nuclear power stations (uranium fission)
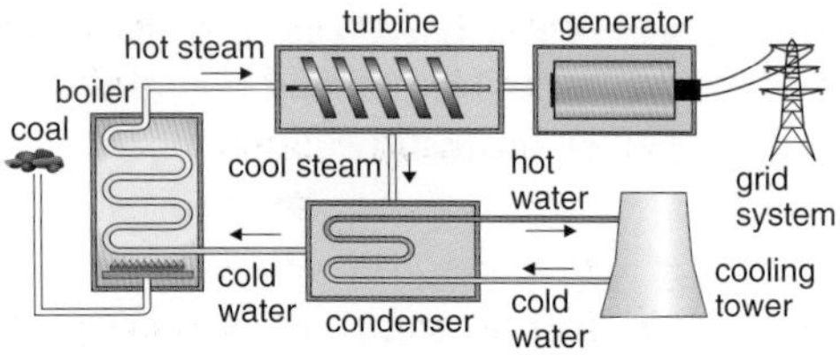</td><td>Uranium nuclei in a reactor split into lighter nuclei (nuclear fission) with the release of very large amounts of kinetic energy. This is used to produce steam, which drives a turbine. The turbine turns a generator to produce electricity.</td></tr>
</table>

Did you know?

The Dinorwig pumped storage hydroelectric power station in Wales uses as much water in 90 minutes as London uses in 24 hours. Because it is in Snowdonia, an area of exceptional natural beauty, all electricity cables from the station are underground, rather than hanging from pylons.

Advantages and disadvantages of using the different energy resources to generate electricity

Energy resource	Advantage	Disadvantage	Other comments
Fossil fuels – coal, oil, natural gas, lignite, turf	● Relatively cheap to start up. ● Moderately expensive to run. ● Large world reserves of fossil fuels.	● All fossil fuels release carbon dioxide on burning and so contribute to greenhouse emissions. ● Burning coal and oil also releases sulphur dioxide gas, which causes acid rain. To combat this the sulphur can be removed from fuels before they are burned, or the sulphur dioxide can be removed from the waste gases (scrubbing) before they enter the atmosphere. ● All fossil fuels are non-renewable. ● As most fossil fuels are burned to produce steam (a slow process), the system responds only very slowly to changes in electrical demand.	● Coal releases the most carbon dioxide and natural gas the least per unit of electricity produced. ● Removing sulphur or sulphur dioxide is very expensive and adds greatly to the cost of electricity production. ● Coal- and oil-fired power stations must be kept running all the time. The furnaces are seriously damaged if they cool down. ● Some gas-powered stations can be switched on and off as required. ● The process is about 30% efficient.
Nuclear fuels – mainly uranium	● Do not produce greenhouse gases like carbon dioxide. ● Do not emit gases which cause acid rain. ● Usually emit very few radioactive materials into the environment.	● The waste products will remain dangerously radioactive for tens of thousands of years. As yet, no one has found an acceptable method to store these materials cheaply, safely and securely for such a long time. ● An accident could release dangerous radioactive material which would contaminate a very wide area. ● Nuclear fission fuels are non-renewable. ● As nuclear fuels are all used to produce steam (a slow process), the system responds only very slowly to changes in electrical demand.	● Nuclear fuel is relatively cheap on world markets. ● Nuclear power station construction costs are much higher than fossil fuel stations, because of the need to take expensive safety precautions. ● Decommissioning – shutting down the power station at the end of its useful life, safely removing the dangerous radioactive waste and returning the site to its former state – is extremely expensive. ● Nuclear power stations must be kept running all the time. ● The processs is about 30% efficient.

Energy resource	Advantage	Disadvantage	Other comments
Wind	● A renewable energy resource. ● Low running costs.	Wind farms can be: ● unsightly (visual pollution) ● very noisy ● hazardous to birds ● unreliable (wind strength is highly variable).	● Modern wind farms have an efficiency of about 40%. ● Unable to respond to changes in electrical demand.
Tides	● A renewable energy resource. ● Low running costs.	Tidal barrages are built across river estuaries and can cause: ● navigation problems for shipping ● destruction of habitats for wading birds and the mud-living organisms on which they feed.	● Tides are predictable, but they vary from day to day and month to month. ● This makes them unsuitable for producing a constant daily amount of electrical energy.
Solar cells and solar arrays	● A renewable energy resource. ● Low running costs. ● Useful where only small amounts of electricity are needed (e.g. calculators).	● Solar cells produce only tiny amounts of electricity. ● They are used where there are very few alternatives (e.g. to produce electric energy in spacecraft) and where the high cost is acceptable.	● A very long pay-back time (20 years). ● Unreliable, because they depend on the amount of sunlight falling on them – this changes with the time of day, the season of the year and the weather. ● A typical solar array is 15% efficient.
Hydroelectric power	● A renewable energy resource. ● Low running costs. ● Can be made very efficient if operated in reverse at night as a pumped storage station, using cheap power from other stations.	Many hydroelectric schemes involve the flooding of river valleys. This can cause: ● problems of relocating people ● destruction of habitats for many animal and plant species.	● Very reliable. ● Very quick to respond to changes in electrical demand – the operators need only increase or decrease the rate of water flow to the turbines. ● Suitable mainly for hilly areas with reliable rainfall.

Ireland's natural fuel resources

Ireland has almost no coal or oil resources. The island is rich in turf (peat), but it is important not to over-exploit these resources industrially because of the damage that can be done to habitat. Ireland does however have an important fossil fuel resource – natural gas from the Celtic Sea. Northern Ireland has another resource – lignite. This is sometimes called **brown coal** because it is rocky like coal, but brown like peat. There are millions of tonnes of lignite reserves around Crumlin and under Lough Neagh. Lignite has almost no sulphur, but is about 50% water by weight.

Questions

1 Most of Ireland's energy needs are supplied by fossil fuels. Name three fossil fuels.

2 Make a copy of the table below and tick (✓) those items which are energy forms.

Quantity	Tick if the quantity is a form of energy
Sound	
Pressure	
Force	
Weight	
Electricity	
Heat	

3 The table below shows six energy resources. Copy the table and tick (✓) the correct boxes to show whether these resources are renewable or non-renewable.

Energy source	Renewable?	Non-renewable?
Gas		
Hydroelectricity		
Oil		
Coal		
Wind		
Tides		

4 A model aircraft has its wings covered with solar panels to drive the propellers and charge the battery. Copy and complete the following sentences to show the energy changes which take place in such an aircraft:

The solar cells change __________ energy into __________ energy. The battery stores __________ energy. As the propellers turn they change __________ energy into useful __________ energy. As the model aircraft gains height, it gains __________ energy. The model aircraft crashes into the ground. As it does so, it produces wasted heat and __________ energy.

5 Why are all power stations in the British Isles built on the coast or close to rivers? (Hint: What is the water used for?)

6 In what ways is the production of electricity in a fossil fuel power station and in a nuclear power station similar? In what ways are these power stations different?

7 Currently nuclear waste is vitrified (turned into a type of glass), stored in strong metal drums and kept deep underground. Why is this an unsatisfactory solution for the long term?

Did you know?

German people are encouraged to install arrays of solar cells on the roof of their homes to produce electricity. Germans can sell the energy to the electricity supplier for about 30 pence a unit. They can then buy the electricity for domestic use at about 10 pence per unit. So the more electricity they can make from solar cells, the less money they have to pay in their bill. But there is a catch – the pay-back time for an array of solar cells is about 20 years!

8 Name the two polluting gases produced by the majority of coal- and oil-burning power stations.

9 Norway has complained that Britain is partly responsible for the destruction of the Norwegian habitat by acid rain. How might this have come about?

10 What are the arguments for and against installing a nuclear power station in Ireland?

11 Imagine you are a government scientist. Write about 100 words giving the advantages of having a nuclear power station rather than one which burns fossil fuels.

12 Why do you think Northern Ireland has not yet mined the lignite resources around Crumlin?

13 Do you think the government's target to have 10% of our electricity production from renewable resources by 2010 is realistic? What can you and your family do to contribute?

14 Explain why so much money and effort are being put into research into renewable forms of energy. Could this money be better spent on other energy forms? Give the reasons for your opinions.

15 The electricity companies say that electricity is a 'clean' fuel. Why is this statement misleading?

The Sun

Almost all energy resources ultimately rely on the energy of the Sun. In the case of fossil fuels we know that these resources come from the dead remains of plants and animals laid down many millions of years ago. Under the Earth's surface, these remains slowly fossilised into coal, peat, gas and oil. But other processes also rely on the Sun's energy. Hydroelectric energy depends on the water cycle, and this process begins when ocean water evaporates as a result of absorbing radiant energy from the Sun. Wind and waves rely on the Earth's weather, which is largely controlled by the Sun. Only geothermal and nuclear energy do not depend directly on the energy emitted by the Sun.

Did you know?

Nuclear fusion is the joining of light hydrogen nuclei to produce helium with the release of vast quantities of energy. The reaction temperature is over 15 000 000 °C. Fusion is the reaction that occurs in the Sun. So far, man has been unable to control fusion on Earth.

Work

Work is only done when a **force** causes **movement**. So although pushing against a wall might make a person tired, no work is done because it produces no movement. Similarly, holding a book at arm's length is doing no work. But, lifting a book from the floor and placing it on a table is doing work because we are applying a force and producing movement.

We can calculate work using the following formula:

> Work done = Force × Distance moved in direction of force
>
> Or
>
> W = F × d

The units in this formula are matched. Force must *always* be measured in **newtons**, but if the distance were in cm, the work would be in Ncm. If the distance were in metres, the work would be in Nm. The Nm occurs so often that physicists have renamed it the **joule** (J).

It is easiest to remember:

W = Fd
W = Work in joules
F = Force in newtons
d = Distance moved in m

Doing work means spending **energy**. The more work a person does, the more energy they need. The energy used is equal to the amount of work done.

Examples

1 How much work is done when a packing case is dragged 4 m across the floor against a frictional force of 45 N? How much energy is needed?

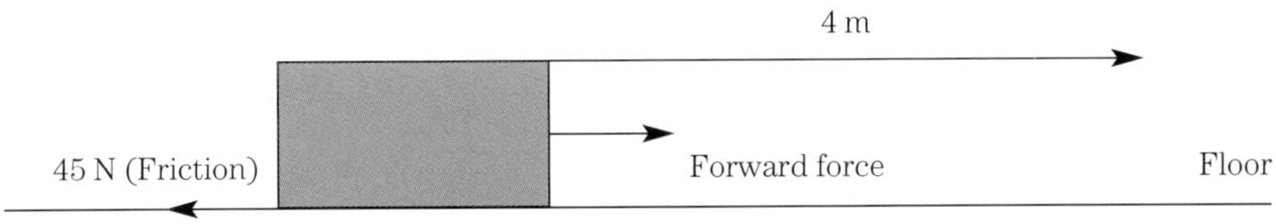

Since the case moves at a steady speed, the forward force must be the same size as the friction force. So the forward force is 45 N.

So work done = F × d = 45 × 4 = 180 J

Energy needed = Work done = **180 J**

2 A crane does 1200 J of useful work when it lifts a load vertically by 60 cm. Find the weight of the load.

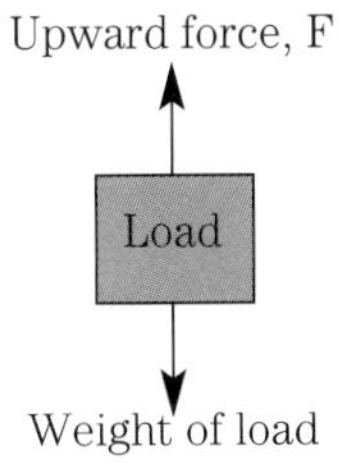

Since the load is being lifted, the minimum upward force is the weight of the load. So,

W = F × d
1200 = F × 0.6 (convert 60 cm to 0.6 m)
F = 1200/0.6 = 2000 N
So, weight of load = **2000 N**

3 How much work is done by an electric motor pulling a 130 N load 6.5 m up the slope shown in the diagram if the constant tension in the string is 60 N.

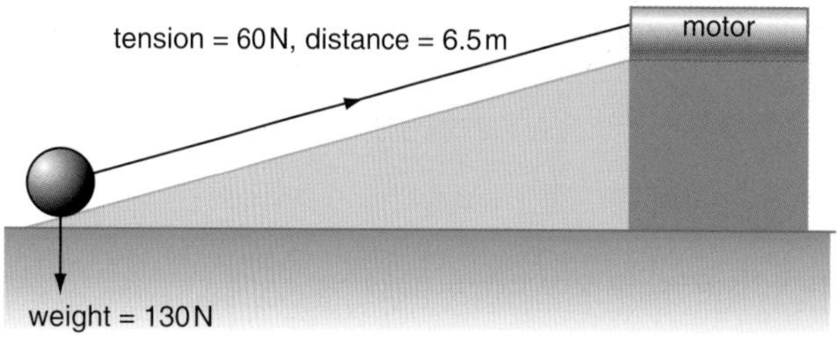

Since the tension force and distance moved are both parallel to the slope, they are both used to find the work done. The weight of the load is not used in this question.

Work = Force × Distance moved in direction of the force = 60 × 6.5 = **390 J**

Work and energy

Energy is the *ability* to do work. So if a machine has 500 J of stored energy, this means it can do 500 J of work. Note that both work and energy are measured in joules.

Example

A battery stores 15 kJ of energy. If the battery is used to drive an electric motor, how high could it raise a 750 kg load if it was lifted vertically?

The battery stores 15 kJ or 15 000 J, so it can do a maximum of 15 000 J of work.

Since a mass of 1 kg weighs 10 N, a mass of 750 kg has a weight of 7500 N. So the motor must produce an upward force of at least 7500 N.

$$W = F \times d$$
$$15\,000 = 7500 \times d$$
$$d = 15\,000/7500 = \mathbf{2\ m}$$

Note that 2 m is the highest that this motor could raise the load. This is because some of the energy in the battery is used to produce heat and sound. In our calculation, we have assumed that *all* the energy in the battery is used to do work against gravity.

Power

Power is the *rate* of doing work. This means that the power of a machine is the work it can do in a second. The formula for calculating power is therefore:

Power = Work done/Time taken
Or
P = W/t

Work is measured in joules and time is measured in seconds, so power must be measured in joules/second or J/s. But the J/s was renamed the **watt** in honour of James Watt, the famous Scottish engineer.

Examples

1 An electric motor is used to raise a load of 105 N. The load rises vertically 2 m in a time of 6 s. Find the work done and the power of the motor.

Work done = Force × Distance = 105 × 2 = 210 J
Power = Work done/Time taken = 210/6 = **35 W**

2 A crane has a power of 2000 W. How much work could it do in an hour?

In power calculations, the unit of time is the second.
So first convert 1 hour to seconds:
1 hour = 60 minutes = 60 × 60 seconds = 3600 seconds

Power = Work done/Time taken
2000 = Work done/3600
Work done = 2000 × 3600 = **7 200 000 J** or **7.2 MJ**

3 A person weighing 550 N runs up the stairs in 3 seconds. The stairs are made of 15 steps each of 14 cm height. Find the person's average power.

Total vertical height = 15 × 14 cm = 210 cm = 2.10 m
Work done = Force × Distance = 550 × 2.10 = 1155 J
Power = Work done/Time taken = 1155/3 = **385 W**

Measuring personal power

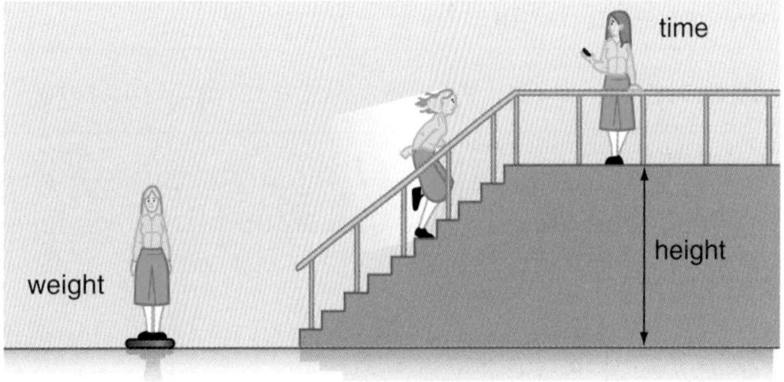

Figure 1 How to measure personal power

To measure personal power, you need to find out how long it takes you to do a given amount of work.

First, find your weight in newtons. The easy way to do this is to find your mass in kilos using bathroom scales, and then use the fact that 1 kg has a weight of 10 N.

Then you need to find the height of a staircase. This can be done by measuring the average height of a riser (stair) and multiplying by the number of risers in the staircase.

Finally, you need to have someone who will time you as you run up the stairs!

Below are typical results:

Measurements	
Mass of student in kg	45
Weight of student in N	450
Height of risers in cm	14.0, 13.8, 13.8, 14.0, 13.9
Average riser height in cm	13.9
Number of risers	30
Staircase height	13.9 × 30 = 417 cm = 4.17 m
Time to run upstairs in s	5.0
Calculations	
Work done	Work = Force × Distance = 450 × 4.17 = 1876.5 J
Power	Power = Work/Time 1876.5/5.0 = **375 W** (approx.)

This figure of 375 W is typical of an average GCSE student. But note that the student could not keep up this power for more than a few seconds. In fact, the average adult has a sustained power of only about 75 W.

Did you know?

The 18th-century engineer James Watt wanted to sell his steam engines to mine owners. At that time pit ponies were used extensively underground to haul coal. Watt wanted to compare the power of these ponies with the power of his engines. Comparison was necessary to convince the mine owners that his engines could do more work every hour than their ponies could. His unit of power was called the 'horsepower'. One horsepower is about 750 watts.

Efficiency

Efficiency is a way of describing how good a device is at transferring energy from one form to another in an intended way.

If a light bulb is rated 100 W, this means that it normally uses 100 J of electrical energy every second. But it might only produce 5 J of light energy every second. The other 95 J are wasted as heat. This means that only 5% of the energy is transferred from electrical energy into light energy. This light bulb therefore has an efficiency of 0.05 or 5%. If the same light bulb were used as a heater, its efficiency would be 95%, because the intended output energy form would be heat, not light.

Efficiency is defined by the formula:

Efficiency = Useful energy output/Total energy input

As efficiency is a ratio, it has no units. Since energy is wasted in every physical process the efficiency of a machine is *always* less than 1.

Examples

1 An electric kettle is rated 2500 W. It produces 2500 J of heat energy every second. The kettle takes 160 seconds to boil some water and during this time 360 000 J of heat energy pass into the water. Find the kettle's efficiency.

Useful energy output (passed into water) = 360 000 J
Total energy input = 2500×160 = 400 000 J
Efficiency = Useful energy output/Total energy input = 360 000/400 000
= **0.9**

So:

- 90% of the electrical energy is used to boil the water.
- 10% of the energy supplied is wasted. Most will be passed through the kettle as wasted heat to the surrounding air. A small amount of heat will be lost as some water evaporates.

2 A motor rated 40 W lifts a load of 80 N to a height of 90 cm in 4 s. Find its efficiency.

Useful energy output = Work done by motor
= Force × Distance
= $80 \times 0.9 = 72$ J

Power = Energy supplied/Time taken
40 = Energy supplied/4
So, Total energy input = $40 \times 4 = 160$ J

Efficiency = Useful energy output/Total energy input
= 72/160 = **0.45**

Did you know?

In the 19th and 20th centuries, many people tried to make perpetual motion machines. The creators hoped these machines would work forever without the continued addition of energy. Sadly, they did not take friction into account. Friction can never be completely eliminated and always causes waste heat or sound. As a result, perpetual motion machines are all doomed to fail.

Gravitational potential energy

When any object with mass is lifted, work is done on it against the force of **gravity**. The greater the mass of the object and the higher it is lifted, the more work has to be done. The work that is done is only possible because some energy has been used. This energy is stored in the object as gravitational potential energy.

When the object is released, it falls back to Earth and the stored energy can be recovered. If the object crashes into the ground, a bang (sound energy) is heard and heat is produced.

Gravitational potential energy = Work done raising load mass (m), against the force of gravity (g), through height (h)
= Weight of mass m × Gravity N/kg × height
= mgh

Gravitational potential energy = mgh

where: m is the mass in kg
g is the gravitational field strength in N/kg
(On Earth g is approximately 10 N/kg)
h is the vertical height in m

In CCEA Science: Double Award and GCSE Science: Physics examinations it is important to remember that 1 kg has a weight of 10 N on Earth. This is just another way of saying that the gravitational field strength, g, on Earth is 10 N/kg. Remember also, however, that the value of g is different at different parts of the Universe. For example, g on the Moon is only about $\frac{1}{6}$th of its value on Earth, approximately 1.6 N/kg.

Examples

1 Find the gravitational potential energy of a mass of 500 grams when raised to a height of 240 cm. Take g = 10 N/kg.
(Note that 500 grams is 0.5 kg and 240 cm is 2.4 m.)
GPE = mgh = 0.5 × 10 × 2.4 = **12J**

2 How much heat and sound energy is produced when a mass of 1.2 kg falls to the ground from a height of 5 m? Take g = 10 N/kg.
Heat and sound energy produced = Original GPE = mgh = 1.2 × 10 × 5 = **60 J**

3 How much gravitational potential energy is stored in the reservoir of a hydroelectric power station if it holds 5 000 000 kg water at an average height of 80 m above the turbines? Take g = 10 N/kg.
GPE = mgh = 5 000 000 × 10 × 80 = **4 000 000 000 J** (or 4×10^9 J)

4 A marble of mass 50 g falls to the Earth. At the moment of impact its kinetic energy is 1 J. From what height did it fall?
GPE = mgh = 1
1 = (50/1000) × 10 × h
(Note the division by 1000 to convert grams to kg)
1 = 0.5 h
h = **2 m**

5 A book of mass 500 g has a gravitational potential energy of 3.2 J when at a height of 4 m above the surface of the Moon. Find the gravitational field strength on the Moon.

$$GPE = mgh = 3.2$$
$$3.2 = 0.5 \times g \times 4 = 2g$$
$$g = 3.2/2 = \mathbf{1.6\ N/kg}$$

Examiner's tip

In all calculations of this type, first write down the appropriate formula, then make the substitutions, and finally carry out the calculations and give your final answer with its unit. Remember, showing your work is always to your benefit. If you make a mistake, the examiner can still give you credit for what you get right!

Questions

16 Competitors in the World's Strongest Man competition must throw a cement block of mass 100 kg over a wall 5.5 m high. How much work is done if the block just clears the top of the wall?

17 A man pushes a lawn mower with a force of 60 N. How much work does he do when he pushes the lawn mower 20 m?

18 The electrical energy used by a boiler is 1000 kJ. The useful output energy is 750 kJ.

a) Calculate the efficiency of the boiler.
b) Suggest what might have become of the energy wasted by the boiler.

19 Explain why the efficiency of a device can never be greater than 1.00 or 100%.

20 A car engine has an efficiency of 0.28. How much input chemical energy must be supplied if the total output useful energy is 140 000 kJ?

21 The power of the motor in an electric car is 3600 W. How much electrical energy is converted into other energy forms in 5 minutes?

22 A crane can produce a maximum output power of 3000 W. It raises a load of mass 1500 kg through a vertical height of 12 m at a steady speed.

a) What is the weight of the load?
b) How much useful work does the crane do lifting the load 12 m?
c) How long does it take the crane to raise the load 12 m?
d) At what speed will the load rise through the air?

23 A barrel of weight 1000 N is pushed up a ramp. The barrel rises vertically 40 cm when it is pushed 1 m along the ramp.

a) Calculate how much useful work is done when the barrel is pushed 1 m along the ramp.
b) To push the barrel 1 m along the ramp requires 1200 J of energy. Calculate the efficiency of the ramp.

Kinetic energy

The **kinetic energy** of an object is the energy it has because it is moving. It can be shown that an object's kinetic energy is given by the formula:

$$\textbf{Kinetic energy} = \frac{1}{2}\,\mathbf{mv^2}$$

where:
m is the mass in kg
v is the speed of the object in m/s

Examples

1 A car of mass 800 kg is traveling at 15 m/s. Find its kinetic energy.

$KE = \frac{1}{2}mv^2 = \frac{1}{2} \times 800 \times 15^2 = 0.5 \times 800 \times 225 = \mathbf{90\,000\ J}$

2 A bullet has a mass of 20 g and is travelling at 300 m/s. Find its kinetic energy. (We must first change the bullet's mass from g to kg by dividing by 1000.)

$KE = \frac{1}{2}mv^2 = \frac{1}{2} \times (20/1000) \times 300^2 = 0.5 \times 0.02 \times 90\,000 = \mathbf{900\ J}$

3 Find the speed of a boat if its mass is 1200 kg and it has a kinetic energy of 9600 J.

$KE = \frac{1}{2}mv^2$

$9600 = \frac{1}{2} \times 1200 \times v^2 = 600 \times v^2$

$v^2 = 9600/600 = 16$

$v = \sqrt{16} = \mathbf{4\ m/s}$

4 The input power of a small hydroelectric power station is 1 MW. If 18 000 000 kg of water flows past the turbines every hour, find the average speed of the water.

1 hour = 60 × 60 seconds = 3600 seconds
Mass of water flowing every second = 18 000 000/3600 = 5000 kg/s

Since the power station produces 1 000 000 J of electrical energy per second, the minimum KE of the water passing every second is 1 000 000 J.

So $KE = \frac{1}{2}mv^2$

$1\,000\,000 = \frac{1}{2} \times 5000 \times v^2$

$v^2 = 1\,000\,000/2500 = 400$

$v = \sqrt{400} = \mathbf{20\ m/s}$

Did you know?

Niagara Falls is approximately 50 m high and it is estimated that about 5 000 000 kg of water flow over the falls every second. This would give it a maximum capacity to produce 2500 MW of electricity. For lots more information about Niagara Falls visit:

www. iaw.com/~falls/
www.city.niagarafalls.on.ca/visitorinsights/

Questions

24 A communications satellite of mass 120 kg orbits the earth at a speed of 3 000 m/s. Calculate its kinetic energy.

25 The viewing platform at the Eiffel Tower in Paris is about 280 m from the ground. Find the gravitational potential energy of a rubber of mass 50 g on the viewing platform. Compare this to the kinetic energy of a 10 g shell travelling at 150 m/s fired from a pistol. Comment on your answer.

26 An oil tanker has a mass of 100 000 tonnes. Its kinetic energy is 200 MJ. Calculate its speed.
(1 tonne = 1000 kg, 1 MJ = 1 Megajoule = 1 000 000 J)

27 A ball of mass 2 kg falls from rest from a height of 5 m above the ground. Copy the table below and complete it to show the gravitational potential energy, the kinetic energy, speed and the total energy of the falling ball at different heights above the surface.

Height above ground in m	Gravitational potential energy in J	Kinetic energy in J	Total energy in J	Speed in m/s
5.0		0	100	0
4.0				4.47
	64			
1.8		64		
0	0			

28 A car of mass 800 kg is travelling at a steady speed. The kinetic energy of the car is 160 000 J. Show carefully that the speed of the car is 72 km per hour.

29 On planet X an object of mass 2 kg is raised 10 m above the surface. At that height the object has a gravitational potential energy of 176 J. Details of three planets are given below. Which one of these three planets is most likely to be planet X?

Planet's name	Mercury	Venus	Pluto
Gravitational field strength, g, in N/kg	3.7	8.8	0.6

30 A bouncing ball of mass 200 g leaves the ground with a kinetic energy of 10 J.

a) If the ball rises vertically, calculate the maximum height it is likely to reach.

b) In practice, the ball rarely reaches the maximum height. Explain why this is so.

Heat transfer

There are three main methods of heat transfer.

1 **Conduction** – occurs mainly in solids. Most liquids are very poor conductors of heat and almost no heat conduction takes place in gases.
2 **Convection** – transfers heat only in liquids and gases.
3 **Radiation** – is the *only* method of heat transfer in a vacuum.

Conduction

Most metals are good conductors of heat. Figure 2 shows an experiment to demonstrate which of three materials is the best heat conductor. The three rods rest on a tripod and a small pin is attached to each one using candle wax as 'glue'. The other ends of the rods are heated equally with a Bunsen flame. To make it a **fair test**, all the rods must be the same length and have the same area of cross section

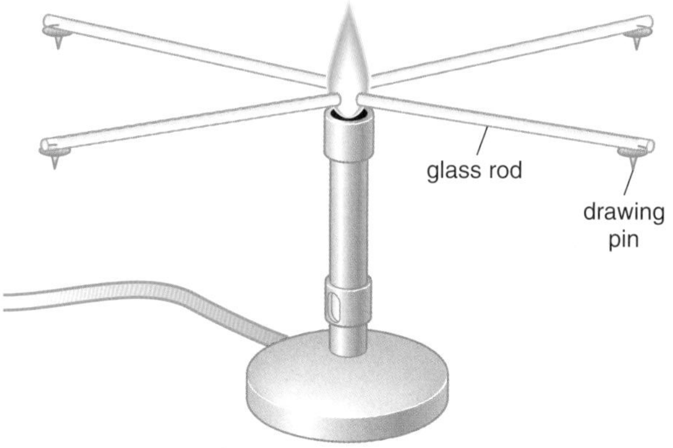

Figure 2 This apparatus can be used to demonstrate heat conduction in different materials

What happens? Heat conducts along all of the rods, but the pins fall off at different times. The pin attached to the copper rod falls first, shortly followed by the pin attached to the aluminium rod. Only after many minutes does the pin attached to the glass rod fall.

The experiment shows that copper and aluminium are good conductors but glass is a very poor heat conductor. Poor conductors are called **insulators**.

Conduction in glass

In solids, the atoms are held together by chemical bonds. Although they cannot move freely around within the solid, they are able to vibrate. The part of the glass in the Bunsen flame absorbs heat energy. This makes the atoms in the end of the rod vibrate faster and with greater amplitude than their neighbours. These vibrations pass from atom to atom through the solid structure, transferring heat (in the form of kinetic energy) as they do so. Only after a considerable time does the energy of the flame reach the other end of the glass rod.

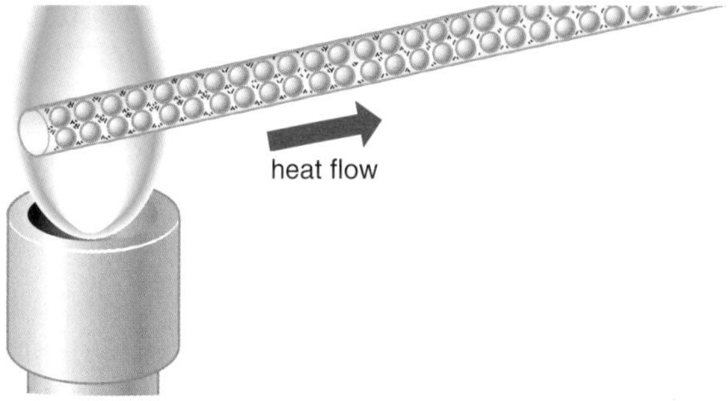

Figure 3 In a glass rod, heat is conducted slowly as the vibrations pass from one atom to the next

Free electron conduction

Why is copper such a good conductor of heat? Unlike glass, copper has **free electrons** in its metallic structure. These are electrons that have escaped from atoms and can move freely throughout the solid. The free electrons absorb heat from the Bunsen flame. This heat allows them to move much faster than before. As they move through the metal, free electrons collide with copper atoms. In these collisions, the electrons give some of their kinetic energy to the atoms and

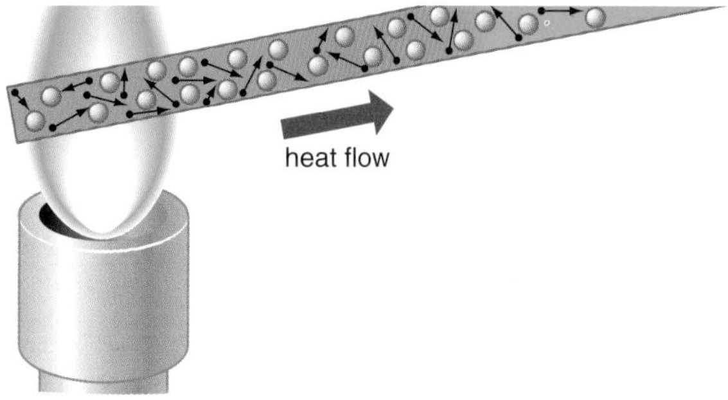

Figure 4 In a metal rod, heat is conducted rapidly through the movement of free electrons

cause them to vibrate with greater amplitude than before. Free electron conduction is very much faster than conduction caused by passing vibrations from atom to atom. So materials with free electrons (and that includes all metals) are the best conductors of heat energy.

It is now clear why liquids are such poor conductors. Most liquids have no free electrons, so they rely on passing vibrations from atom to atom. But because the atoms in a liquid are constantly moving, conduction cannot take place in an orderly way. Liquid metals are exceptions to this rule. At room temperature mercury is a liquid, but it is also a metal, so it conducts heat using its free electrons. This is one of the reasons why it was used for many years in thermometers. But because mercury is extremely poisonous, most modern liquid thermometers use coloured alcohol instead of mercury.

Did you know?

Another liquid metal – **liquid sodium** – is used to conduct the heat away from the reactor core in nuclear submarines. The heat conducted from the reactor is then used to produce electricity to power the submarine below the waves.

Figure 5 In this nuclear submarine, liquid sodium is used to conduct heat

Why does the metal blade of a knife always feel cooler than the plastic handle when taken from a drawer? The first thing to understand is that the handle and the blade are at the *same temperature* and that your hand is warmer than both of them. But because the metal blade is a better conductor than the plastic handle, the blade conducts heat away from your hand faster than the plastic, making it feel colder. Touching very cold metals can cause heat to be conducted from your hand so rapidly that it can give you a serious 'burn'.

The reverse happens if a knife is removed from hot water. As the blade is hotter than your skin, heat is conducted from the blade into your hand faster than heat from the handle. The blade therefore feels hotter than the handle.

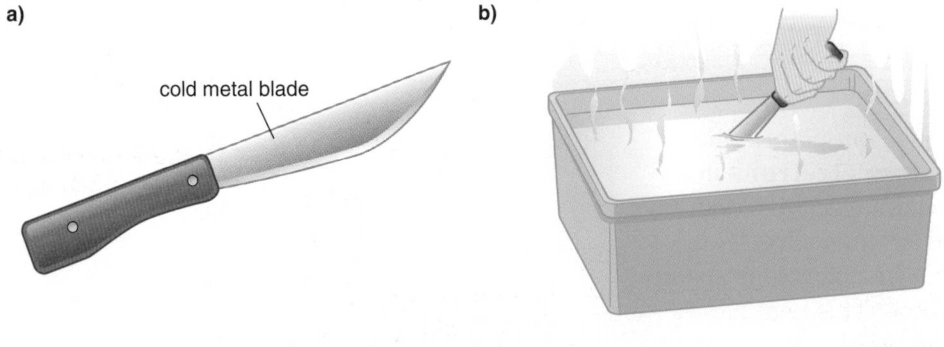

Figure 6a When the knife is at room temperature, the metal blade will feel colder than the handle

b When the knife is hotter than the hand, the metal blade will feel hotter than the handle

Evaporation

Evaporation is another way that heat can transfer from a liquid to the air above it. In a liquid, the fast-moving particles near the surface are likely to escape into the atmosphere, becoming a gas, taking kinetic energy with them. Since only the fastest particles (those with most kinetic energy) are able to do this, the particles remaining in the liquid have less average energy than they had before. This means that the liquid has lost heat energy and becomes cooler. The energy of the Sun causes evaporation at the surface of the Earth's oceans. This drives the water cycle.

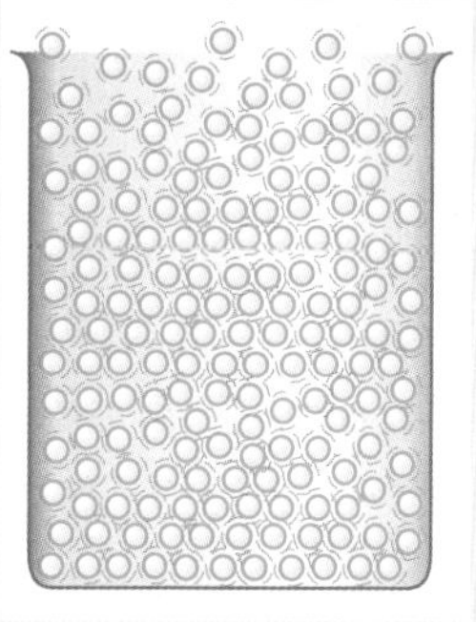

Figure 7 Evaporation occurs at the surface of a liquid

Air – nature's insulator

What happens when we hold a live match a few centimetres away from a Bunsen flame? The heat reaching the match head is not enough to light the match. This is because air is a very poor conductor of heat.

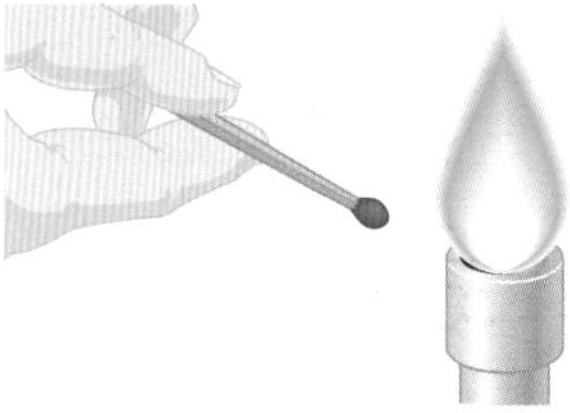

Figure 8 Why won't the match light?

Convection

Convection in air

Convection occurs when the fastest-moving particles in a hot region of a gas or liquid move to a cool region, taking their heat energy with them. It occurs only in liquids and gases because the atoms in solids are not free to move from place to place. Convection is explained by changes in the density of the material.

Convection in air can be demonstrated by the glass chimney experiment shown in Figure 9. First a straw is lit and the flame blown out. Note that the smoke rises when the straw is held in the air. Then the smoky straw is held over each chimney in turn.

When the smoky straw is over the candle flame, the smoke rises.

When the straw is held over the other chimney, the smoke falls. If the straw is held in position for long enough, the smoke will eventually be seen in the horizontal section and then rising above the candle flame.

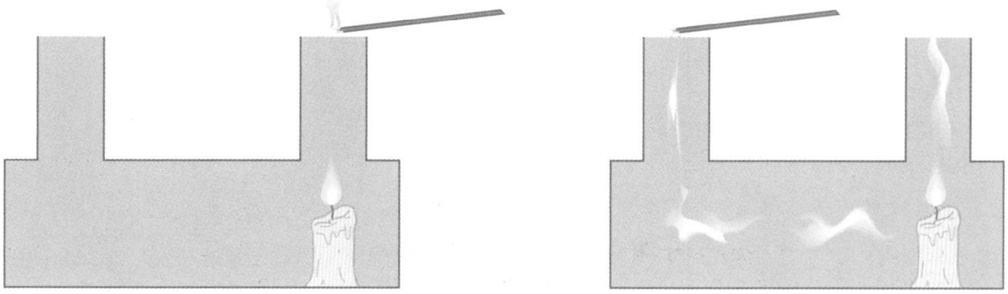

Figure 9 Demonstrating convection currents in air

Why does the smoke fall down the chimney?

- The air around the candle flame becomes very hot.
- The air molecules near the flame are moving faster than those in normal air.
- The hot air molecules are further apart than those in normal air (air has expanded).
- The density of the hot air is less than that of normal air, so the hot air rises up the chimney.
- Cooler air moves along the horizontal tunnel to replace the air which has gone up the chimney.
- The moving smoke follows the motion of the cooler air.

Convection in a liquid

Figure 10 shows convection in water.

The movement of the purple dye in the water shows the convection current.

What causes convection currents in water?
As the water at the bottom of the flask warms up, the molecules gain kinetic energy. This extra energy causes the following to happen:

- the molecules vibrate with greater amplitude
- the warm water therefore expands
- the density of the warm water is less than that of the cold water
- the warm water rises
- cooler water flows downwards to replace the upward-moving warmer water
- cool water at the top falls as it is replaced by warm water.

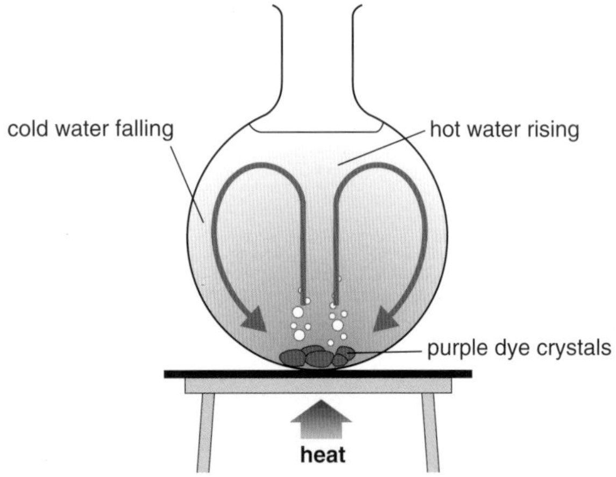

Figure 10 Demonstrating convection currents in a liquid

Did you know?

Water has a maximum density at 4 °C. This means that the water at the bottom of a pond is likely to be around 4 °C at all times of the year. This explains why in winter, ice develops on the surface of a pond (0 °C), while the plants and animals near the bottom have a warmer environment in which to live.

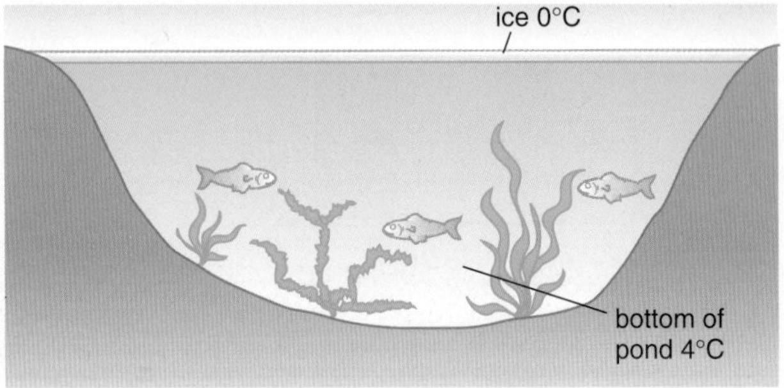

Reducing heat loss from your home

Heat is lost through the roof, walls, windows and floor of a home as shown in Figure 11. Different materials and devices have been designed to reduce this heat loss.

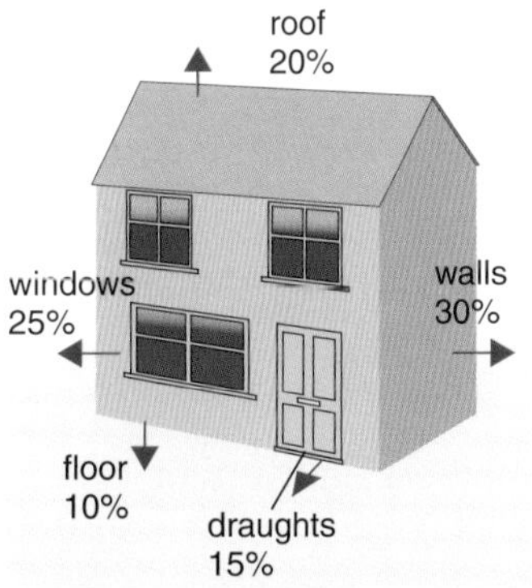

Figure 11 Heat loss from a house

Device	Pay-back time (using money saved on heating bills)	How losses are reduced
Cavity wall insulation	3 years	• The cavity between the outside walls is filled with fibreglass, mineral wool or foam. • Mineral wool and foam both trap air in tiny pockets. • Trapped air reduces heat loss through walls by convection and conduction.
Loft (attic) insulation	1.5 years	• Fibreglass or mineral wool fibres trap air. • Trapped air reduces heat loss through the roof by convection and conduction.
Double glazing	40 years	• Thick glass is used to reduce heat loss through windows by conduction. • Trapped air reduces heat loss by convection and conduction.
Thick curtains and carpets	Variable (depends on quality)	• Reduces draughts. • Trapped air reduces heat loss through windows and floors by convection and conduction.

Radiation

Radiation is the method of heat transfer that takes place without the need for any particles. It is the way by which the Earth receives heat energy from the Sun through the vacuum of space. The heat energy is transferred as **infrared waves**, one of the members of the **electromagnetic spectrum**.

All objects radiate energy (emit radiant heat). The hotter an object is, the more radiation it emits. All objects also absorb radiant heat. If an object is hotter than its surroundings, it emits more radiant heat than it absorbs, so its temperature falls. If an object is cooler than its surroundings, it absorbs more radiant heat than it emits, so its temperature rises.

Giving out radiation (radiation emission)

Figure 12 shows an experiment in which a thick piece of copper is covered with gloss (shiny) white paint on one side and matt (non-shiny) black paint on the other. The copper has been heated with a Bunsen burner until it is very, very hot.

If you were to hold your hand about 30 cm from the gloss white side then hold your hand about the same distance from the black side, you would notice that your hand would feel very much hotter facing the matt black side. This is because the matt black surface is the better emitter of radiant heat.

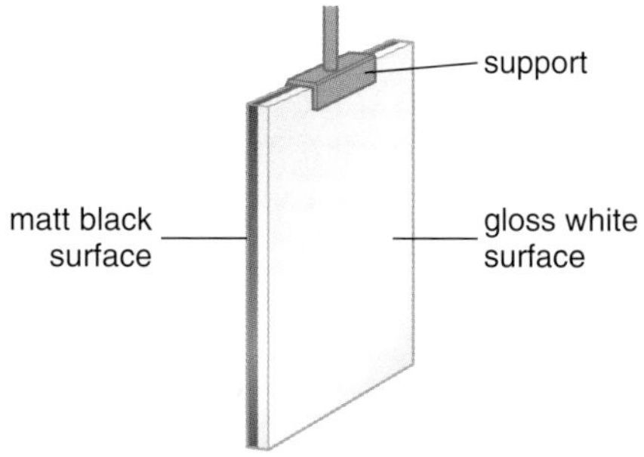

Figure 12 Investigating radiation emission

Rules to remember

- Black surfaces are the best emitters of radiation.
- White surfaces are the worst emitters of radiation.
- Matt surfaces are better emitters than gloss surfaces.

Taking in radiation (radiation absorption)

Figure 13 shows two sheets of thin aluminium, one painted gloss white and the other matt black. A cork is fixed to the back of each vertical plate with candle wax as 'glue'. The plates are placed equal distances away from a Bunsen burner. When the burner is lit, each plate receives the same quantity of radiant heat, but in a very short time the wax on the matt black plate will melt and the cork will fall off. The white plate stays much cooler and the cork takes much longer to fall off.

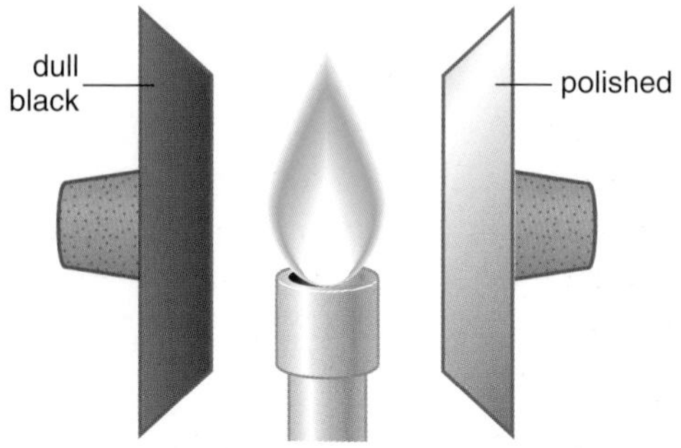

Figure 13 Investigating radiation absorption

Rules to remember

- Radiant heat falling on a surface is partly absorbed and partly reflected.
- Matt black surfaces are good absorbers (and poor reflectors) of radiation.
- Gloss white surfaces are poor absorbers (and good reflectors) of radiation.

Radiation summary

Matt black surfaces are	Gloss white surfaces are
Good emitters and absorbers of radiation	Poor emitters and absorbers of radiation
Poor reflectors of radiation	Good reflectors of radiation

The greenhouse effect

Most of the infrared radiation from the Sun is reflected back into space. But some of it reaches the Earth's surface where it is absorbed. The Earth itself then radiates part of this energy back into its atmosphere.

The infrared energy which is radiated by the Earth has a longer wavelength than the waves which come from the Sun. This long-wavelength radiation is then absorbed by the carbon dioxide (and other greenhouse gases such as methane and water vapour) in the atmosphere, keeping the Earth reasonably warm. This effect is known as the **normal greenhouse effect** and without it, life on Earth would be impossible for humans.

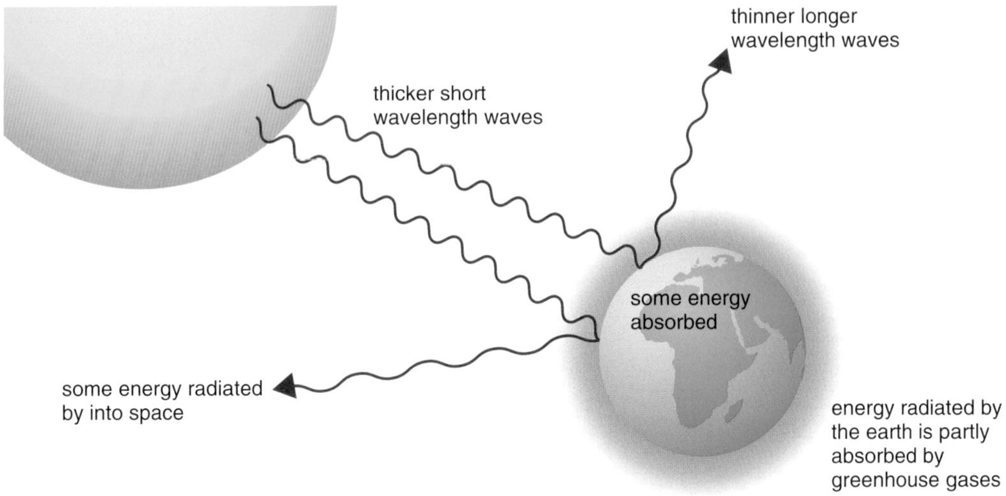

Figure 14 The greenhouse effect

As more and more fossil fuels are burned, the amount of carbon dioxide in the atmosphere is increasing. This has the effect of absorbing more of the energy radiated from the Earth, so making the atmosphere warmer. This effect is called **global warming.** The major danger of such warming is that the polar ice-caps begin to melt, causing widespread flooding. There may also be drastic changes in climate with storms, droughts and famines becoming more and more common.

Some scientists are concerned that global warming might increase so much that it becomes irreversible. As the air temperature increases, more and more dissolved carbon dioxide passes from oceans, lakes and rivers into the atmosphere. This causes more global warming which causes further carbon dioxide to pass into our atmosphere, and so the process continues. This effect is called the **runaway greenhouse effect** and would be catastrophic for life on Earth.

Did you know?

Venus is the hottest planet in the Solar System, although Mercury is closer to the Sun. Scientists are now fairly certain that there was a runaway greenhouse effect on Venus. The surface temperature on Venus is over 460 °C and the atmosphere is over 95% carbon dioxide.

Applications of heat transfer

Vacuum flasks

The **vacuum flask** was designed by James Dewar in order to keep liquids cold. But the flask works equally well as a way of keeping liquids hot. Today it is commonly used as a picnic flask to keep tea, coffee or soup hot. How does it work?

- The flask is made of a double-walled glass bottle. There is a vacuum between the two walls. The vacuum stops all heat transfer by conduction or convection through the sides.
- The glass walls facing the vacuum are silvered. Their shiny surfaces reduce heat transfer by radiation to a minimum.
- The stopper is made of plastic and is often filled with cork or foam to reduce heat transfer by conduction through it.
- The outer, sponge-packed plastic case protects the inner, fragile flask against physical damage.

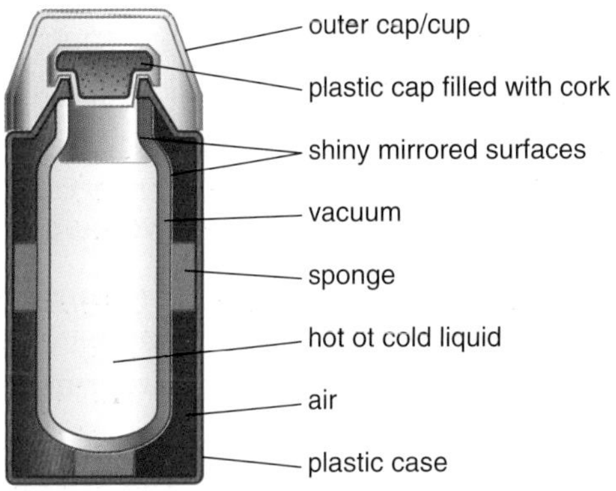

Figure 15 A crosss-section through a vacuum flask

Solar panels

A solar panel absorbs sunlight and uses the energy to heat water in the following process:

- The sunlight passes through a glass window and falls onto a blackened metal sheet.
- The metal is in a draught-proof enclosure to minimise heat loss by convection.
- The blackened metal absorbs almost all of the energy in the sunlight and its temperature often rises to over 100 °C.
- The heat stored in the blackened metal is then transferred to water flowing in a nearby pipe.

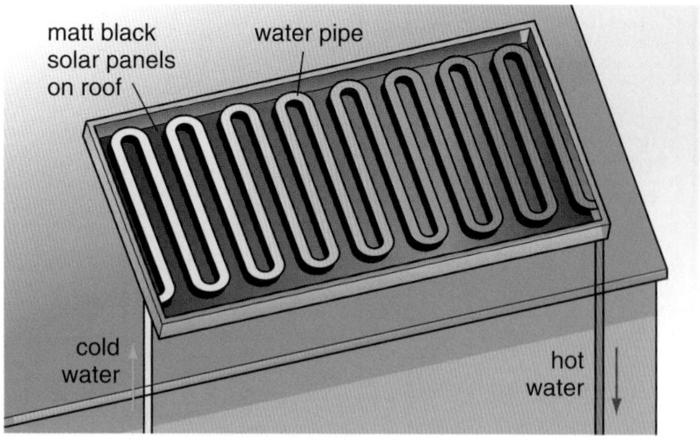

Figure 16 How a solar panel works

Solar panels are ideal for use where large volumes of hot water are needed, such as swimming pools and hospital laundries.

Did you know?

Northern Ireland is one of Europe's major manufacturers of solar panels. They are made by a company in Bangor. If you ever fly into Singapore airport, look closely at the terminal building – the solar panels on the roof were built in Ireland!

Questions

31 As food is cooled in a fridge, heat energy is transferred to a coolant. The coolant, usually a liquid with a low boiling point, passes through pipes at the back of the fridge. The pipes are usually painted black and have thin metal 'fins' attached.

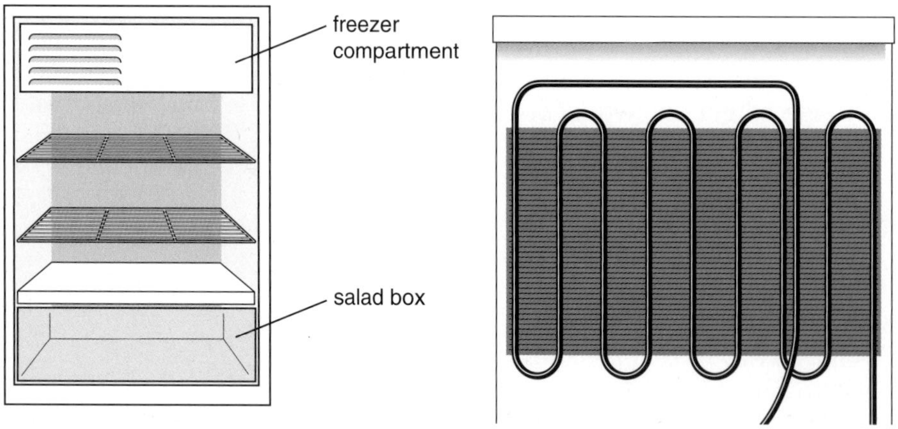

a) Why are the pipes painted black?
b) Why are the pipes mounted on thin metal fins?

32 Container ships are used to carry fruit and vegetables all over the world. The hold of the ship has two metal walls with an insulator in-between.

a) What is the purpose of the insulating material?
b) Give the name of a suitable insulator for this purpose.
c) What makes this insulator effective?

33 Which part of an oven is hottest, the top or the bottom? Why is this so? What is the purpose of the fan in a fan-assisted oven?

34 What is meant by saying that the pay-back time for double glazing is 40 years? Suggest a reason, other than that they might look good and last a long time, why people have their windows double glazed.

35 Suggest a reason why the roof of a house in a very hot country is often painted white.

36 Computer chips can produce a lot of heat. The chips must not be allowed to become too hot, however, otherwise they will be damaged. They are often attached to a heavy piece of copper metal with black fins as shown in the diagram. Such a piece of metal is called a heat-sink. What four features of the design of this type of heat-sink make it suitable for its purpose?

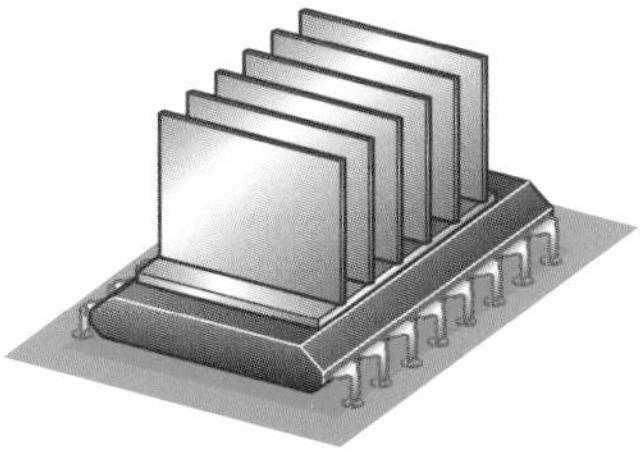

Expansion

Most solids, liquids and gases expand when they are heated. If this expansion is resisted, very large forces are created. Sometimes these forces are useful and sometimes they are a nuisance.

The expansion of different materials can be demonstrated using the apparatus shown in Figure 17.

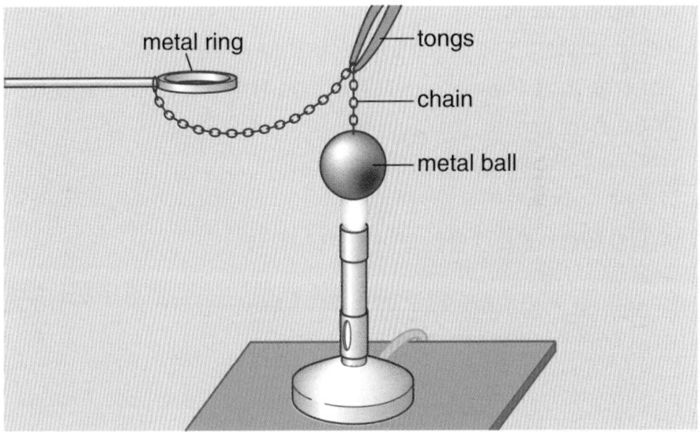

Figure 17 The ball and ring experiment

Ball and ring experiment

When the ball is cold, it just passes through the ring. But when heated, the ball expands and is no longer able to pass through the ring. To allow the hot ball to pass through the ring, we need to heat the ring also.

The thermoscope and the bubbling flask

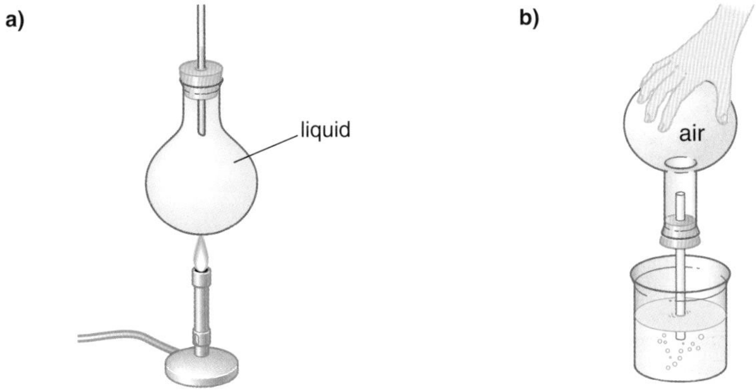

Figure 18 Demonstrating the expansion of (a) a liquid and (b) a gas

Thermoscope

When the flask in Figure 18a is heated, the liquid in the capillary tube is first observed to fall and then to rise. The liquid level falls at first because the flask temperature rises before that of the liquid. When the flask temperature rises, the flask itself expands causing the liquid level to fall. Later, as the liquid temperature rises, the liquid expands and rises up the capillary tube. The higher the liquid temperature, the higher it rises up the tube. This early thermometer was first used by Galileo and was called a thermoscope.

Bubbling flask

The warmth of a person's hand is enough to cause the air in the flask to expand and bubble out through the water (Figure 18b).

In general, for the same temperature increase:

- gases expand very much more than liquids
- liquids expand very much more than solids.

Forces in expansion

We can demonstrate the very large forces involved in expansion using the apparatus shown in Figure 19.

The strong, flat iron bar A has a screw thread on one end. The cast iron retaining pin passes through the hole at one end of the bar. The bar is then heated strongly with a Bunsen flame. When the bar is very hot, the knurled nut at B is tightened so the cast iron pin is held tight against the pillars (C). As bar A cools, it gets shorter and the force exerted on the pin is enough to snap it in two.

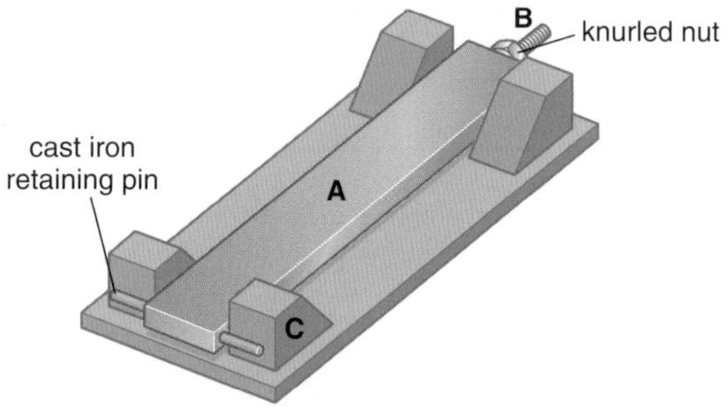

Figure 19 The forces of expansion are so strong in metals that they cause the cast iron pin to snap

Allowance for expansion

Engineers and architects need to be aware of the huge forces which occur in expansion and make allowances for them.

Railway lines

Railway lines used to be laid on wooden sleepers with gaps between them to allow for expansion in summer and contraction in winter. Today they are more likely to be laid in 1 km lengths and bolted onto much stronger concrete sleepers. Despite this an **expansion joint** between the rails is still necessary to avoid buckling in hot weather.

Bridges

Civil engineers allow for expansion in bridges in hot weather in one of two ways. They can either fit expansion joints, as in Figure 20, or they can fix one end of the bridge while allowing the other end to expand over rollers as in Figure 21.

Figure 20 An expansion joint in a bridge

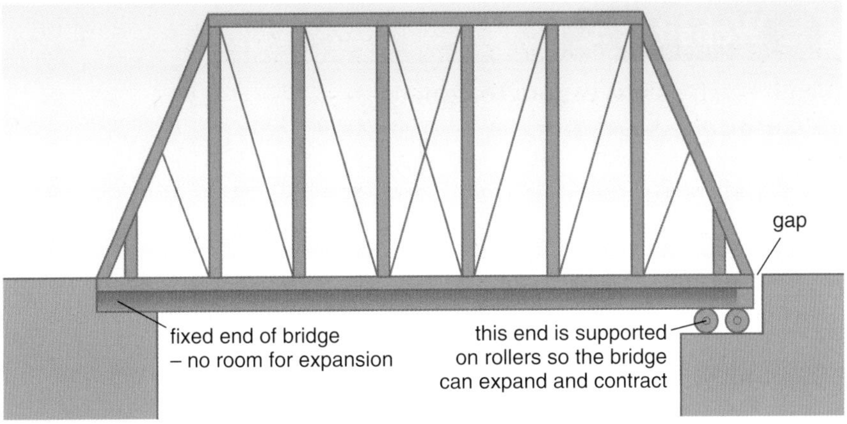

Figure 21 Expansion rollers on a bridge

The bimetallic strip

If equal lengths of two different metals are welded together so that they cannot move separately, they form a **bimetallic strip**. When heated, one metal will expand more than the other, so the strip bends. The metals used are often copper and iron. Copper expands more than iron, as shown in Figure 22. Bimetallic strips are frequently used as heat detectors and switches.

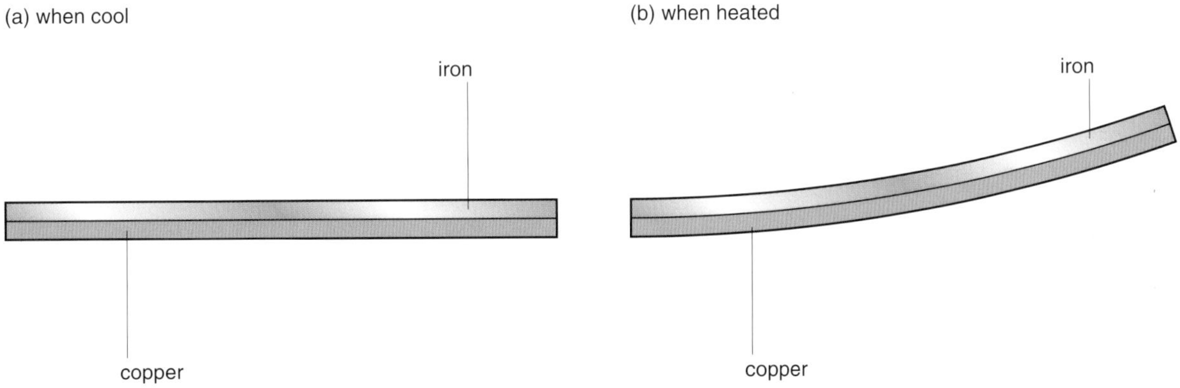

Figure 22 The bimetallic strip bends when heated and becomes straight again when cool

Fire alarm

When the temperature rises, the bimetallic strip in the fire alarm bends. The lower copper metal expands more than the inner iron metal, so the strip bends, closing the gap at the contacts. This completes the circuit so setting off the alarm.

In practice a latching circuit is used to prevent the ringing alarm stopping if the temperature later falls.

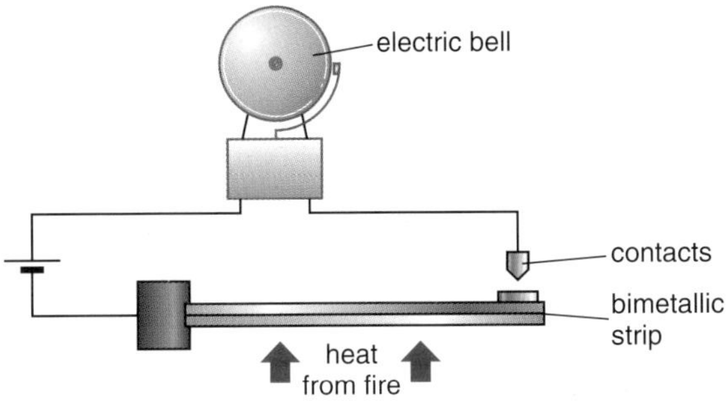

Figure 23 The bimetallic strip bends when warm to complete the fire alarm circuit

Websites

Use your favourite search engine (such as **www.google.com** or **www.excite.com**) and search using the keywords:

fossil + fuel	energy + power
coal	uranium
oil	hydroelectric
natural + gas	geothermal
energy + work	tidal + energy

www.geocities.com/Athens/Aegean/8438/menuenergy.html

www.purchon.com/physics

www.crest.org/hydro
For information on hydroelectricity

www.crest.org/bioenergy
For information on bioenergy

www.crest.org/geothermal
For information on geothermal energy

www.schoolzone.co.uk

www.howstuffworks.com

www.baynet.co.uk/colliery
For information on coal products

www.w5online.co.uk
For information about W5 in Belfast

www.visualphysics.com

www.electricity.org.uk
For information on electricity

www.sodaconstructor.com
For information about model construction

www.foe.co.uk
Friends of the Earth website

www.bbc.co.uk/sia
Interactive science from the BBC

www.schoolscience.co.uk/content/4/physics/corus/heat
For information on heat transfer in metals

www.s-cool.co.uk
For general information on energy transfer (select GCSE/physics/energy transfer)

www.bbc.co.uk/schools/gcsebitesize/physics/energy
For useful help with exam revision

Exam questions

1 A satellite orbits the Earth.

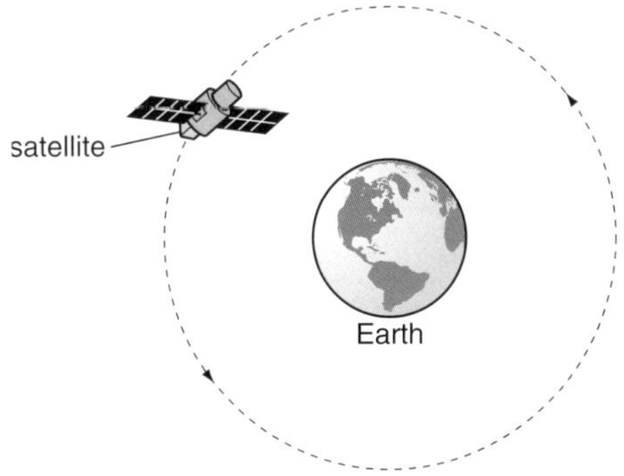

a) Name the two main types of energy possessed by the satellite in its orbit. *(2 marks)*

b) The diagram below shows a wind farm. This is a site where turbines have been set up.

(i) Copy and complete the boxes below to show the useful energy change which takes place in a wind turbine.

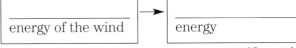

Input		**Useful output**
______ energy of the wind	→	______ energy

(2 marks)

(ii) The wind is a renewable energy source. What does this mean? *(1 mark)*

(iii) Give two other examples of renewable energy resources. *(2 marks)*

2 In Scotland hydroelectric power makes a significant contribution as a source of electricity.

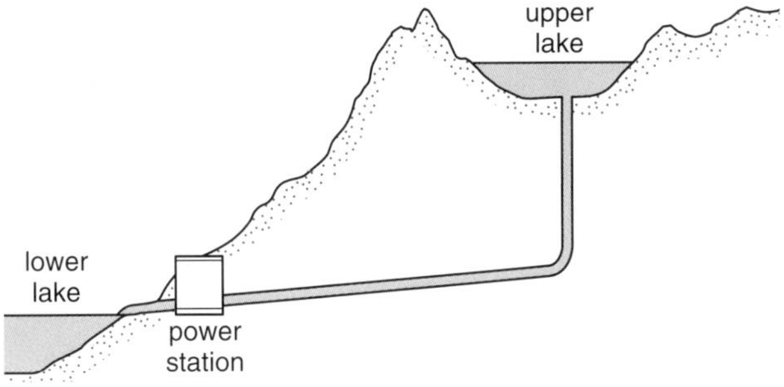

Copy and complete the boxes below to show the energy changes taking place in a hydroelectric power station.

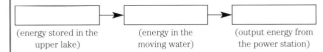

______	→	______	→	______
(energy stored in the upper lake)		(energy in the moving water)		(output energy from the power station)

(3 marks)

3 A tidal barrage in France generates electricity. One environmental effect of using the tides to generate electricity is to reduce the greenhouse effect by decreasing the consumption of fossil fuels.

a) Explain fully how this reduces the greenhouse effect. *(2 marks)*

b) Apart from the above environmental issue, state one advantage and one disadvantage of generating electricity from the tides. *(2 marks)*

4 The apparatus shown below was set up to study how heat was transmitted through different materials. After a few minutes of heating, the wax on the mercury-filled test tube melts and the cork falls off. The wax on the water-filled test tube takes much longer to melt

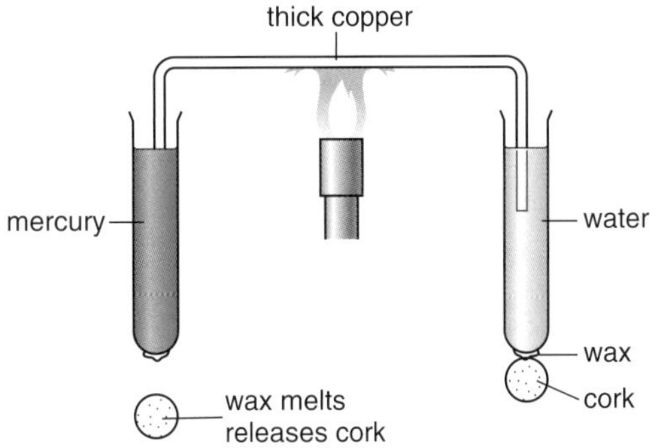

a) Name the main method by which heat from the Bunsen flame reaches the mercury and the water. *(1 mark)*

b) What does this experiment tell you about heat transfer in mercury and water? *(1 mark)*

The diagram shows a simple experiment to examine the heat given out by a Bunsen flame. The corks are attached to the metal plates by wax, which soon melts

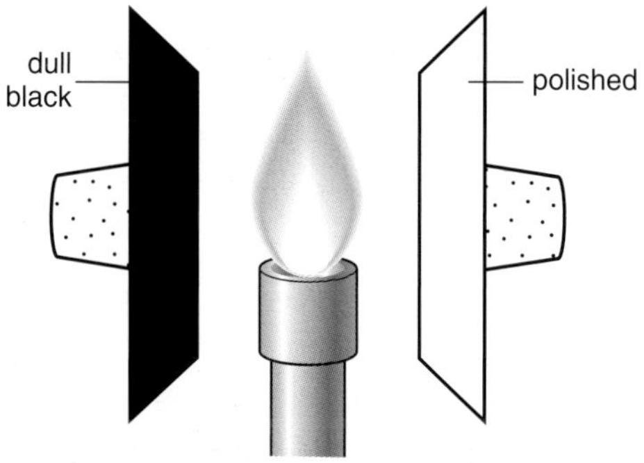

c) Name the main method by which heat reaches the metal plates from the Bunsen flame. *(1 mark)*

d) Describe and explain what happens after a few minutes of heating. *(1 mark)*

5 a) An electric kettle is half full of water.

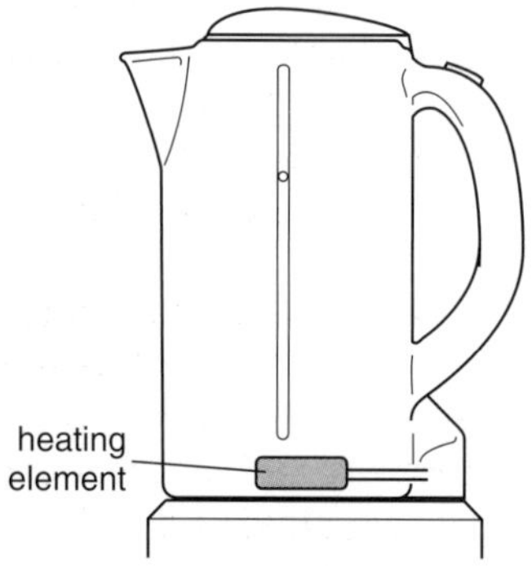

(i) Name the process by which heat energy is spread throughout the water. *(1 mark)*

(ii) Copy the diagram of the kettle and use arrows to draw the directions of the currents set up in the water by the heating element. *(1 mark)*

b) A saucepan containing cold water is placed on a hot plate. The water is heated through the base of the saucepan. Name this process of heat transfer. *(1 mark)*

c) The base of the saucepan is made of steel and the handle is made of wood. These materials are chosen for their thermal properties.

(i) Why is steel used for the base? *(1 mark)*

(ii) Why is wood used for the handle? *(1 mark)*

6 The diagram shows two spoons being held in ice-water. One is made of steel and the other is made of plastic.

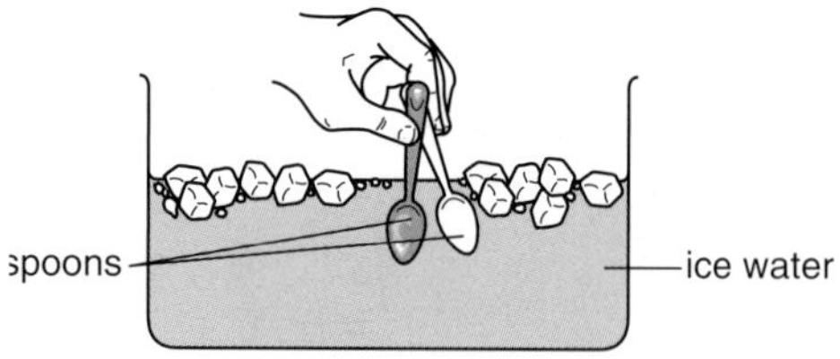

a) Which one will feel colder? *(1 mark)*

b) Explain fully the reason for your answer to a). *(2 marks)*

7 The diagram below shows an experiment in which water can be boiled at the top of a test tube while ice cubes are held at the bottom of the tube by a metal gauze.

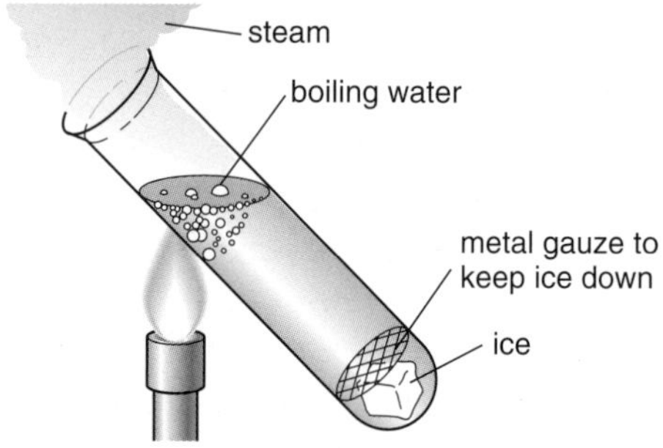

a) (i) Why do convection currents not carry heat down to the ice? *(1 mark)*

(ii) What does this experiment tell us about the ability of water to conduct heat? *(1 mark)*

The diagram below shows an experiment sometimes used in radiation investigations. The surfaces of the box are painted. One is matt black, another is shiny black, another is shiny white and the fourth is matt white. The metal box is filled with very hot water. Identical thermometers are held equal distances from the four side surfaces of the metal box and the temperature on each is recorded.

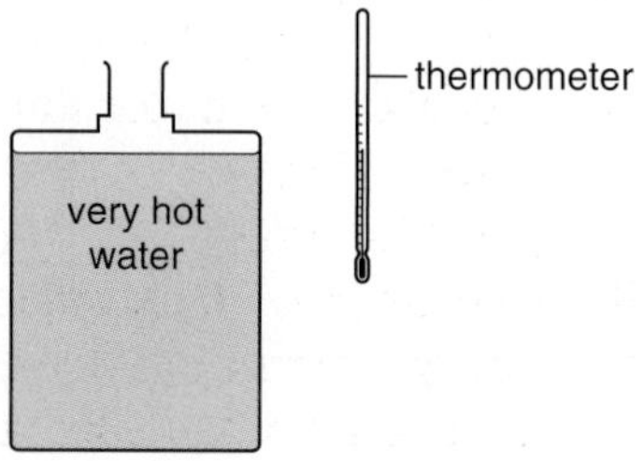

b) (i) Explain why the experiment works best if the thermometer bulbs are blackened. *(1 mark)*
(ii) Why is it important that the thermometers are all the same distance from the surface of the cube? *(1 mark)*
(iii) Which one of the four surfaces gives out the most radiant heat? *(1 mark)*
(iv) Which one of the four surfaces gives out the least radiant heat? *(1 mark)*
(v) How could you tell from the thermometers which surface was giving out most radiant heat? *(1 mark)*

8 a) The most common energy resources used in Europe today are: oil, natural gas, coal, nuclear energy, hydroelectric and wind energy.
(i) Choose one non-renewable energy resource from the list above and say why it is non-renewable. *(2 marks)*
(ii) Choose one renewable energy resource from the list above and say why it is renewable. *(2 marks)*
(ii) Give one advantage that non-renewable energy resources have over renewable energy resources. *(1 mark)*

b) It has been estimated that 1×10^8 (100 000 000) kg of water flows over Niagara Falls every second. The falls are 50 metres high.
(i) Calculate the gravitational potential energy lost every second by the water flowing over the falls ($g = 10\ m/s^2$). *(3 marks)*
A feasibility study has shown that only 0.008 (0.8%) of the available potential energy could be converted into electrical energy by a hydroelectric power station built on the falls.
(ii) Calculate the maximum power output of such a hydroelectric power station. *(3 marks)*
(iii) Explain why all hydroelectric power stations are dependent on the energy of the Sun. *(2 marks)*

c) Domestic hot water is normally stored in a copper cylinder.
(i) By what process is heat lost from the water into the walls of the cylinder? *(1 mark)*
(ii) Explain how the heat loss from the copper cylinder is reduced by painting it shiny white. *(2 marks)*
(iii) Explain fully how covering the cylinder with a jacket of fibre-glass wool reduces the rate of heat loss. *(2 marks)*

d) The process of heat transfer in metals involves the movement of particles. A metal bar is at the same constant temperature as its surroundings. Describe the motion of:
(i) the atoms in the metal. *(2 marks)*
(ii) the free (delocalised) electrons. *(2 marks)*
The metal bar is now heated at one end with a Bunsen flame.
(iii) What particles are mainly responsible for conduction of heat throughout the bar? *(1 mark)*
(iv) Describe how the motion of these particles changes due to the heating. *(1 mark)*
(v) Describe how the energy is transferred from these particles to the atoms of the metal. *(1 mark)*

e) The diagram below shows a vehicle with a winch attached. The winch is connected to a tree by rope. As the winch winds in the rope, the vehicle moves forward towards the tree. The winch uses 500 W of input electrical power. It has an efficiency of 0.6.

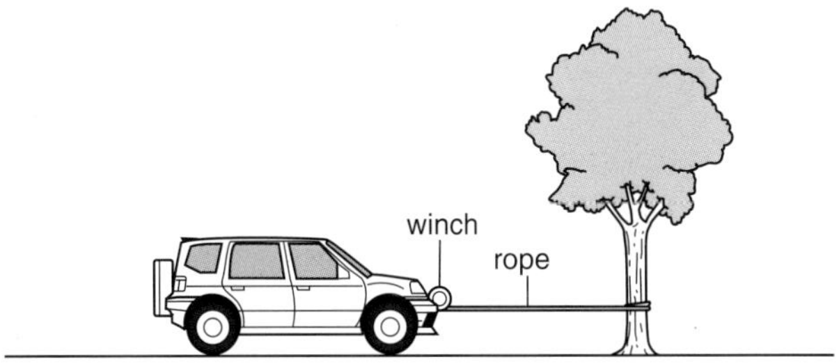

(i) Calculate the useful output power of the winch. *(3 marks)*
(ii) Write down the useful work done by the winch in 1 second. *(1 mark)*
(iii) The pulling force in the rope is 1200 N. Calculate the constant speed at which the vehicle moves forward. *(3 marks)*

9 a) How much work is done by a tractor when it lifts a load of 8000 N to a height of 1.8 m?

(3 marks)

b) The output power of the tractor is 5.2 kW. Calculate the time it takes to do 26 000 J of work.

(3 marks)

The efficiency of the tractor is 0.26 (or 26%).

c) If the output power of the tractor is 5.2 kW, calculate the input power.

(3 marks)

10 Stephen weighs 550 N. How much work does he do in climbing up to a diving board which is 3.0 m high?

(3 marks)

11 Saltburn is a seaside resort in Yorkshire. There is a considerable drop from the cliff top to the beach. In 1884 an inclined tramway was built to carry passengers from the beach to the cliff top.

Two identical tramcars were used each with a water tank underneath it. The tramcars were connected by a steel cable which passed around a large pulley at the top. The tramcar which happens to be at the top has water added until there is enough to raise the tramcar at the bottom of the tramway.

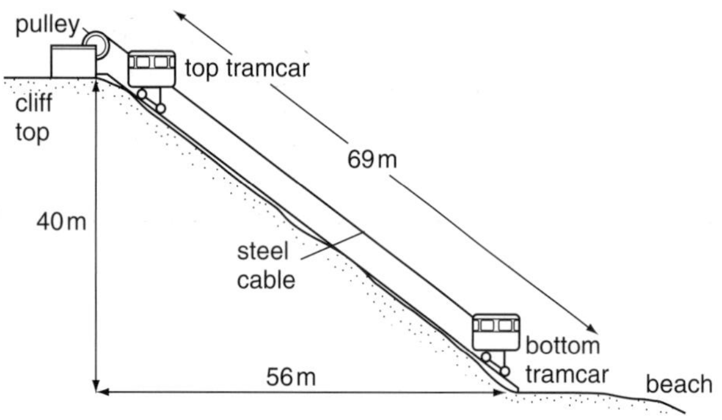

a) On one journey the weight of the lower tramcar and its passengers was 24 000 N. Ignoring friction, calculate the work done, in kJ, in bringing the tramcar from the beach to the cliff top.

(3 marks)

b) The time for this journey was 20 seconds. Calculate the power needed to raise the tramcar.

(3 marks)

c) On this journey the energy provided by the upper car as it descended was 1200 kJ. Calculate the efficiency of the tramway on this journey.

(3 marks)

d) During the journey certain energy changes take place. Complete the table below by stating whether the energy listed in the first column increases, decreases or remains unchanged as the top tramcar descends at a constant speed.

Energy	Increases/decreases/ unchanged
Potential energy of the top tramcar	
Kinetic energy of the top tramcar	
Kinetic energy of the bottom tramcar	
Potential energy of the bottom tramcar	
Heat energy	

(5 marks)

Chapter 2

Forces

Learning objectives

By the end of this chapter you should know:

- That balanced forces produce no change in movement
- That unbalanced forces produce a change in movement or direction
- Newton's First and Second Law
- The relationship between force, mass and acceleration
- How to distinguish between mass and weight
- How to calculate the weight of a body
- What happens when a body falls
- What is meant by terminal velocity
- What density is and how to calculate it
- How to determine density experimentally
- How to investigate experimentally the relationship between force and the extension of a helical spring
- Hooke's Law and be able to use it to solve simple problems
- The meaning of elastic limit
- The factors which affect the moment of a force
- The principle of moments
- Some different examples of lever
- The term centre of mass and understand how the stability of an object depends on the position of the centre of mass and the width of its base
- How to describe an experiment to locate the centre of mass of an irregular lamina
- How to use the relationship between pressure, force and area
- That pressure is measured in pascals.
- How simple hydraulic machines work using the transmission of pressure by liquids
- How to carry out simple calculations on hydraulic machines

Balanced and unbalanced forces

A **force** has both size and direction. The size of the force is measured in **newtons** (N). When drawing forces in diagrams it is usual to represent the direction of the force by an arrow and the size of the force by the length of the arrow drawn to scale.

A horizontal force of 50 N acting to the right may be represented by

→ 50 N

A horizontal force of 150 N acting to the left may be represented by

150 N ←

If the forces are equal in size and opposite in direction, then the forces are balanced. **Balanced** forces do not change the velocity of an object.

Figure 1 shows a car travelling at a steady speed of 30 km/h in a straight line under the action of two equal and opposite forces: the thrust exerted by the engine and drag.

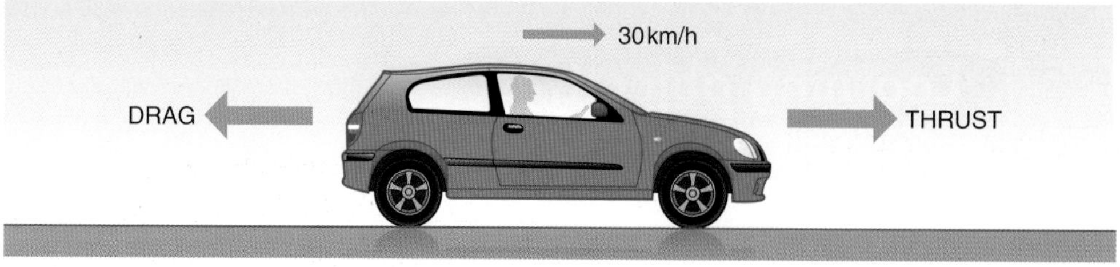

Figure 1

If an object is stationary (not moving), it will remain stationary.

In a tug of war like that in Figure 2, two teams pull against each other. When both teams pull equally hard, the forces are balanced and the rope does not move. But when one team starts to pull with a larger force, the rope moves. When this happens the two forces are no longer balanced.

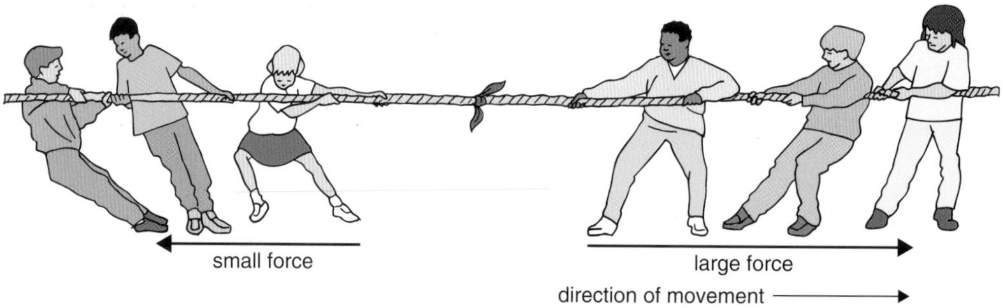

Figure 2 The forces in this tug of war are unbalanced, as the team on the right is pulling with a larger force

Unbalanced forces will change the velocity of an object. Since velocity involves both speed and direction, unbalanced forces can make an object speed up, slow down or change direction.

Unbalanced forces applied to the handlebars will make the cyclist in Figure 3 change direction. This means the velocity of the cyclist will change even though the speed may stay the same.

Figure 3

An object will only accelerate when an unbalanced force acts on it. It then accelerates in the direction of the unbalanced force. If the driving force on a car is greater than the drag force, the car will accelerate or speed up.

Figure 4 This car is accelerating

If the driver then decides to apply the brakes, the driving force will be smaller than the braking force and the car will decelerate or slow down.

Figure 5 This car is decelerating

A car is travelling in a straight line along a motorway.

Table 1 shows in which situations there is an unbalanced force on the car.

Table 1

Situation	Unbalanced force acting
The car's speed is increasing	✓
The car's speed is decreasing	✓
The car's speed is constant	
The car starts going round a bend	✓

Did you know?

There are four fundamental forces in the Universe that account for all interactions between matter and energy. They are known as the strong nuclear, weak nuclear, electromagnetic and gravitational forces. The most powerful of these is the strong nuclear force which is 100 times stronger than the next strongest, the electromagnetic force.

Newton's Laws

All that we have said about forces so far is summarised by **Newton's First Law**:

> A body stays at rest, or if moving it continues to move with uniform velocity, unless an unbalanced force makes it behave differently.

Linking unbalanced forces, mass and acceleration

It is possible for one person to push a car, however the acceleration of the car would be small. The more people that push the car, the larger the acceleration. So, the larger the force, the larger the acceleration.

Figure 6

Even four people would find it difficult to push a van, because the mass of a van is far larger than the mass of a car. The larger the mass, the smaller the acceleration.

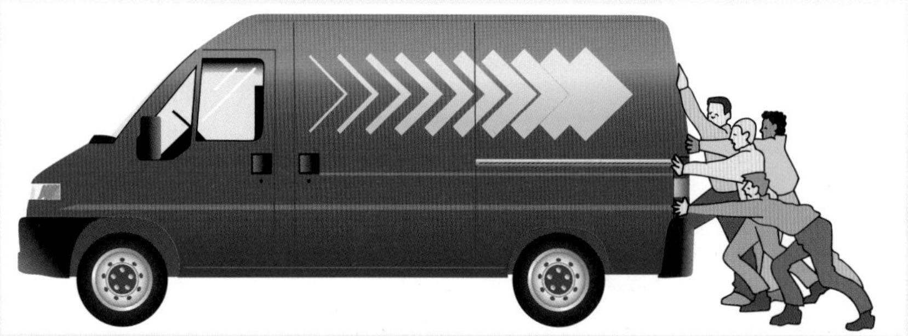

Figure 7

The size of the force needed to accelerate a mass can be worked out using **Newton's Second Law.**

$$\underset{(N)}{\text{Unbalanced force}} = \underset{(kg)}{\text{Mass}} \times \underset{(m/s^2)}{\text{Acceleration}}$$

Or

$$F = m \times a$$

Newton's Second Law tells us that for a given body, the greater the force, the greater is the acceleration.

This law also explains why some very large articulated lorries take a long distance to stop. When the stopping force is constant, the deceleration is inversely proportional to the mass of the lorry.

Examples

1 Calculate the force needed to give a train of mass 250 000 kg an acceleration of 0.5 m/s^2.

$F = m \times a$
$= 250\,000 \times 0.5$
$= \mathbf{125\,000\ N}$

2 A forward thrust of 400 N exerted by a speedboat enables it to go through the water at constant velocity. The speedboat has a mass of 500 kg. Calculate the thrust required to accelerate the speedboat at 2.5 m/s^2.

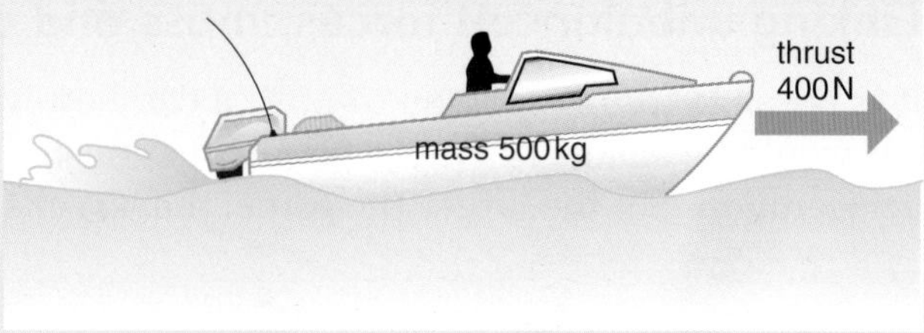

Note the phrase 'at constant velocity'. This is a clue to use Newton's First Law. If the thrust exerted by the engine is 400 N, there must be an equal and opposite force of 400 N due to the drag of the water on the boat. To calculate the force to accelerate the speedboat we should draw a force diagram.

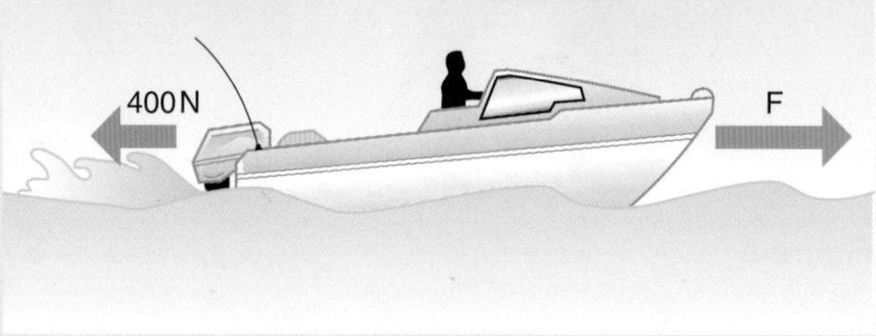

Unbalanced force = Mass × Acceleration
$(F - 400) = 500 \times 2$
$F - 400 = 1000$
$F = \mathbf{1400\ N}$

Summary of balanced and unbalanced forces

- Balanced forces have no effect on the movement of an object. If it is stationary it will remain stationary; if it is moving it will carry on moving at the same speed and in the same direction.
- Unbalanced forces will affect the movement of an object.
- An unbalanced force on an object causes its velocity to change – it accelerates. The greater the force, the greater the acceleration.
- The greater the mass of an object, the greater the force needed to make it accelerate.

Questions

1 A bicycle and rider have a total mass of 90 kg and travel along a horizontal road at a steady speed. The forward force exerted by the cyclist is 40 N.

a) Explain why the cyclist does not accelerate.

b) The rider increases the forward force to 70 N. Calculate the acceleration.

2 A car accelerates at 3.0 m/s^2 along a road. The mass of the car is 1200 kg and all the resistive forces add up to 400 N. Calculate the forward thrust exerted by the car's engine.

3 The diagram below shows the forces on a car of mass 800 kg.

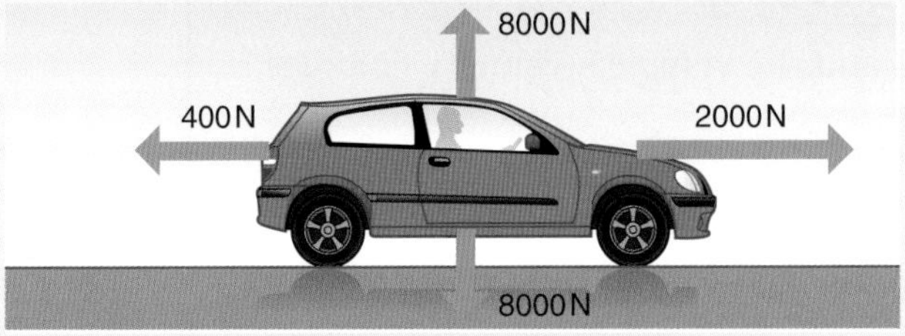

a) In what direction will the car accelerate?

b) Calculate the size of the car's acceleration.

4 The blades of a helicopter exert an upward force of 25 000 N. The mass of the helicopter is 2000 kg.

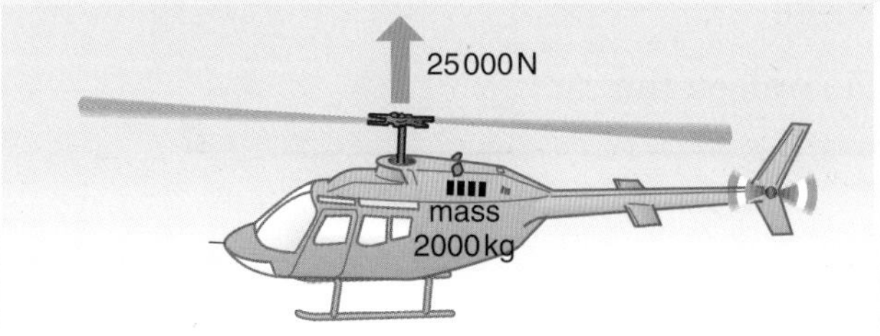

a) Calculate the weight of the helicopter.

b) Calculate the acceleration of the helicopter.

5 A forward thrust of 300 N exerted by a speedboat engine enables the speedboat to go through the water at a constant speed. The speedboat has a mass of 500 kg.

Calculate the thrust required to accelerate the speedboat at 2 m/s^2.

6 A car of mass 1200 kg accelerates at 3 m/s^2 along a road. Calculate the forward thrust exerted by the car engine if all resistive forces add up to 400 N.

7 A car and driver are travelling at 24 m/s and the driver decides to brake, bringing the car to rest in 8 seconds. The mass of the car and driver is 1200 kg.

a) Calculate the deceleration of the car.

b) Calculate the size of the unbalanced force which brings the car to rest.

8 A cyclist and her bicycle have a combined mass of 60 kg. When she cycles with a forward force of 120 N, she moves at a steady speed. However, when she cycles with a forward force of more than 120 N, she accelerates.

a) Explain, in terms of forces, why the girl moves at a steady speed when the force is 120 N.

b) Calculate her acceleration when the forward force is 300 N.

9 A Land Rover's brakes are applied and the vehicle's velocity changes from 50 m/s to zero in 5 seconds.

a) Calculate the acceleration of the Land Rover.

b) The resultant force causing this acceleration is 18 000 N. Calculate the mass of the Land Rover.

10 A car of mass 1000 kg is travelling at 20 m/s and collides with a wall. The front of the car collapses in 0.1 seconds by which time the car is at rest.

a) Calculate the deceleration of the car.

b) Calculate the force exerted by the wall on the car.

Mass, weight and free fall

In everyday life the terms mass and weight are used interchangeably. In physics, however, we must be very careful to distinguish clearly between mass and weight.

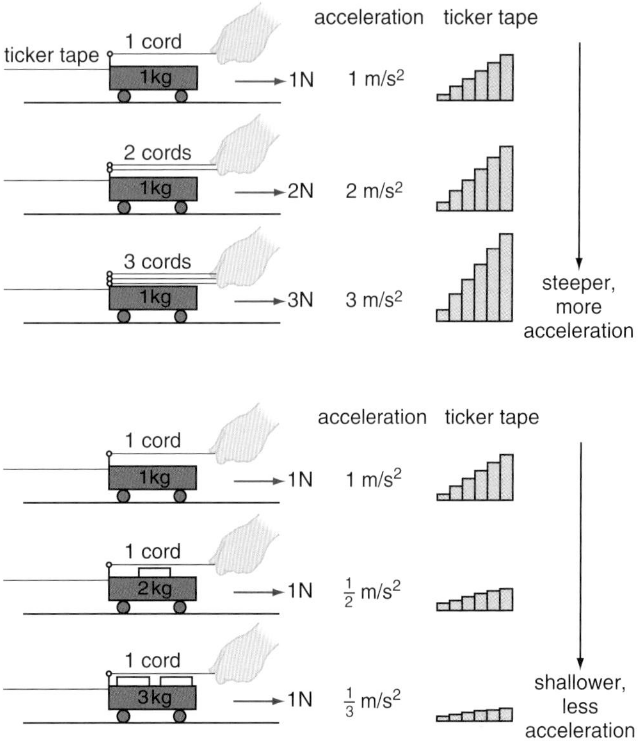

Figure 8a Experiment 1: Keep the mass constant and change the force
b Experiment 2: Keep the force constant and change the mass

What is mass?

Mass is defined as the amount of matter in a body. Mass is measured in kilograms (kg). It is another example of a scalar quantity.

However, Newton's Second Law of motion allows a more exact definition to be made. In Figure 8 you can see that a more massive trolley accelerates more slowly than a less massive trolley for the same force applied. Massive objects have an inbuilt reluctance to start moving: this is called **inertia** (from the Latin for laziness).

Did you know?

Large oil tankers turn off their engines two miles before reaching port.

What is weight?

Weight is a force and is a measure of the size of the gravitational pull on an object exerted, in our case, by the Earth. Near the surface of the Earth, there is a force of 10 N on each 1 kg of mass. We say that the Earth's **gravitational field strength**, g, is 10 N/kg.

The weight, W, of an object is the force that gravity exerts on it. The formula for weight is:

$$\underset{(N)}{\text{Weight}} = \underset{(kg)}{\text{Mass}} \times \underset{(m/s^2)}{\text{Acceleration (due to gravity)}}$$

Or

$$W = m \times g$$

Weight is measured in newtons (N). It is a vector quantity, so it has direction as well as size.

The value of g is roughly the same everywhere on the Earth's surface. But the further you move away from the Earth, the smaller g becomes.

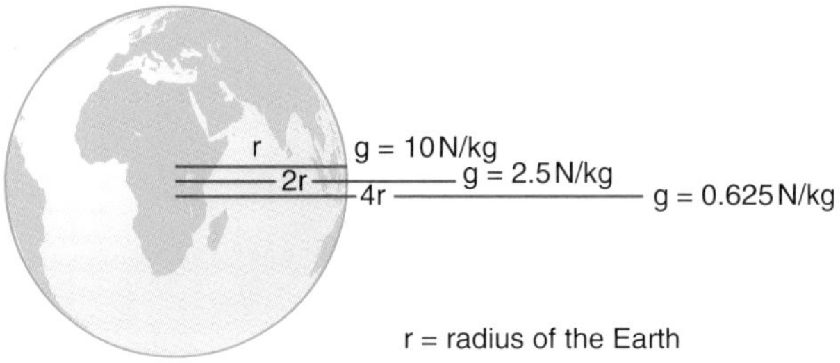

Figure 9 The gravitational field strength, g, decreases with distance from the Earth

The Moon is smaller than the Earth and pulls objects towards it less strongly. On the Moon's surface the value of g is 1.6 N/kg.

In deep space, far away from the planets, there are no gravitational pulls, so g is zero, and therefore everything is weightless.

Example

What is the weight of a 70 kg man on
a) the Earth where g = 10 N/kg, b) the Moon where g = 1.6 N/kg?

a) $W = m \times g$
$= 70 \times 10$
$= 700$ N

b) $W = m \times g$
$= 70 \times 1.6$
$= 112$ N

The size of g also gives the gravitational acceleration, because from Newton's Second Law:

Acceleration = Force/Mass
Or g = Weight/Mass

So an alternative set of units for g is m/s^2.

Did you know?

Your weight at the equator is slightly less than your weight at the North Pole because of the Earth's shape. If your mass was 40 kg, your weight at the North Pole would be 400 N while on the equator it would be 397.5 N.

Table 2 Comparing mass and weight

Mass	Weight
scalar	vector
measured in kg	mesured in N
never varies	varies from place to place

Free fall

Galileo showed that two lead balls of different diameter hit the ground at the same instant when dropped from the top of the leaning tower of Pisa.

All bodies in the absence of air resistance fall at the same rate of 10 m/s^2 near the surface. It is a common misconception to think that a more massive object falls faster than a less massive one. It is true that there is a greater force on the more massive object but the acceleration, which is the ratio of force to mass, will be the same for both bodies.

$a = F/m$ or in this case $g = W/m$

This means that if there is no air resistance, the speed of a falling object will increase by 10 m/s every second. In a vacuum, where there is no air resistance, all falling objects accelerate at the same rate.

When the glass tube in Figure 10 is evacuated and then turned upside down, the penny and piece of paper fall together. Although the penny has more mass than the piece of paper, gravity will exert a larger force on the penny giving both objects the same acceleration, i.e. the ratio of weight to mass is the same for both the penny and the piece of paper.

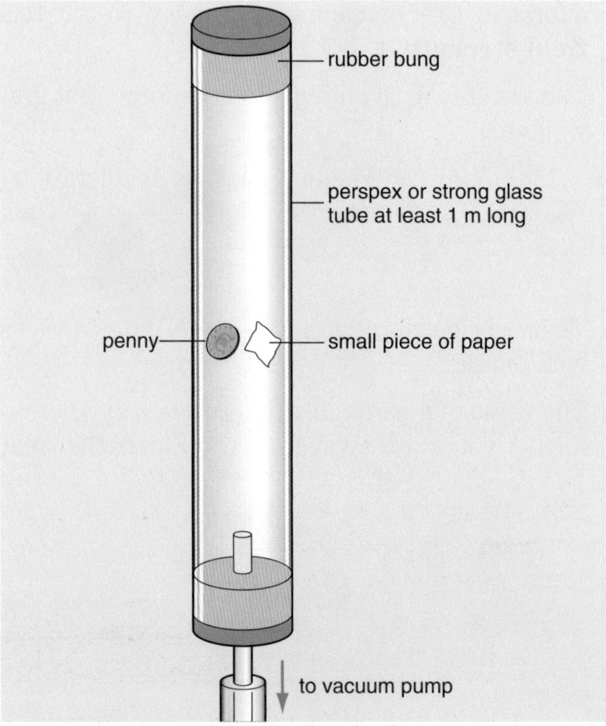

Figure 10 Investigating falling bodies in a vacuum

Usually air resistance does act on a falling body. Air resistance can only be ignored if the force it exerts is very small. When sky-divers jump from a plane, the forces on them are unbalanced so the sky-divers accelerate.

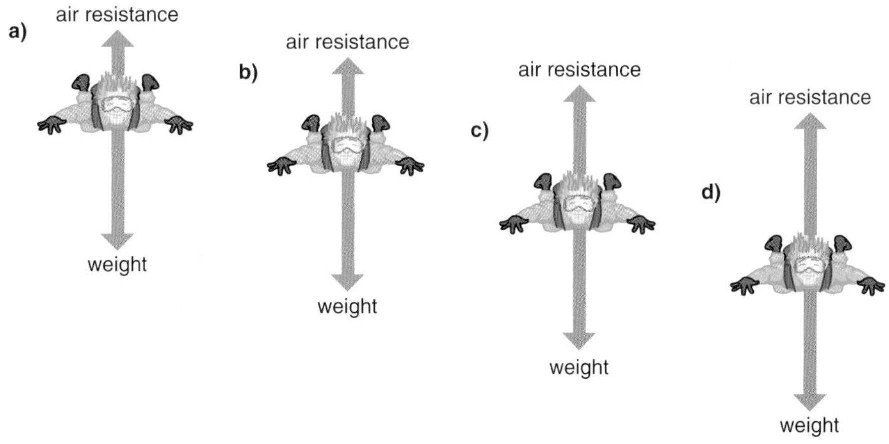

Figure 11 The weight of the sky-diver stays the same, but air resistance increases with speed. Eventually air resistance = weight, and the sky-diver reaches his terminal velocity

The faster the sky-diver falls, the larger the air resistance, so the smaller the acceleration. Eventually the downward force due to gravity and the upward force due to air resistance will be balanced. The sky-diver will stop accelerating and start to fall at a constant speed. At this point the sky-diver has reached his **terminal velocity**.

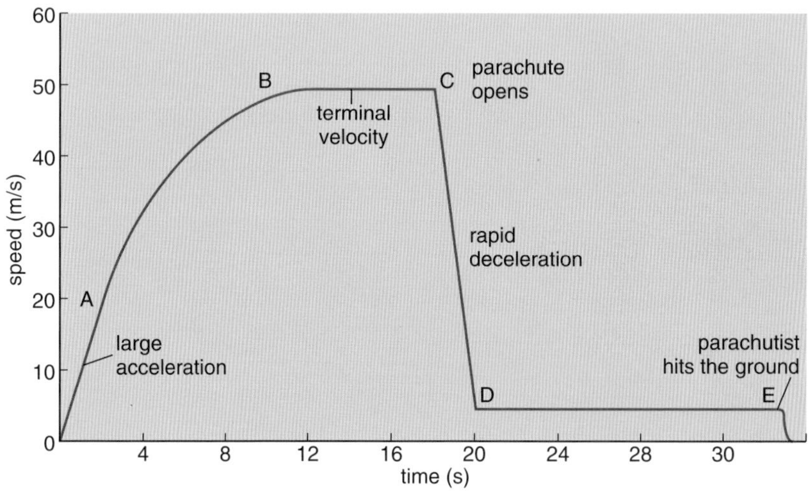

Figure 12 A speed–time graph for a sky-diver

Opening the parachute increases the air resistance. Since the force of gravity stays the same, it will take less time before the two forces are balanced. This gives the sky-diver a lower terminal velocity. Terminal velocity depends on the size of the air resistance force.

Air resistance is affected by the shape of an object. If the sky-diver pulls his arms and legs in line with his body, air resistance is reduced. It will take longer for the upward and downward forces to balance, so the sky-diver reaches a higher terminal velocity. Terminal velocity depends on the shape of an object.

Figure 13 This sky-diver has reached his terminal velocity

Did you know?

An air hostess, Vesna Volovic, fell over 10 kilometres without a parachute and survived!

Questions

11 Julie said, 'My weight is 35 kg.' What is wrong with this statement and what do you think her weight really is?

12 A ball bearing is gently dropped into a tall cylinder of oil which resists its motion. Describe what will happen to the ball bearing.

13 An astronaut standing on the surface of the Moon releases a hammer and a feather from the same height. What will happen and why?

14 Why does a parachute slow down a falling parachutist?

15 Explain the shape of each section, AB, BC, CD and DE, of the graph in Figure 12.

Density

The spectators at a football match are densely packed on the terraces, whereas the footballers on the pitch are well spread out. In a similar way, different materials have different **densities**. Some materials, such as lead, have large atoms which are very tightly packed together. We say that lead is a very dense material. In contrast, polystyrene has very small, well-spaced-out atoms.

Figure 14 Concorde is made from aluminium to give it low density and high strength

In Physics, a fairer comparison between materials such as lead and polystyrene is made using the concept of density.

The density of a material is defined as the mass per unit volume.

It is calculated using the formula:

$$\text{Density} = \frac{\text{Mass}}{\text{Volume}}$$

The unit of density is the kilogram per cubic metre (kg/m^3). Occasionally you will also see the unit gram per cubic centimetre (g/cm^3).

The density of lead is 11 g/cm^3, which means that a piece of lead of volume 1 cm^3 has a mass of 11 g. Therefore 5 cm^3 of lead has a mass of 55 g.

Knowing the density of a substance, the mass of any volume of that substance can be calculated. This enables engineers to work out the mass (and hence the weight) of a structure if they know from the plans the volumes of the materials to be used and their densities.

Did you know?

The Earth is the densest planet in our Solar System.

Example

Taking the density of Mercury as 14 g/cm^3, find
a) the mass of 7 cm^3 of mercury and
b) the volume of 42 g of mercury.

a) $\text{Density} = \frac{\text{Mass}}{\text{Volume}}$

$14 = \frac{\text{Mass}}{7}$

$\text{Mass} = 14 \times 7 = \mathbf{98\ g}$

b) $\text{Density} = \frac{\text{Mass}}{\text{Volume}}$

$14 = \frac{42}{\text{Volume}}$

$\text{Volume} = 42/14 = \mathbf{3\ cm^3}$

Table 3 The densities of some common substances

Substance	Density in g/cm^3	Density in kg/m^3
Aluminium	2.7	2700
Iron	8.9	8900
Gold	19.3	19 300
Pure water	1.0	1000
Ice	0.9	900
Petrol	0.8	800
Mercury	13.6	13 600
Hydrogen	0.09	90
Air	1.3	1300

Measuring density

To determine the density of a substance we need to measure a) its mass and b) its volume. The density, d, will then be given by the ratio of its mass (m) to its volume (V), i.e.

$$d = \frac{m}{V}$$

Regularly-shaped object

The mass of such an object is found using a top-pan balance and the volume by measuring its dimensions with a ruler and using the appropriate formula.

For example:

Volume of a rectangular block = Length × Breadth × Height
Volume of a cylinder = π × Radius^2 × Height

Irregularly-shaped object

If the shape of the object is too irregular for the volume to be determined using formulae, then a displacement method is used as shown in Figure 15. As before, the mass is found using a top-pan balance and the density calculated as outlined previously.

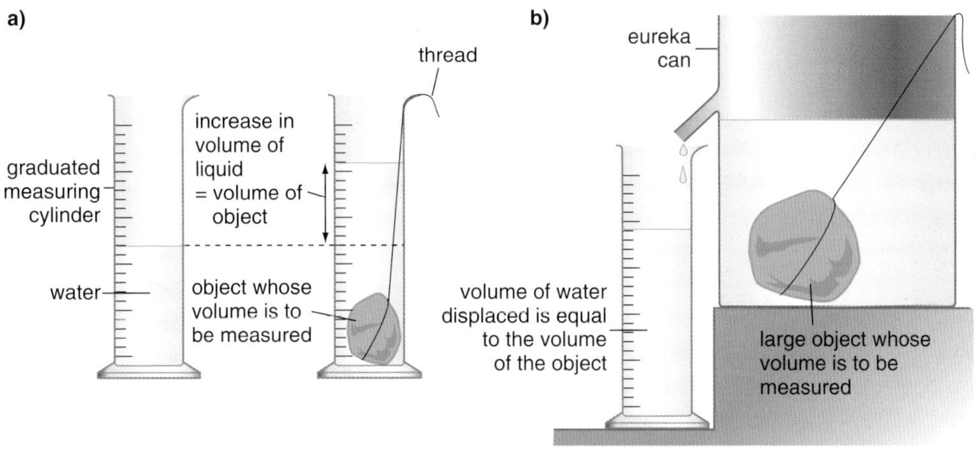

Figure 15a The volume of a small object can be measured in a measuring cylinder

b Measuring the volume of a large object requires a Eureka can

Liquid

In this method, first find out the mass of a dry, empty, graduated cylinder. The liquid under test is then poured into the cylinder and the volume measured. The mass of the cylinder and liquid is then measured (see Figure 16).

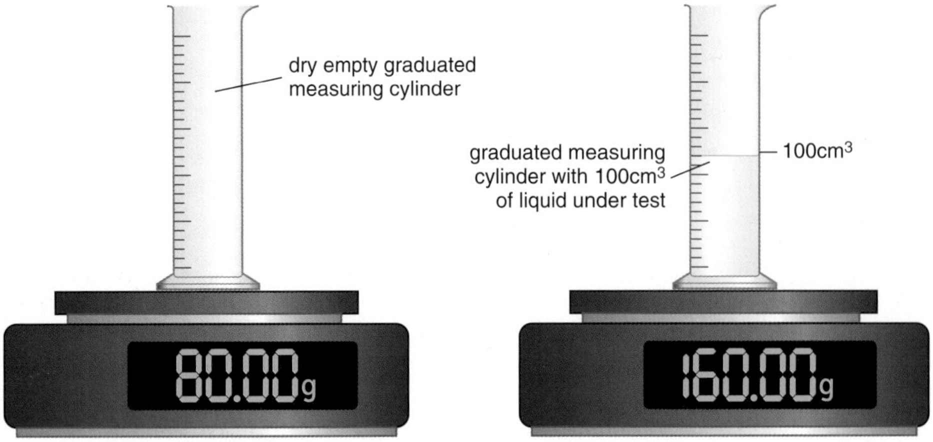

Figure 16 Calculating the density of a liquid

The mass of the specified volume of liquid is determined by subtracting the mass of the empty cylinder from the combined mass of cylinder and liquid. The density of the liquid is found as before, by dividing the mass of the liquid by its volume.

Questions

16 Consult Table 3 on page 43 to find which substance, of mass 57.9 g, has a volume of 3 cm^3.

17 Aluminium has a density of 2.7 g/cm^3.

a) What is the mass of 20 cm^3 of aluminium?

b) What is the volume of 54 g of aluminium?

18 A piece of steel of mass 120 g has a volume of 15 cm^3. Calculate its density.

19 Calculate the mass of air in a room of dimensions 10 m by 5 m by 3 m, if air has a density of 1.26 kg/m^3.

20 A stone of mass 60 g is lowered into a measuring cylinder causing the liquid level to rise from 15 cm^3 to 35 cm^3 . Calculate the density of the stone in g/cm^3.

21 The capacity of a petrol tank in a saloon car is 0.08 m^3. Calculate the mass of petrol in a full tank if the density of petrol is 800 kg/m^3.

22 The mass of an evacuated steel container, of volume 1000 cm^3, is 350 g. The mass of the steel container when full of air is 351.2 g. Calculate the density of air.

23 100 identical copper rivets are put into an empty measuring cylinder and 50 cm^3 of water are added. What is the volume of

a) 100 copper rivets?

b) 1 copper rivet?

c) If all the copper rivets together have a mass of 180 g, calculate the density of copper.

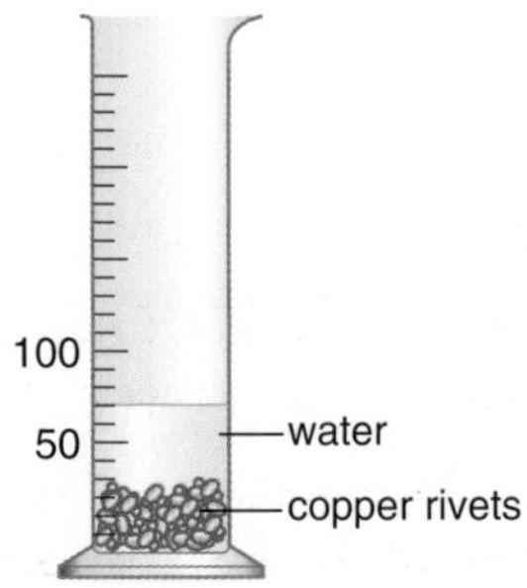

Hooke's Law

When a helical spring is loaded, it stretches.

The **natural length** is the normal length of the spring without a load on it.

The **extended length** is the length of the spring when loaded.

The difference between the extended and natural lengths is known as the **extension**:

i.e. Extension = Extended length − Natural length

Figure 17 shows a simple experiment to investigate the behaviour of a helical spring. The steps involved in this experiment are given below:

1 Measure the natural length of the spring.

2 Add 100 g (weight = 1.0 N) mass hanger.

3 Measure the extended length of the spring.

4 Calculate and record the extension.

5 Add a second 100 g slotted mass.

6 Repeat measurements and record results in a table, as shown.

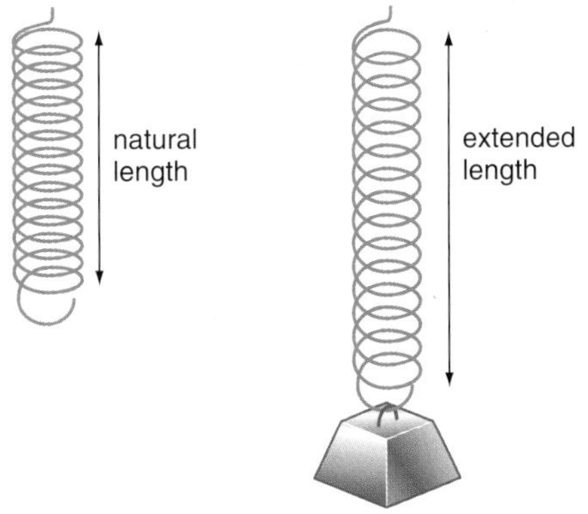

Figure 17

Load in N	Extended length in cm	Extension in cm
1		
2		
3		
4		
5		
6		

7 Draw a graph of load (N) on the y-axis versus extension (cm) on the x-axis.

The graph produced should show a straight line such as AB in Figure 18.

This experiment shows that the extension of a spring is proportional to the load. A material that behaves in this way is said to obey **Hooke's Law**:

> Extension is proportional to the load, provided the elastic limit is not exceeded.

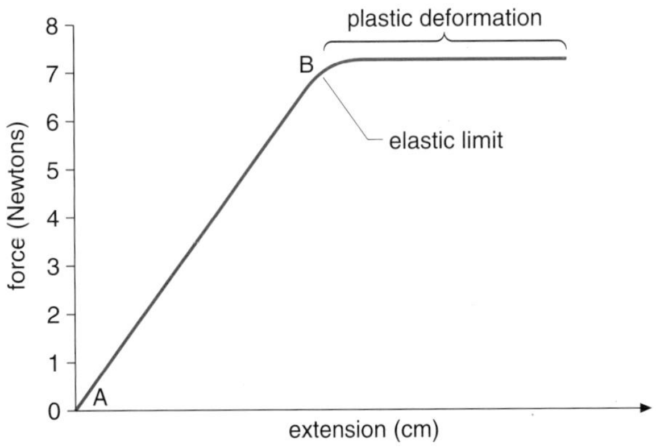

Figure 18

At point B the spring has reached its **elastic limit**, so no longer obeys Hooke's Law. Over the region AB of the graph, the spring shows elastic behaviour. This means that when the load is removed, the spring returns to its original length and shape.

If a load of more than 7 N (i.e. beyond point B) is applied to this spring, it goes beyond its elastic limit and so changes its shape permanently. When the load is removed, the spring does not return to its original shape. This is called **plastic deformation**.

Questions

24 The table shows the total length of a spring when different loads are applied.

Load in N	Total length in cm
2	12
3	15

a) What extension is produced in the spring by a load of 1 N?
b) Calculate the original length of the spring.

25 The spring in a chest expander has a natural length of 24 cm. A force of 1 N stretches the spring 0.4 cm. Calculate the force needed to stretch the spring to a total length of 60 cm.

26 The following results were obtained from a stretching experiment.

Force on the spring in N	0	1	2	3	4	5	6
Extension in cm	0	1.5	3.0	4.5	6.0	7.5	9.0

Force on the spring in N	0	1	2	3	4	5	6
Extension in cm	0	3.5	7.5	11.5	15.5	18.5	20

Plot graphs of force against extension for these results and mark any regions that follow Hooke's law.

27 Hannah is investigating Hooke's Law. She applied different loads to the same helical spring. She obtained the following incomplete set of results.

Load in N	0	3	6	9	12
Length of spring in cm	6	8	10	12	14
Extension in cm					

a) Complete the last row of Hannah's table of results.
b) Explain whether or not Hooke's Law was obeyed in Hannah's experiment.

Moments and levers

Moment of a force

Door handles are usually placed as far from the hinges as possible so that the door opens and closes easily. A much larger force would be needed if the handle was near the hinges. Similarly, it is easier to tighten or loosen a nut with a long spanner than with a short one.

The **turning effect** or **moment** of a force depends on two factors:

1 the size of the force
2 the distance the force is from the turning point or **pivot**.

(Occasionally you may see the word fulcrum which is the old English word for pivot.)

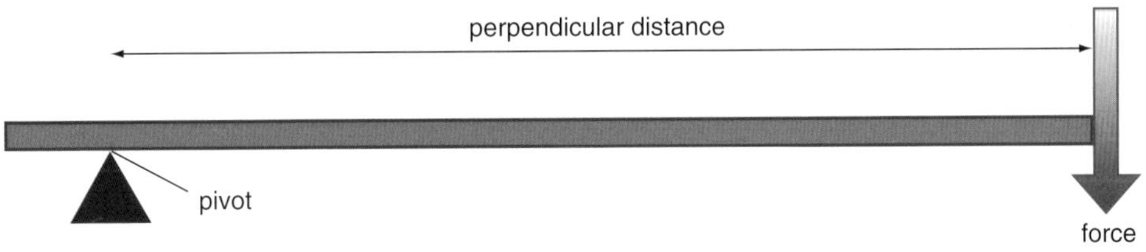

Figure 19 Calculating the moment of a force

The moment of a force is measured by multiplying the force by the perpendicular distance (the distance at right angles) of the line of action of the force from the pivot. This can be written as:

Moment of a force = Force × Perpendicular distance from the pivot

The unit of the moment of a force is the newton metre (Nm), when the force is measured in newtons (N) and the distance from the pivot is measured in metres (m).

Did you know?

Archimedes claimed that he could lift the Earth! He maintained that if he had a very long lever pivoted on the Atlas mountains, he could quite easily lift the Earth.

Example

Find the moment of a 100 N force applied at a perpendicular distance of 0.3 m from the centre of a nut.

Turning moment = Force × Perpendicular distance
= 100 N × 0.3 m
= 30 Nm

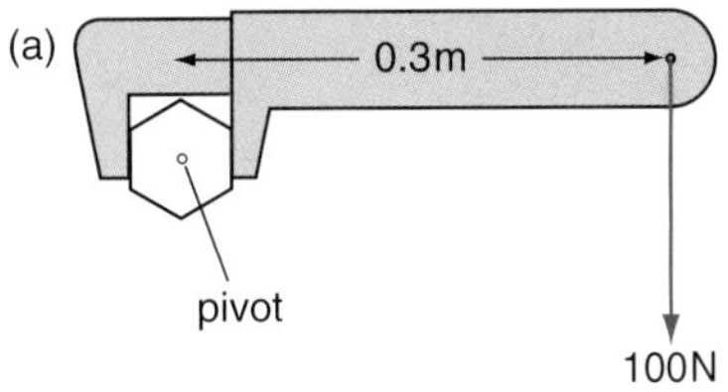

Investigating the principle of moments

The **principle of moments** can be investigated using the following method:

- Suspend and balance a metre stick at the 50 cm mark using twine.
- Adjust the position of the twine so that the rule does not rotate.
- Hang unequal masses, m_1 and m_2 (100 g slotted masses), from either side of the metre stick as illustrated in Figure 20.
- Adjust the position of the masses until the metre stick is balanced (in equilibrium) once again.

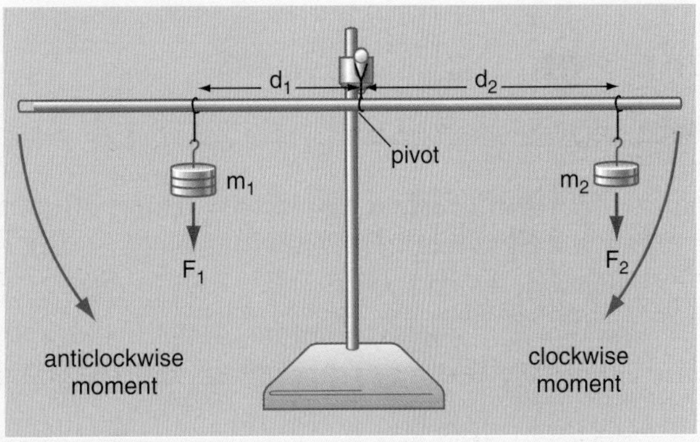

Figure 20 Experiment to investigate the principle of moments

- Gravity exerts forces F_1 and F_2 on the masses m_1 and m_2. Remember that a 100 g slotted mass is equivalent to 1 N. Record the results in the table and repeat for other loads and distances.

m_1 (g)	F_1 (N)	d_1 (cm)	$F_1 \times d_1$ (Ncm)	m_2 (g)	F_2 (N)	d_2 (cm)	$F_2 \times d_2$ (Ncm)

- The force F_1 is trying to turn the metre stick anticlockwise and $F_1 \times d_1$ is its moment. F_2 is trying to turn the metre stick clockwise, its moment is $F_2 \times d_2$.
- When the metre stick is balanced (i.e. in equilibrium), the results should show that the anticlockwise moment $F_1 \times d_1$ equals the clockwise moment $F_2 \times d_2$.

The principle of moments is as follows:

When a body is in equilibrium the sum of the clockwise moments about any point equals the sum of the anticlockwise moments about the same point.

Another very important consequence of the fact that the body is in equilibrium is that the forces acting on the metre stick in any direction must balance. The upward forces must balance the downward forces. This idea is very useful when doing problems.

Example

A boy, weighing 600 N, sits 6 m away from the pivot of a see-saw, as shown below.

a) What force 9 m from the pivot is needed to balance the see-saw.
b) Find the size of the upward force exerted by the pivot.

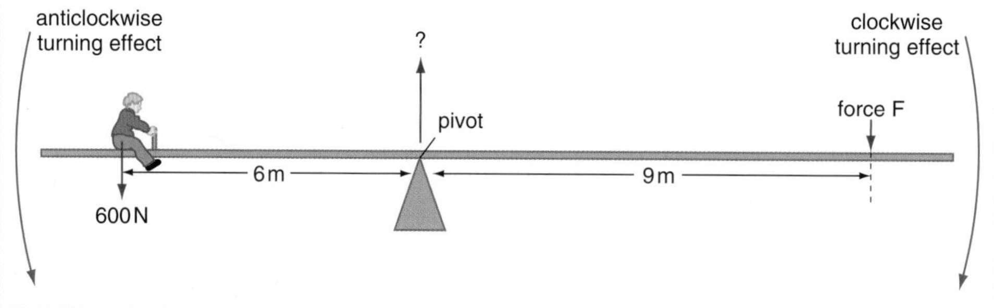

a) The force F exerts a clockwise turning effect about the pivot while the boy's weight exerts an anticlockwise turning effect. Since the see-saw is balanced, we can write

$$\text{Clockwise moment} = \text{Anticlockwise moment}$$
$$F \times \text{Distance from pivot} = 600\text{ N} \times \text{Distance from pivot}$$
$$F \times 9\text{m} = 600\text{ N} \times 6\text{ m}$$
$$F = \frac{600 \times 6}{9}$$

hence F = **400 N**

b) Also, since the body is balanced (in equilibrium):
The upward force at the pivot = The sum of the downward forces acting on the see-saw
= 400 N + 600 N
The upward force at the pivot = **1000 N**

Levers

Levers are very simple machines used frequently in everyday life. All levers work in the same sort of way. The lever turns about a point called the pivot (or fulcrum). A force – the **effort** (E) – is applied, usually near one end, and the load (W) is moved by the other end (see Figure 21).

Figure 21 A simple lever

In general, the effort, load and pivot can be arranged in three different ways. These are illustrated in Figure 22.

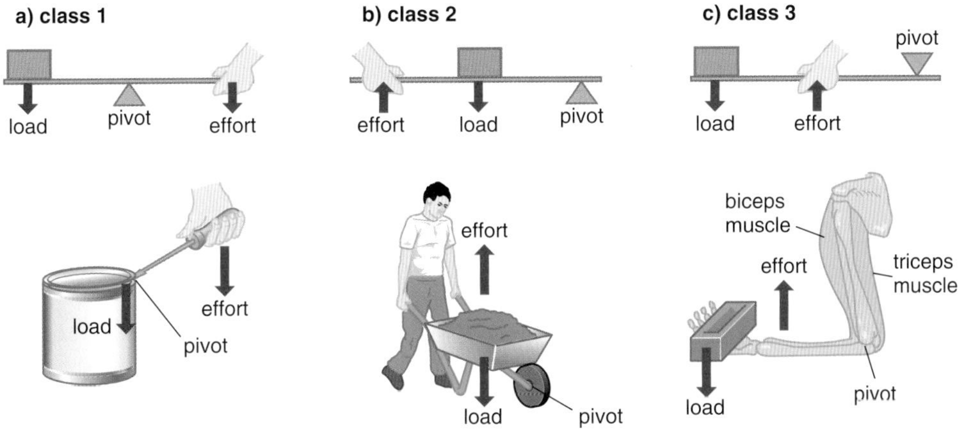

Figure 22 The three classes of levers, with a practical example of each

Figure 23 shows some examples of double levers.

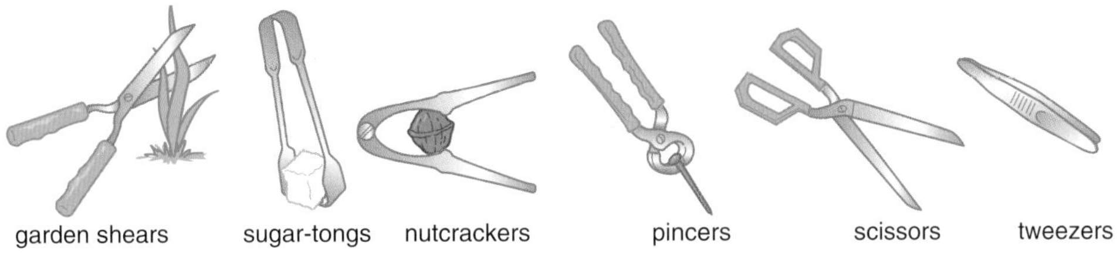

Figure 23 All these tools use the principle of a double lever

Questions

28 The diagram shows a car park barrier. The weight of the barrier is 150 N and its centre of mass is 0.9 m from the pivot.

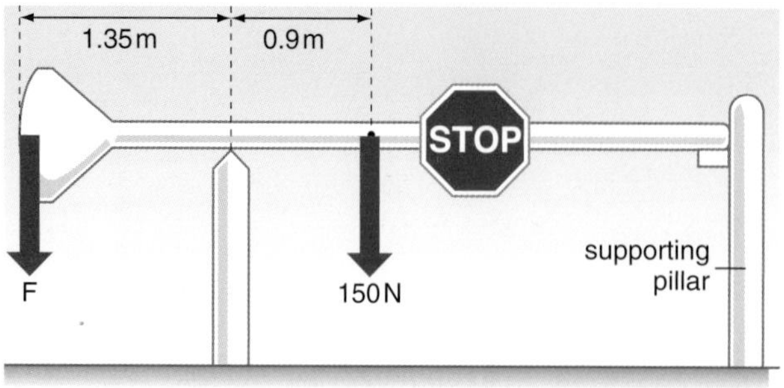

a) Calculate the size of the clockwise moment produced by the barrier's weight about the pivot.

b) Calculate the size of the force, F, on the left of the pivot which will just lift the barrier off the supporting pillar.

29 A uniform metre rule is pivoted at its midpoint. A load of 4 N acts on the right-hand side at a distance of 36 cm from the pivot.

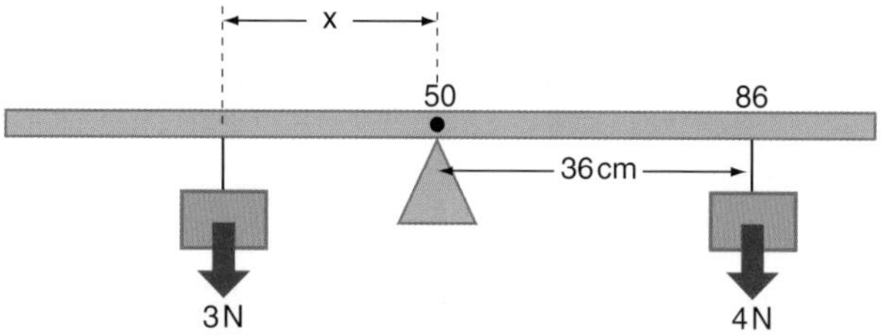

Calculate the distance from the pivot where you would place a 3 N weight to balance the metre rule.

30 The diagram below shows a plan view of a gate pivoted at C. The boy at A is pushing on the gate with a force of 100 N and a man at B is pushing in the opposite direction so that the gate does not move.

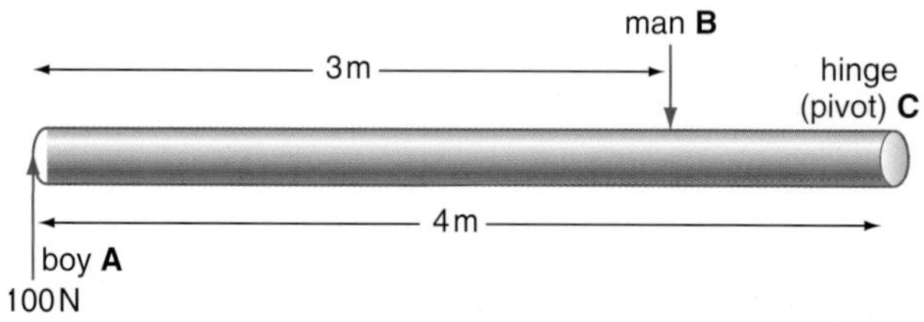

a) Calculate the moment of the force exerted by the boy about C.

b) What is the moment of the force exerted by the man about C?

c) What size of force is exerted by the man?

31 The centre of mass (see page 52) of an 80 cm snooker cue is 15 cm from its thick end. The cue balances on a pivot 40 cm from its thick end when a force of 5 N is applied to the thin area.

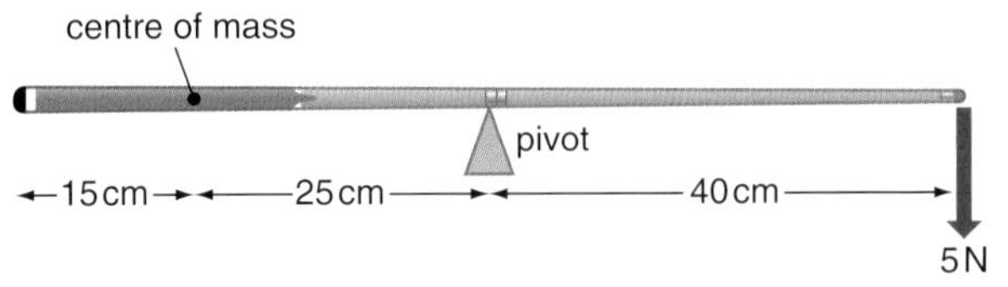

a) Calculate the moment of the 5 N force about the pivot and state the direction in which it acts.

b) Calculate the weight of the snooker cue.

32 A wheelbarrow and its load together weigh 600 N. The distance between the pivot and the wheelbarrow's centre of mass is 75 cm.

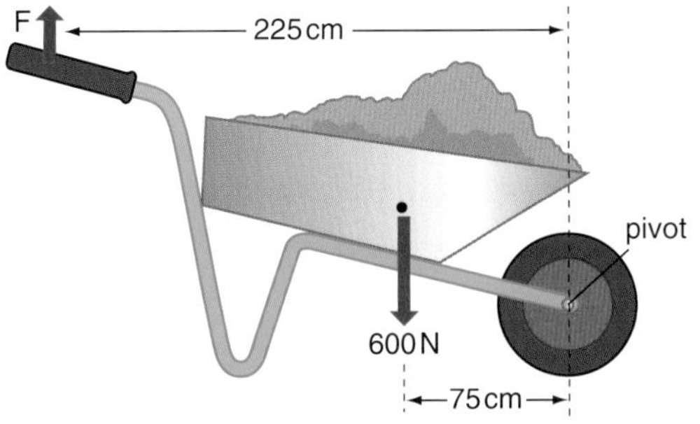

The distance between the handles and the pivot is 225 cm.

Calculate the size of the smallest force, F, needed to lift the wheelbarrow at the handles.

33 The diagram shows a side view of a uniform paving slab of weight 100 N.

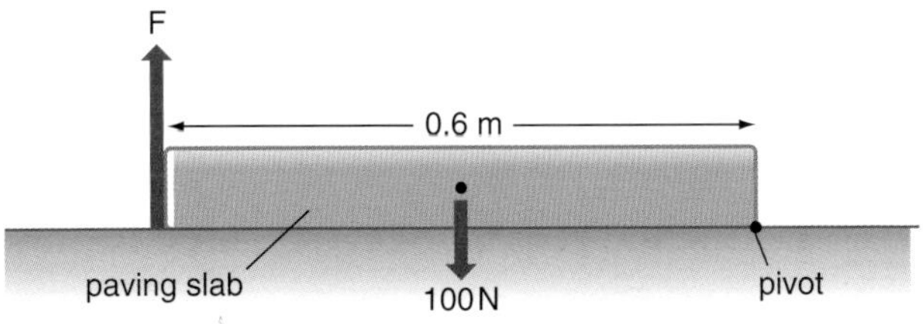

Calculate the smallest force, F, needed to lift the paving slab.

Centre of mass and stability

All objects have a point at which we can consider all their weight to be concentrated. This point is referred to as the **centre of mass**, sometimes called the **centre of gravity** of the object.

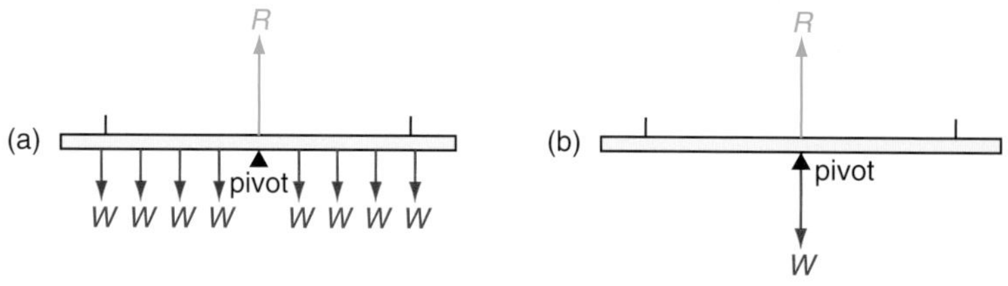

Figure 24

Figure 24a shows a metre stick that is balanced about its midpoint. You could imagine the metre stick as consisting of a series of 10 cm sections. The mass of each section is pulled towards the centre of the Earth by the force of gravity, so there are several small forces acting on the metre stick. But it is possible to replace all of these forces by a single resultant force acting through its centre of mass, G. This force may be balanced by the reaction exerted by the pivot, as illustrated in Figure 24b.

The centre of mass may be regarded as the point of balance. If a body has a regular shape, such as a flat disc or a rectangular sheet of metal, then the centre of mass is at its geometrical centre.

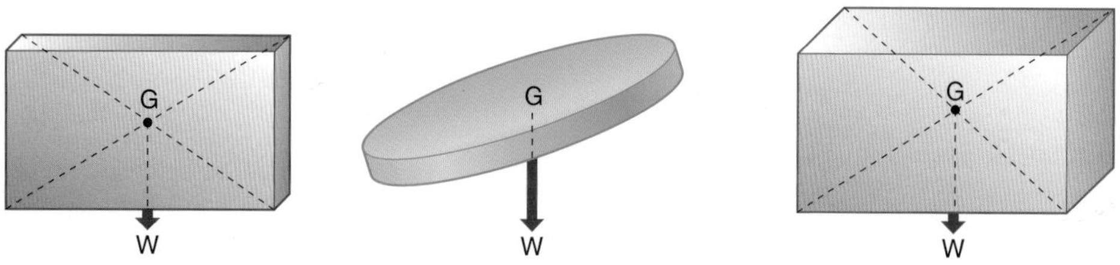

Figure 25 Working out the centre of gravity for regular objects

Flat triangular shapes are a little more difficult. In such cases, lines called **medians** are drawn from the corners of the triangle to the midpoints of the opposite sides. Where the medians intersect is the centre of mass.

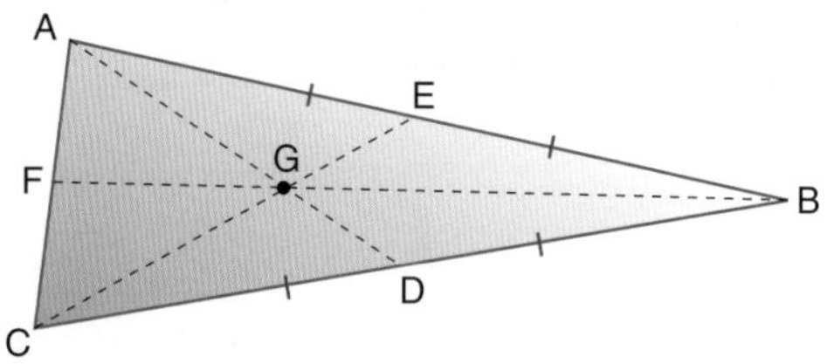

Figure 26 Where the medians intersect is the triangle's centre of mass

To find the centre of mass of an irregularly-shaped lamina

A **lamina** is a body, the shape of which is in the form of a flat thin sheet.

For this experiment, it is important to realise that when a body is suspended so that it can swing freely, it will come to rest with its centre of mass vertically below the point of suspension.

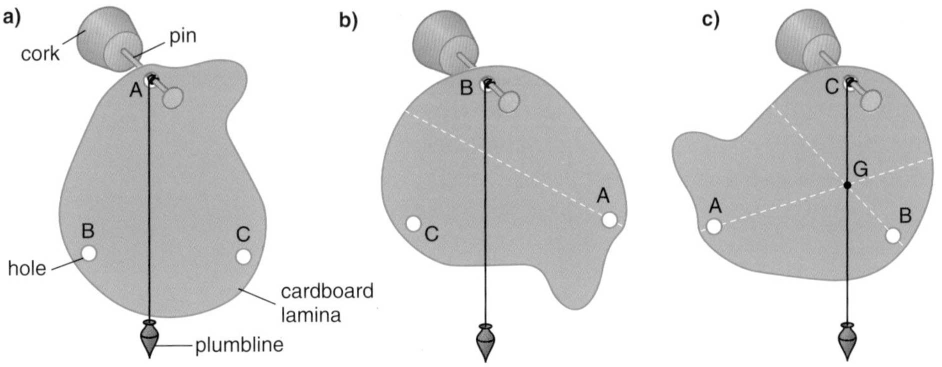

Figure 27 To find the centre of mass of an irregular lamina

The stages involved in this investigation are given below:

- Hang an irregularly-shaped sheet of cardboard from a pin, embedded into a cork.
- Hang a plumb-line from the same pin.
- When the cardboard settles, mark the vertical line with a pencil.
- Repeat from two further points.

The intersection of the vertical lines from the three points of suspension will fix the centre of mass.

Equilibrium and stability

A body is in **equilibrium** when both the resultant force and resultant turning effect on it are zero. There are three types of equilibrium which are determined by what happens to the object when it is given a small push.

1 A ball on a flat piece of ground is in **neutral equilibrium**. When given a gentle push, the ball rolls, keeping its centre of mass at the same height above the point of contact with the ground.

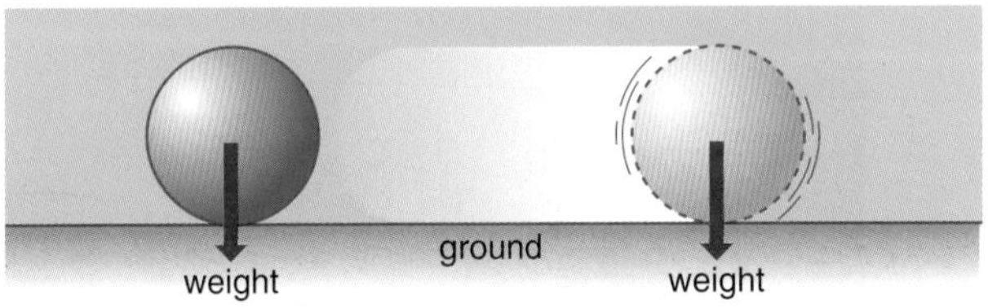

Figure 28 This ball is in neutral equilibrium with the ground

2 A tall radio mast is in **unstable equilibrium**. It is balanced with its centre of mass above its base, but a small push from the wind will move its centre of mass downwards. To prevent the mast toppling, it is stabilised with cables.

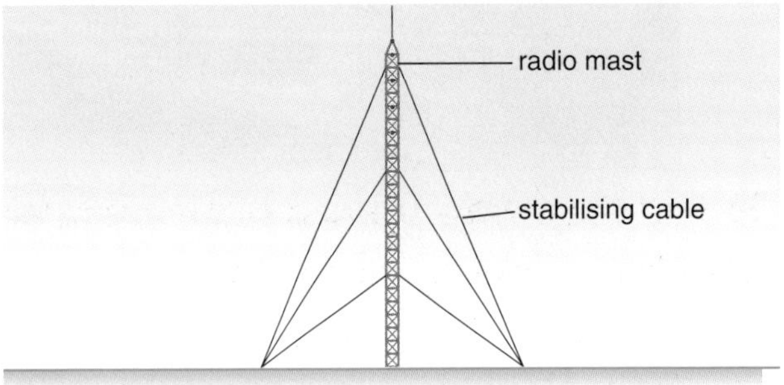

Figure 29 This radio mast is in unstable equilibrium

3 A car on the road is in **stable equilibrium** (Figure 30a). If the car is tilted, (b), the centre of mass is lifted. In this position, the action of the weight keeps the car on the road. In (c), the centre of mass lies above the wheels, so the car is in a position of unstable equilibrium. If the car tips further, (d), the weight provides the turning effect to turn the car over. Cars with a low centre of mass and a wide wheelbase are the most stable on the road.

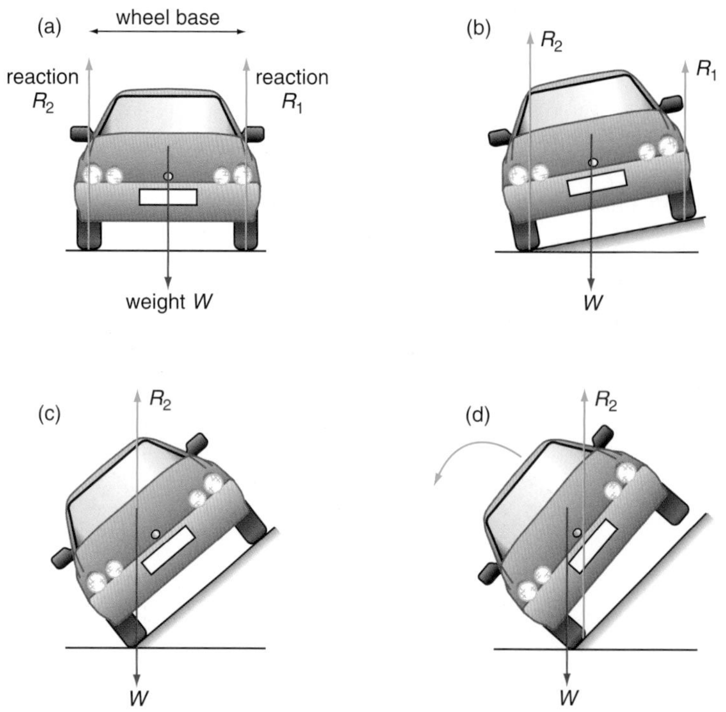

Figure 30 As the car tilts further, it becomes more and more unstable until at position (d), it topples over

Figure 31 This racing car is extremely stable because of its low centre of mass and wide wheelbase

Questions

34 The diagrams represent thin sheets of plastic.

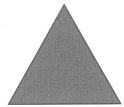

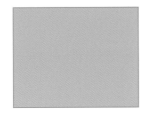

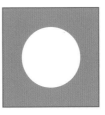

a) Copy out the diagrams and draw construction lines to show where the centre of mass of each plastic sheet is.
b) The central circular portion (shaded) has been cut out. If the centre of the circle is at the centre of the square, where will the centre of mass of this plastic sheet be?

35 a) What is meant by the centre of mass of an object?
b) The diagram below shows a pencil with a penknife attached balancing on its point.

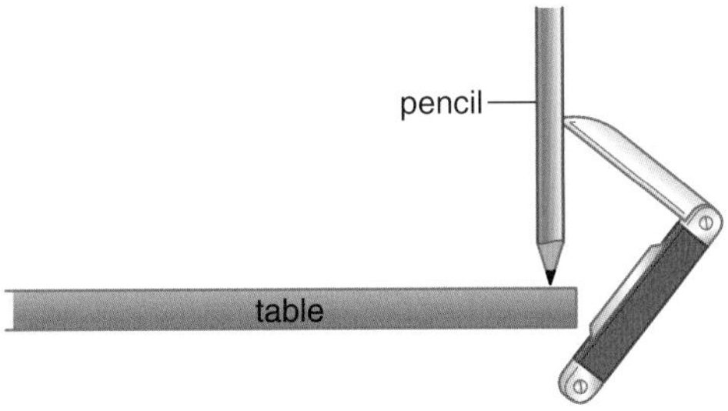

(i) Explain why this happens.
(ii) What would happen if the knife blade were closed slightly?

c) This diagram shows a piece of cardboard. Copy the diagram exactly and mark a possible position for the centre of mass.

36 The diagram below shows a cross-section through a racing car.

a) Copy the diagram and mark with a cross the approximate position of the centre of mass.
b) What two features of the car give it great stability?

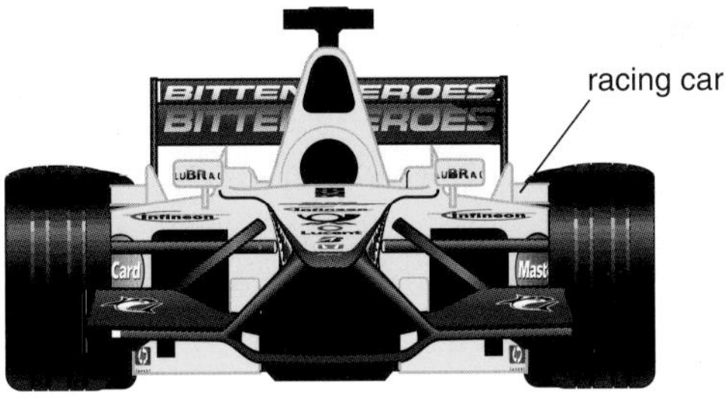

37 The diagrams below show cross-sections through two drinking glasses.

a) Copy the diagrams and mark with a cross the approximate position of the centre of mass of each glass.

b) Which glass is likely to be more stable?

c) Give two reasons for your answer to part b).

38 a) The diagram below shows a solid cone in stable equilibrium. Draw two further diagrams to illustrate a solid cone in (i) unstable and (ii) neutral equilibrium.

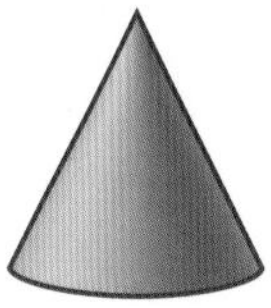

b) These diagrams show the cross-sections of two similarly-shaped table lamps, A and B. The bases in each case are solid.

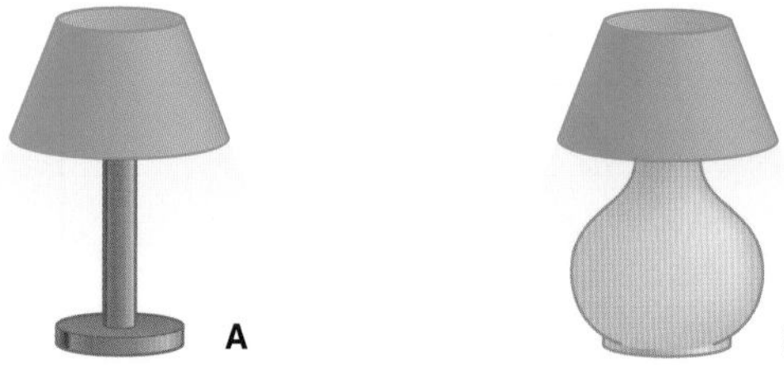

(i) Copy the diagrams and mark with a cross where you might expect the centre of mass to be.

(ii) Which lamp is likely to be more stable?

(iii) Give two reasons for your answer to part (ii).

39 a) The diagram shows a T-shaped lamina, in which QR is twice as long as AB.

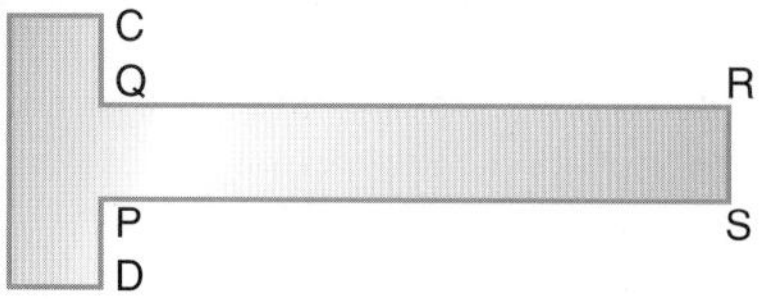

Copy the diagram and on it:

(i) Mark with a dot labelled X the centre of mass of the rectangle ABCD.

(ii) Mark with a dot labelled Y the centre of mass of the rectangle PQRS.

(iii) Mark with a dot labelled Z the approximate position of the centre of mass of the whole shape.

b) Sketch the shape of a lamina in which the centre of mass falls outside the shape itself. Mark on the sketch approximately where the centre of mass lies.

Pressure

Figure 32 illustrates a concrete slab lying on each of its sides on soft ground. The weight of the slab is the same irrespective of the side it is resting on, however the effect on the soft ground depends on the area of contact.

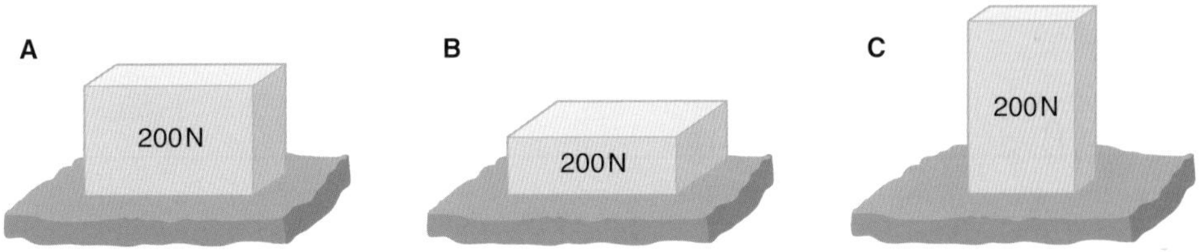

Figure 32

When the slab is lying on side A, the area of contact is very large but the force per m^2 is very small, hence the effect on the soft ground will be minimal. In contrast, the force per m^2 exerted by side C is very large, so the effect on the soft ground will be large.

We use the term **pressure** to describe how force is distributed normally (at right angles) over an area. If the force is spread out over a large area, as in the case of side C, we say that the pressure exerted on the ground is small. If the force is concentrated on a small area, as in the case of side A, we say that the pressure is large.

Pressure is defined as the ratio of the normal force to the area of contact.

$$\text{Pressure} = \frac{\text{Force}}{\text{Area}}$$

Or

$$P = \frac{F}{A}$$

When the units of force are in newtons (N) and the units of area are in m^2, then the units of pressure are in N/m^2 which are more properly called **pascals** (Pa).

The calculations for the pressure exerted by the concrete slab on each of its sides are given in Table 4.

Table 4 The pressure exerted by the slab on each of its sides A, B and C

Side of block in	A	B	C
Weight in N	200	200	200
Area of contact in m^2	4	2	1
Pressure in Pa	50	100	200

More often than not the normal force will be the weight of an object.

$$\text{Pressure} = \frac{\text{Weight}}{\text{Area}}$$

Examiner's tip

In calculations, the units for pressure may be in N/cm^2 or even N/mm^2. Use the units that the question demands – under no circumstances will you be expected to convert mm^2 or cm^2 to m^2.

It is clear from the pressure equation that the pressure that an object exerts is inversely proportional to the area of contact assuming the force does not change. In other words, as the area of contact increases, the pressure decreases and vice versa.

This fact has many practical applications, as shown in Figure 33.

a) A chef will spend time sharpening the carving knife before cutting the joint of meat, as a small area of contact means enormous cutting pressure.

b) The area of contact between the blade of an ice skate and the ice is very small. This results in very large pressure on the ice, producing a layer of water between the blade and the ice, reducing the frictional force and making skating effortless.

c) The weight of a woman when concentrated on a stiletto heel results in a very large pressure – so large that floors are easily damaged.

d) A JCB digger has very large rear wheels, so its huge weight is spread out. Consequently, the pressure which the JCB exerts on the soft ground is small, preventing it from sinking.

e) Snow shoes are used to make walking in snow much easier. The large area of the shoes reduces the pressure on the snow and so prevents sinking.

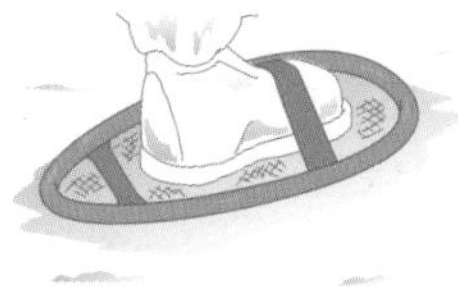

f) In some places, the ground is so soft that houses are built on rafts of concrete. The large area of concrete spreads the weight of the house, so it doesn't sink into the ground.

Figure 33

Example

A high-sided lorry has a side of $40\ m^2$. The wind exerts a pressure of 500 Pa on the side of the lorry. Calculate the force exerted by the wind on the lorry.

$$\text{Pressure} = \frac{\text{Force}}{\text{Area}}$$

$$\text{Force} = \text{Pressure} \times \text{Area}$$

$$\text{Force} = 500 \times 40$$

$$\text{Force} = \mathbf{20\,000\ N}$$

Questions

40 Explain each of the following:
a) You cannot push your thumb through a wooden desk, but with the same force, you can push a drawing pin into the wood.
b) When a fireman rescues a dog which has fallen through the ice on a frozen lake, he puts his ladder on the ice first and then crawls out to the dog on the ladder.
c) A Chieftain tank will not sink into soft ground.
d) A carpenter will sharpen his chisel before he starts work.

41 A girl weighs 600 N and the area of both her feet is 150 cm^2. Calculate the pressure she exerts on the floor. Give your answer in N/m^2.

42 A power washer can produce a fine water jet with a force of 56 000 N on an area of 0.005 m^2. Calculate the pressure which the washer can exert on the ground.

43 A large metal box is 0.8 m long, 0.5 m wide and 0.4 m deep. The box weighs 320 N. Calculate the areas of each of its faces and hence find the maximum and minimum pressures which the box can exert on the ground.

44 A ballet dancer standing on one of her points has a weight of 400 N. Calculate the pressure she exerts on her point if the area of her point is 2 cm^2.

45 A concrete slab measures 1 m $\times$ 0.5 m and exerts a pressure of 1000 Pa on the ground. Calculate the weight of the concrete slab.

46 Jim has a weight of 750 N. When standing on one foot he exerts a pressure of 3 N/cm^2 on the ground.
a) Calculate the area of contact between Jim's shoe and the ground.
b) How will the pressure exerted on the ground by Jim be affected if Jim now stands with both shoes on the ground?

47 A tractor has a mass of 3000 kg and the total area of its wheels in contact with the ground is 0.75 m^2. Calculate the pressure which the tractor exerts on the ground.

Hydraulics

Hydraulic machines, such as JCB diggers and car lifts in garages, are capable of exerting enormous forces. How do they do it?

Figure 34 Both these machines use hydraulic forces to lift huge weights

What is a hydraulic system?

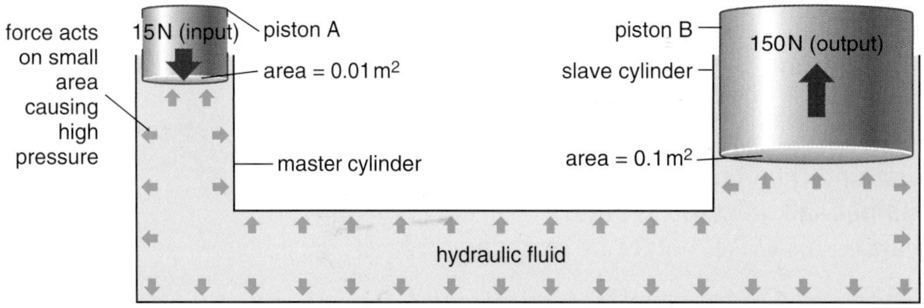

Figure 35 In this hydraulic system, the high pressure is transmitted by the fluid from the smaller piston, where the pressure is the same. As a result, the force is larger on piston B

Figure 35 illustrates a simple hydraulic system. A liquid is used to transmit a force to where it is needed. A force (the effort) is applied to a liquid using the master cylinder and piston. This puts the liquid under pressure. Liquids are virtually incompressible, so the pressure is transmitted instantaneously and evenly throughout the liquid. This causes a force to be applied at the slave piston. The size of the force depends on the relative cross-sectional areas of the pistons. It does not depend on the shape or angle of the interconnecting pipework.

Why liquids are incompressible

In a gas, the molecules are far apart and can easily be compressed. However, in a liquid the molecules are already very close together. Very large forces are needed to push them even a little closer. Because liquids are not compressible, if a force is applied at one end of a hydraulic system most of the force is passed on to the other.

Why is the applied force magnified?

Since the pressure is the same everywhere within the system, the pressure on both pistons must be the same.

Consider the lifting system in Figure 35.

$$\text{Pressure (Pa)} = \frac{\text{Force (N)}}{\text{Area (m}^2)}$$

Therefore

$$\frac{\text{Force applied to master cylinder (N)}}{\text{Cross-sectional area of master cylinder (m}^2)} = \frac{\text{Force applied to slave cylinder (N)}}{\text{Cross-sectional area of slave cylinder (m}^2)}$$

This can be rearranged to give

$$\text{Force applied to master cylinder (N)} = \text{Force applied to slave cylinder (N)}$$

$$= \frac{\text{Cross-sectional area of slave cylinder (m}^2)}{\text{Cross-sectional area of master cylinder (m}^2)}$$

Example

Let the area of piston A = 0.01 cm² and the force at A = 15 N.

Pressure at A = Force/Area = 15/0.01 = 1500 N/cm²

This means that if the area of piston B = 0.1 cm², then the force at B is:

Pressure = Force/Area

1500 = ?/0.1

Rearranging gives force exerted on slave piston (B) = **150 N**.

In other words, the hydraulic system will magnify the force. The larger the ratio of the areas of the pistons, the greater will be the output force.

Hydraulic braking systems

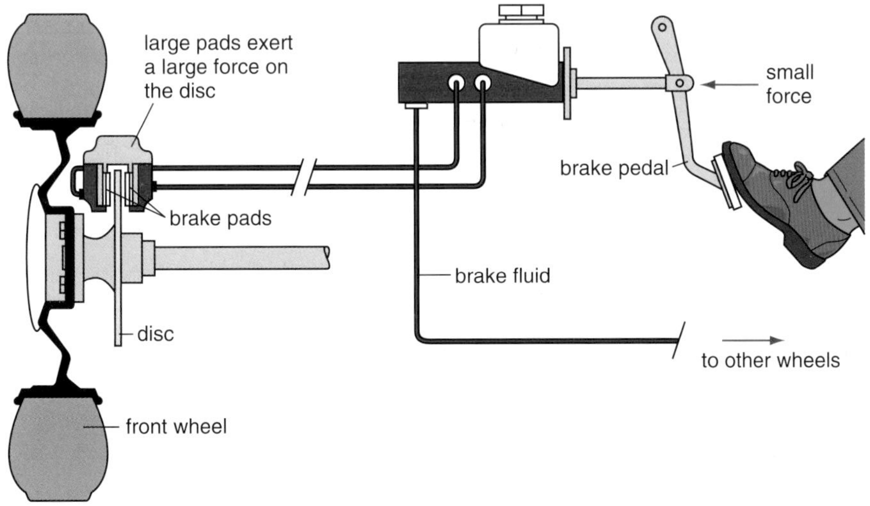

Figure 36 The hydraulic braking system of a car

When the brake pedal in Figure 36 is pressed, a force is applied to the piston of the master cylinder. The four slave cylinders apply a force to the brake pads to stop each of the wheels turning. All four pistons have the same cross-sectional area, so all apply the same braking force. What do you think would happen if the forces were different?

There are many useful applications of hydraulic systems:

- forces are transferred around JCB diggers through hydraulic hoses
- hydraulic lifts are used to raise cars in garages
- machine presses.

Questions

48 A brake master cylinder piston has an area of 1 cm^2. The piston in the brakes has an area of 5 cm^2. The master cylinder is pushed with a force of 600 N.

a) Calculate the pressure on the master cylinder piston.

b) What is the pressure on the brake piston?

c) Calculate the force applied to the brakes.

d) Explain why water is not used in car braking systems.

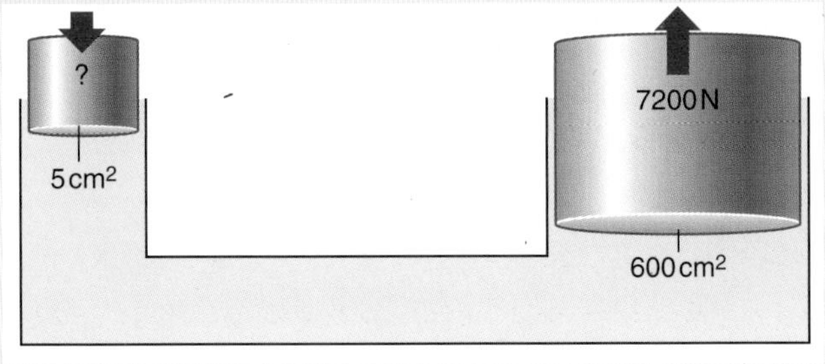

49 A hydraulic press has pistons with areas of 5 cm^2 and 600 cm^2. What force is needed on the smaller piston to support a load of 7200 N?

50 What properties of liquids make them suitable for use in hydraulic machines such as car brakes?

61 In a hydraulic brake, a force of 600 N is applied to a piston of area 5 cm^2.

a) What pressure is transmitted throughout the liquid?

b) If the other piston has an area of 20 cm2, what is the force exerted on it?

Websites

Use your favourite search engine (such as **www.google.com** or **www.excite.com**) and search using the key words:

Terminal velocity

Density

Hooke's Law

Principle of moments

Hydraulics

www.marshall.tstc.edu/pages/applied/mom2.html

www.explorescience.com/activities/activity_list.cfm?categoryID=10

http://library.thinkquest.org/10796/

www.marshall.tstc.edu/pages/applied/mom4.html

Exam questions

1 a) State Hooke's Law.

(2 marks)

b) The manufacturers of car seat belts are required by law to test how they behave when different forces are applied to them. A particular seat belt gave the following results.

Load in kN	Seat belt length in cm	Extension in cm
0	120.5	0
0.5	122.0	1.5
1.0	123.5	3.0
1.5	125.0	4.5
2.0	126.5	6.0
2.5	129.0	8.5
3.0	132.5	12.0

(i) What is the natural (unstretched) length of this seatbelt?

(2 marks)

(ii) Up to what load in kN does this seat belt obey Hooke's Law? Explain the reason(s) for your answer.

(3 marks)

(iii) When the load is removed the seat belt always gets shorter. In one case a load of 5 kN is applied and then removed and in another case a load of 1 kN is applied and then removed. In what way, if any, does the length of seat belt after the load is removed compare in these two cases?

(2 marks)

(iv) When a car is involved in a major accident it is wise to replace the seat belts. Use your knowledge as to how materials behave when stretched to suggest a reason why this is so.

(1 mark)

c) (i) Explain what is meant by density.

(2 marks)

(ii) Describe briefly how you could use a measuring cylinder half filled with water to find the volume of a bracelet. In your description state what measurements you would make and what calculation you would carry out.

(4 marks)

(iii) A certain bracelet has a volume of 2.4 cm^3 and a mass of 46 g. Calculate its density. Show clearly how you get your answer.

(3 marks)

(iv) The bracelet is made from a metal which is almost 100% pure. Use your answer to part (iii) and the table below to find out what the metal is.

Metal	Copper	Gold	Lead	Platinum
Density in g/cm^3	8.9	19.3	11.3	21.5

(1 mark)

2 a) State the principle of moments. *(3 marks)*

b) A hydraulic jack can be used to lift heavy objects. The diagram below shows a simplified version of such a jack.

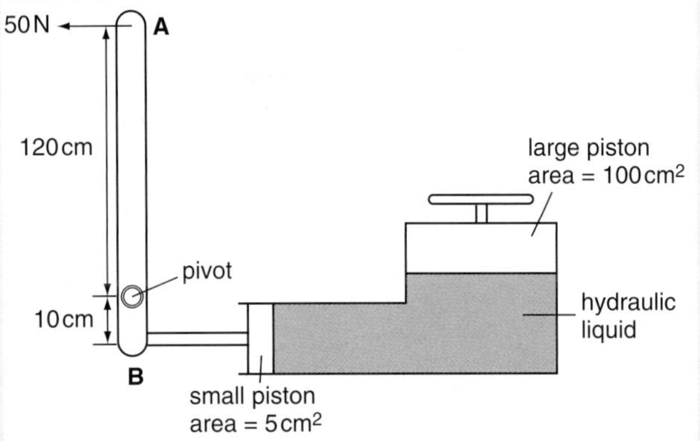

(i) Explain, in terms of force and pressure, how the movement of the small piston to the right causes the large piston to rise. *(2 marks)*

(ii) Susan pulls the lever at the end A with a force of 50 N. Show that the force produced at B on the lever is 600 N. *(4 marks)*

(iii) The area of the small piston is 5 cm^2. Calculate the pressure acting on the liquid when the force on the small piston is 600 N. Show clearly how you get your answer. *(4 marks)*

(iv) The area of the large piston is 100 cm^2. Calculate the force exerted on the large piston due to the hydraulic liquid. Show clearly how you get your answer. *(2 marks)*

c) A heavy ball, of mass 10 kg, is dropped from a height of 5 metres.

(i) What is the potential energy lost by the ball during this fall? Show clearly how you get your answer. *(5 marks)*

(ii) Calculate the velocity of the ball at the bottom of the fall. Show clearly how you get your answer. *(4 marks)*

3 a) (i) Explain what is meant by density. *(1 mark)*

Data relating to a particular concrete slab are given below.

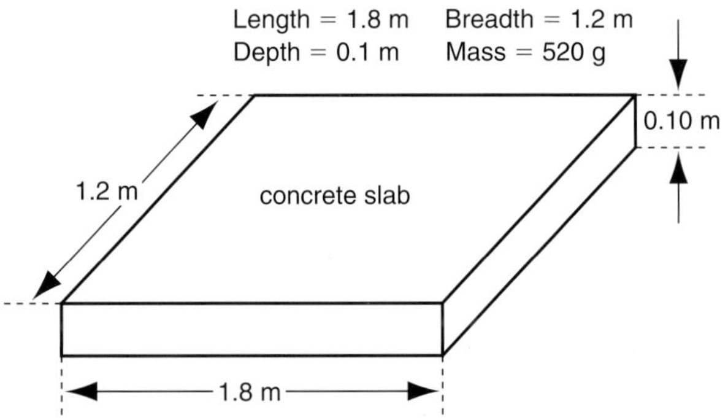

(ii) Use the data in the table to calculate the volume of this concrete slab. Show clearly how you get your answer. *(4 marks)*

(iii) For bridge construction the concrete slabs must have a density of at least 2350 kg/m^3. Is this particular slab dense enough to be used for bridge construction? Show clearly how you get your answer. *(4 marks)*

(b) (i) Explain what is meant by pressure. *(1 mark)*

An oil jet is used to cut brittle candy into bars as shown below.

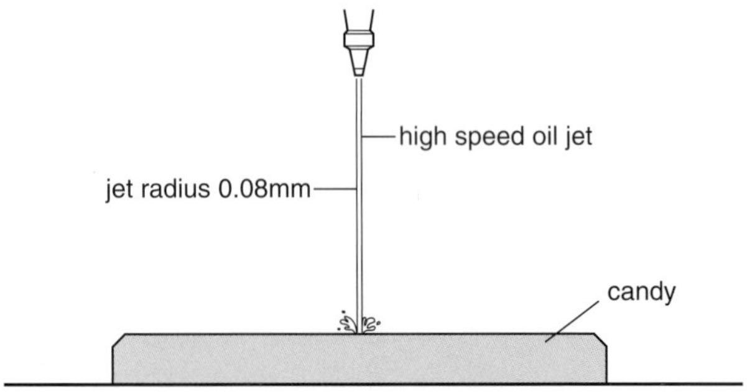

(ii) The jet has a radius of 0.08 mm at the surface of the candy. Calculate the surface area of the candy in contact with the oil jet, giving your answer in mm^2 and in m^2. Show clearly how you get your answer. *(4 marks)*

The pressure of the oil jet on the candy is 180 MPa.

(iii) What pressure, in pascals, is exerted by the oil jet on the candy.
(1 mark)

(iv) Use your answers to parts (ii) and (iii) to calculate the force which the oil jet exerts on the candy.
(3 marks)

c) (i) Explain what is meant by the centre of mass of an object.
(1 mark)

The diagram below shows a wheelbarrow at rest on level ground.
The weight of the wheelbarrow and its contents is 1500 N.

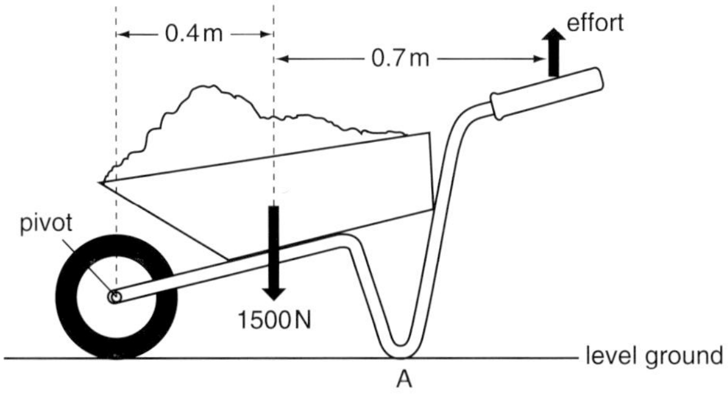

(ii) Use the values on the diagram to calculate the moment of the 1500 N force about the pivot.
Show clearly how you get your answer.
(5 marks)

(iii) Use your answer to part c)(ii) to calculate the effort that must be applied to the handles, if the wheelbarrow is just to lift off the ground at A.
Show clearly how you get your answer.
(4 marks)

(iv) What is the upward vertical reaction (supporting force) from the ground through the pivot, when the wheelbarrow is just lifted off the ground by the effort?
Show clearly how you get your answer.
(2 marks)

Chapter 3

Motion

Learning objectives

By the end of this chapter you should know:

- The difference between distance and displacement
- How to calculate speed
- The difference between speed and velocity
- How to define and calculate acceleration
- How to draw a distance–time graph
- How to calculate speed from the gradient of a distance–time graph
- How to draw a velocity–time graph
- How to calculate acceleration from the gradient of a velocity–time graph
- That the area under a velocity–time graph is the displacement
- That friction is a force that opposes motion
- The factors which affect braking distance
- Several examples of circular motion
- How to define centripetal forces
- Some examples of forces which provide the centripetal force
- What happens when the centripetal force is removed

Motion in a straight line

Distance and displacement

The **distance** between Belfast and Coleraine is 100 km.

But the **displacement** of Belfast from Coleraine is 100 km south-east. We can define displacement as distance *in a specified direction*. Displacement is represented by an arrow. The length of the arrow is proportional to the distance and the direction of the arrow is in the same direction as the displacement (see Figure 2).

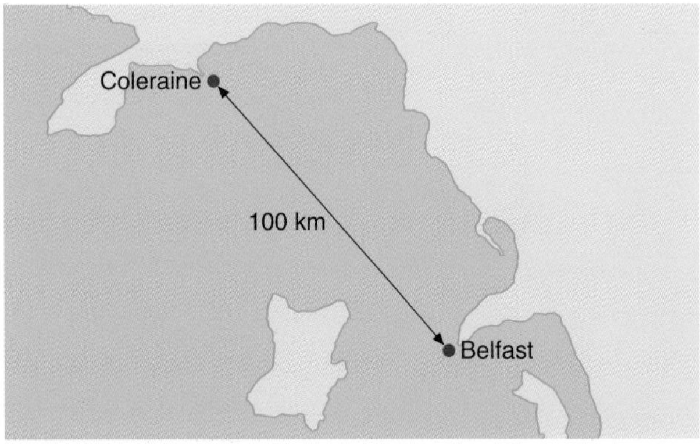

Figure 1 The distance between Coleraine and Belfast

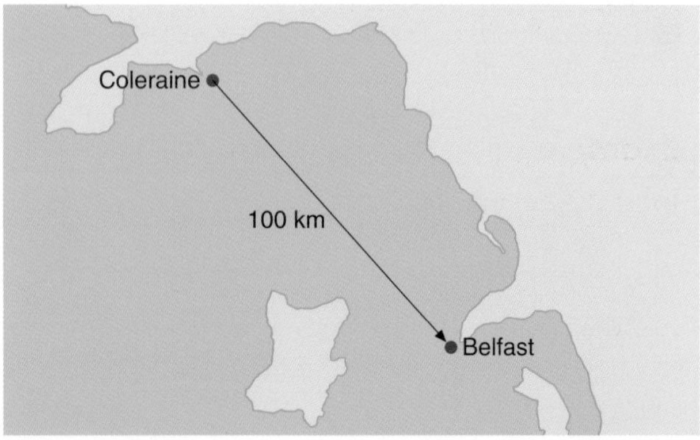

Figure 2 The displacement of Belfast from Coleraine

The return journey from Coleraine to Belfast and then back again is a distance of 200 km but the displacement is 0 km!

We say that distance is a **scalar quantity** – a quantity with size only – whereas displacement is a **vector quantity**, as it has size *and* direction.

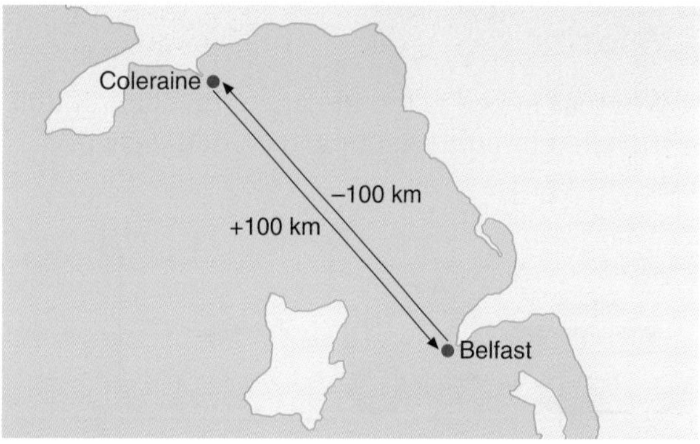

Figure 3 The displacement on a return journey is 0 km

Speed

If a car travels between two points on a road, its average speed can be calculated using the following formula:

$$\text{Speed} = \frac{\text{Distance moved}}{\text{Time taken}}$$

If distance is measured in metres (m) and time in seconds (s), speed is measured in metres per second (m/s).

For example, if a car travels from Coleraine to Belfast in 2 hours, its average speed is:

$$100\ \text{km}/2\ \text{h} = 50\ \text{km/h}$$

The speedometer would certainly not read 50 km/h for the whole journey but might vary considerably from this value. The driver may decide to stop for a rest or he might overtake another car and be travelling faster than 50 km/h. Hence we talk about the **average speed**, the formula for which is:

$$\text{Average speed} = \frac{\text{Total distance travelled}}{\text{Time taken}}$$

To find the actual speed at a particular moment in time, we would need to know the distance travelled in a very short interval of time.

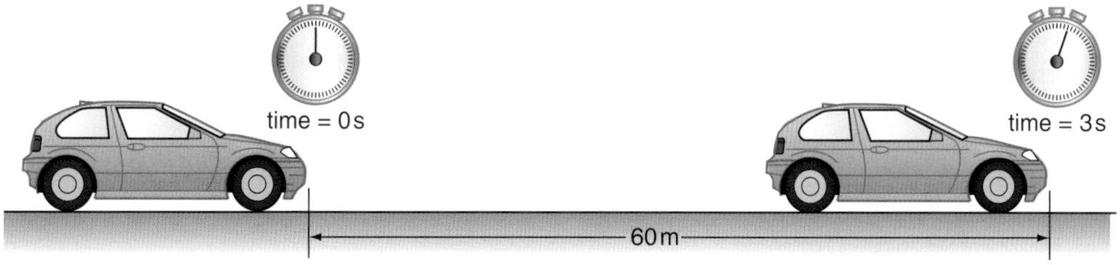

Figure 4 Measuring speed

Example

Find the speed of a car which travels 60 m in 3 s.

$$\text{Speed} = \frac{\text{Distance}}{\text{Time}}$$

$$= \frac{60\ \text{m}}{3\ \text{s}}$$

$$= \mathbf{20\ m/s}$$

Did you know?

The fastest passenger airliner is the Russian Tupolev Tu-144. It is reported to have reached a maximum speed of 1600 miles/hour or Mach 2.4.

Velocity

Whereas speed is the distance travelled in unit time, **velocity** is the distance travelled in unit time in a specified direction.

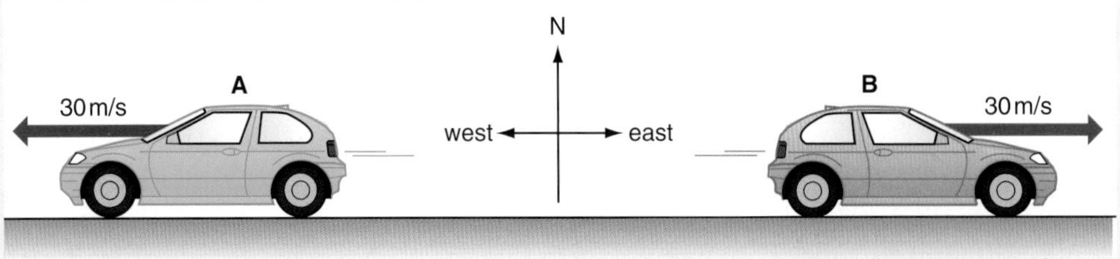

Figure 5 These two cars have the same speed, but a different velocity

Looking at Figure 5, car A has the same speed as car B but a different velocity. Car A's velocity is 30 m/s due west while car B has a velocity of 30 m/s due east.

Speed is a scalar quantity and velocity a vector quantity.

$$\text{Velocity} = \frac{\text{Distance travelled in a specified direction}}{\text{Time taken}}$$

Because displacement is the distance travelled in a specified direction, we can rewrite the formula for velocity as:

$$\text{Velocity} = \frac{\text{Displacement}}{\text{Time taken}}$$

The units for speed and velocity are the same, metres per second (m/s), though occasionally, you will see the units of kilometres per hour (km/h).

The car in Figure 6 is moving at a steady or constant speed of 20 m/s along a straight road and then goes round a bend.

The speed of the car at A, B and C is 20 m/s, but the velocity changes as it travels from B to C. This is because velocity is a vector quantity and although the size of the velocity may be constant at 20 m/s, its direction is constantly changing, so its velocity is constantly changing.

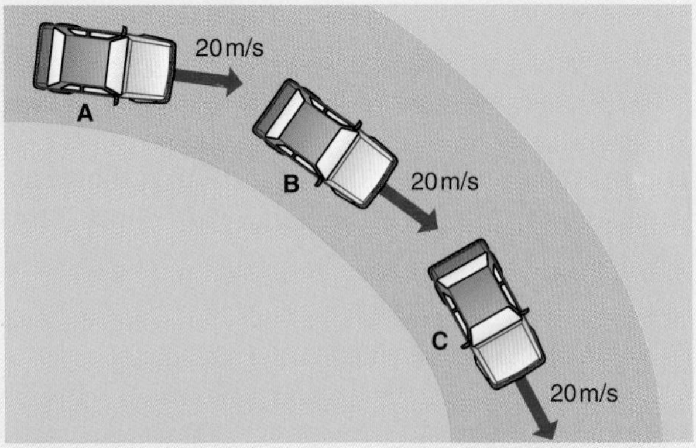

Figure 6 The velocity of the car changes as it goes around the bend

Acceleration

When the velocity of a body increases or decreases we say it accelerates. Consider the example in Figure 7. The car starts from rest (velocity = 0), but after one second its velocity has increased to 3 m/s. After two seconds its velocity has increased by 3 m/s to 6m/s. We say that the car's velocity increases by 3 m/s in one second due east, i.e. its **acceleration** is 3 m/s^2 due east.

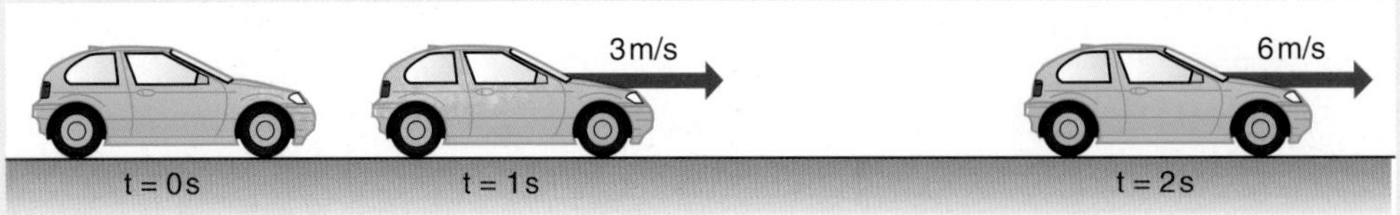

Figure 7 This car is accelerating

We can define acceleration as the change in velocity in unit time.

$$\text{Acceleration} = \frac{\text{Change in velocity}}{\text{Time taken}}$$

Acceleration is measured in metres per second per second, written as m/s^2. Because acceleration is a vector quantity, it can be shown using an arrow (often double-headed). Alternatively, a '+' or '−' sign can be used to indicate whether the velocity is increasing or decreasing.

For example:

$+3\ m/s^2$ (velocity increasing by 3 m/s every second)
$-3\ m/s^2$ (velocity decreasing by 3 m/s every second)

A negative acceleration is called a **deceleration** or a **retardation**.

A uniform acceleration means a constant (steady) acceleration.

In terms of symbols:

If v = final velocity
u = initial velocity
t = time taken

Then v − u = change in velocity

$$\text{Acceleration, } a = \frac{v - u}{t}$$

Multiplying across by t

$$at = v - u$$

$$v = u + at$$

Questions

1 A car travels 800 m in 40 s.

a) What is its average speed?
b) Why is its actual speed usually different from its average speed.

2 A car has a steady speed of 10 m/s.

a) How far does the car travel in 9 s?
b) How long does it take the car to travel 220 m?

3 Explain the difference between

a) distance and displacement, and
b) speed and velocity.

4 Calculate the average speed of each object.

a) 

this runner travels 400 m in 44 s

b) 

this car travels 175 miles in 3 hours

c) 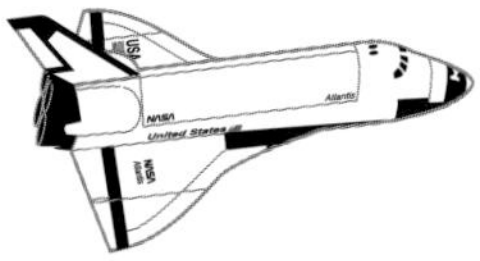

this shuttle travels 43750 miles in 2.5 hours

5 a) A train has an acceleration of 3 m/s^2. What does this tell you about the velocity of the train?
b) A bus has a deceleration of 2 m/s^2. What does this tell you about the velocity of the bus?

6 A car takes 8 s to increase its velocity from 3 m/s to 30 m/s. What is its acceleration?

7 A motorbike, travelling at 25 m/s, takes 5 s to come to a halt. What is its deceleration?

8 An aircraft on take-off has a uniform acceleration of 4 m/s^2.
a) What velocity does the aircraft gain in 5 s?
b) If the aircraft passes a point on the runway at a velocity of 28 m/s, what will its velocity be 8 s later?

9 A ball is thrown vertically upwards in the air, leaving the hand at 30 m/s. The acceleration due to gravity is 10 m/s^2.

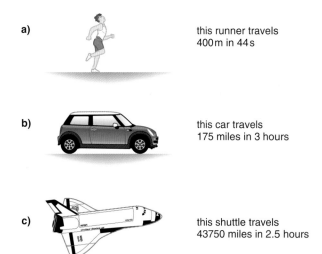

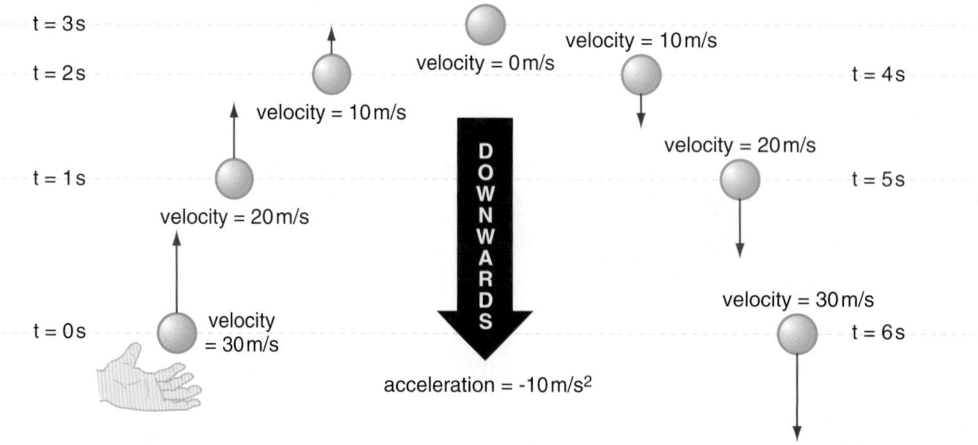

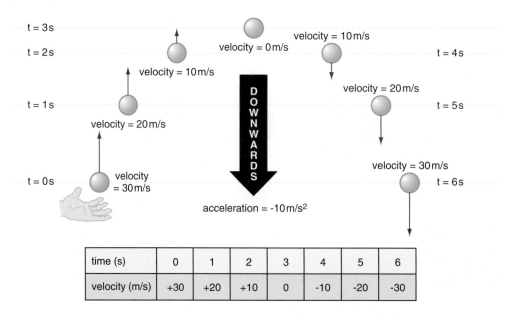

time (s)	0	1	2	3	4	5	6
velocity (m/s)	+30	+20	+10	0	-10	-20	-30

Draw a graph to show the motion of the ball. Plot velocity on the y-axis and time on the x-axis.

Graphs and motion

Graphs are a very useful way of displaying the motion of objects. There are two main types of graphs used in Physics:

1 Distance–time graphs **2** Velocity–time graphs.

1 Distance–time graphs

A **distance–time** graph is a plot of distance on the y-axis versus time on the x-axis.

The simplest type of distance–time graph is shown in Figure 8.

This graph illustrates that although the time increases steadily, the distance travelled is not changing. The body must be **stationary**.

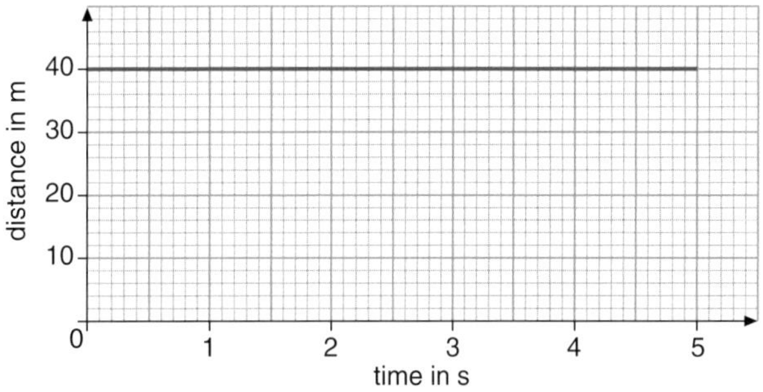

Figure 8 A simple distance–time graph of a stationary body

A horizontal line on a distance–time graph means that the body is stationary.

In contrast, Figure 9 shows that the distance is increasing by 5 m in every second, i.e. the body is travelling with uniform speed covering equal distances in equal units of time.

$$\text{The slope of the graph} = \frac{AB}{OB}$$

$$= \frac{20 - 0}{4 - 0}$$

$$= \frac{20}{4}$$

$$= \mathbf{5\ m/s}$$

The speed the body is travelling is 5 m/s.

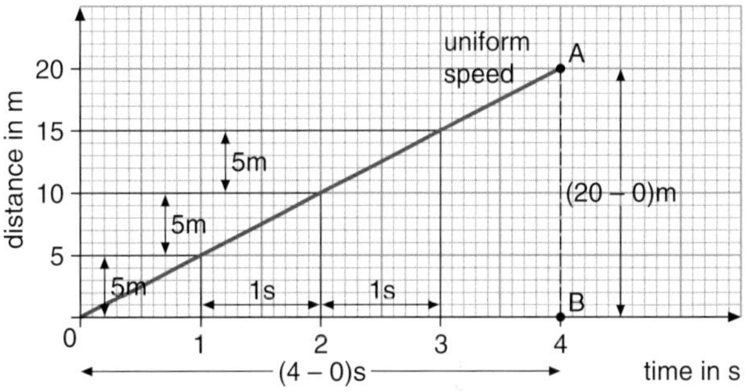

Figure 9 A distance–time graph of a body moving with uniform speed

The slope or gradient of a distance–time graph represents the speed.

When the velocity is changing, the slope of the distance–time graph changes. In Figure 10, the slope is increasing which means that the body is accelerating.

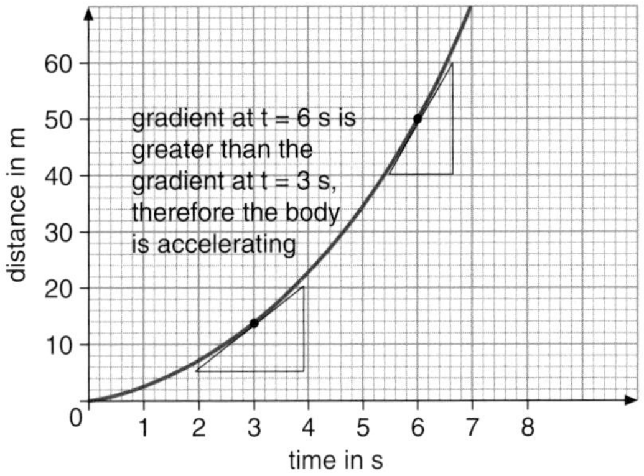

Figure 10 A distance–time graph for a body which is accelerating

2 Velocity–time graphs

A **velocity–time graph** is a plot of velocity on the y-axis versus time on the x-axis.

The simplest type of velocity–time graph is shown in Figure 11.

This graph shows that while time is increasing, the velocity remains at a constant (steady) 30 m/s. The car is not accelerating.

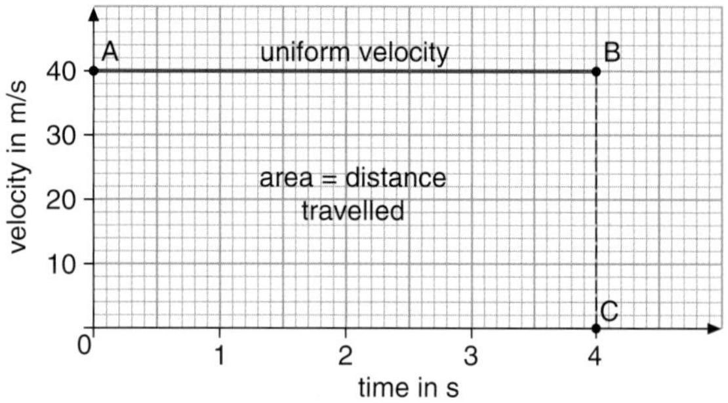

Figure 11 A velocity–time graph for a car going at a constant velocity

> The area under a velocity–time graph represents the displacement travelled.

For example, in Figure 11, the area of the rectangle OABC is:

$= OA \times OC$

$= 40 \text{ m/s} \times 4 \text{ s}$

$= \mathbf{160\ m}$

The displacement travelled by the car is 160 m.

In Figure 12,OD is the velocity–time graph for a body accelerating uniformly from rest.

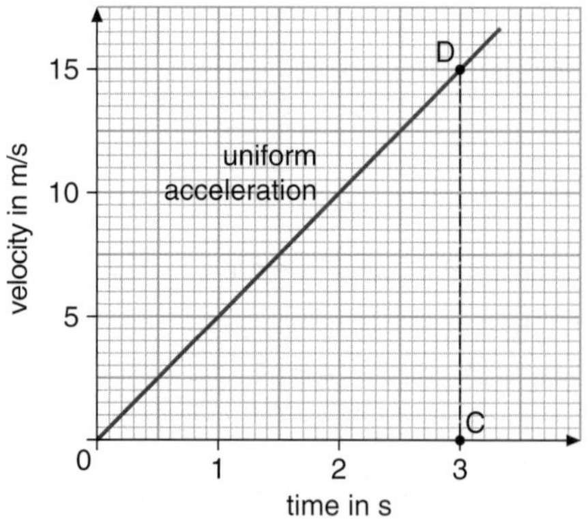

Figure 12 A velocity–time graph for a body accelerating uniformly

> The slope or gradient of a velocity–time graph represents the acceleration of the body.

For example, in Figure 12:

$$\text{Acceleration} = \text{gradient} = \frac{DC}{OC}$$

$$= \frac{15 - 0}{3 - 0}$$

$$= \frac{15}{3}$$

$$= \mathbf{5\ m/s^2}$$

Futhermore, the area of the triangle OCD gives the displacement travelled.

$$\text{Displacement} = \text{Area of triangle OCD}$$

$$= \frac{1}{2} \times OC \times CD$$

$$= \frac{1}{2} \times 3 \times 15$$

$$= \mathbf{22.5\ m}$$

The relationship between average velocity, time and displacement

Consider a general graph, see Figure 13, of a body uniformly accelerated from an initial velocity u to a final velocity v under an acceleration a for a time of t seconds.

The area of the trapezium is the displacement s.

s = Average of the parallel sides × base

$= \frac{1}{2}(v + u)t$

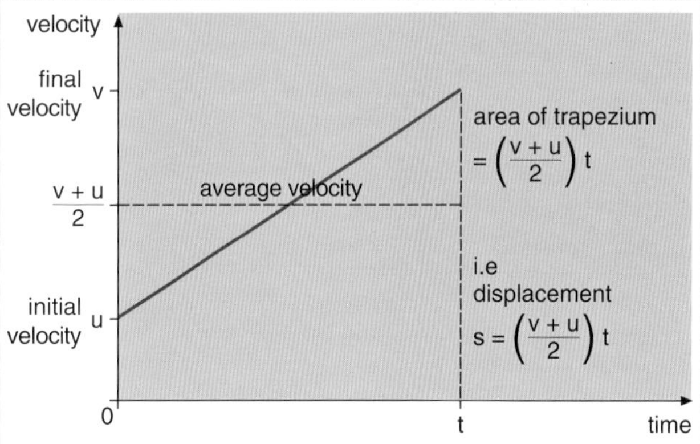

Figure 13 Graph showing relationship betwween velocity, time and displacement

Questions

10 Paul and Jim set off at the same time from their separate houses to walk to a nearby shop.

The table below shows the distances travelled by Paul to the shop.

Distance walked by Paul in m	0	3	6	9	12	15	18	21
Time elapsed in seconds	0	1	2	3	4	5	6	8

a) Draw a graph of distance against time for Paul's journey.

The table below shows the distances travelled by Jim to the same shop.

Distance walked by Jim in m	0	2	4	6	8	10	12	14
Time elapsed in seconds	0	1	2	3	4	5	6	7

b) Draw a graph of distance against time for Jim's journey on the same axis.

c) Use the graphs to answer the following questions.
 (i) Which walker is going faster?
 (ii) How long does it take Paul and Jim to walk 11 m?
 (iii) How far apart are Paul and Jim after 2.5 s?
 (iv) Is Paul's speed steady?
 (v) What is Jim's average speed?

11 Study the velocity–time graph below and describe in words the motion of the object.

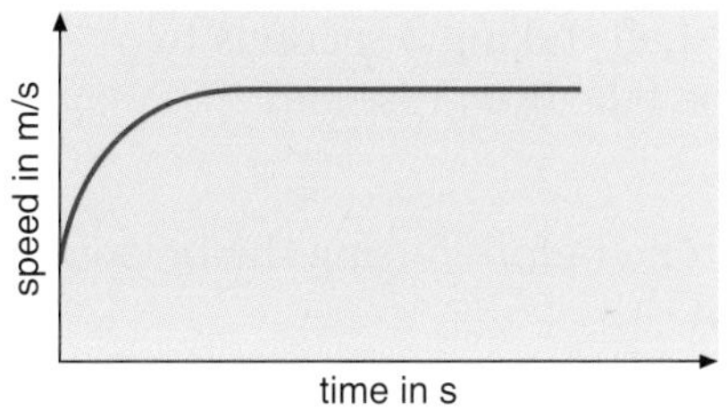

12 The diagram below shows a velocity–time graph for a car accelerating away from a junction. Calculate:

a) the acceleration during the first 5 s and
b) the total displacement.

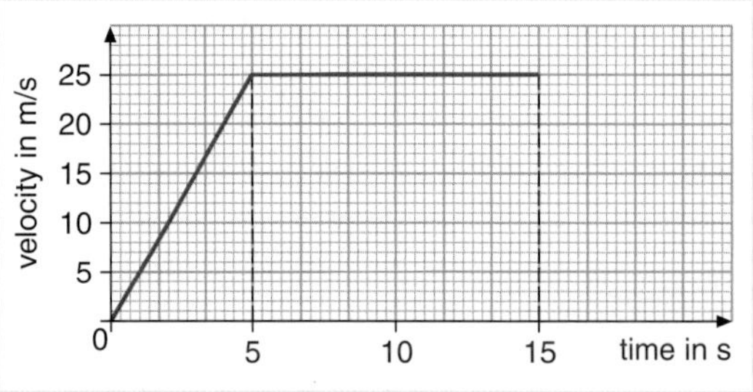

13 The sketch graph below represents a journey in a lift in a hospital.

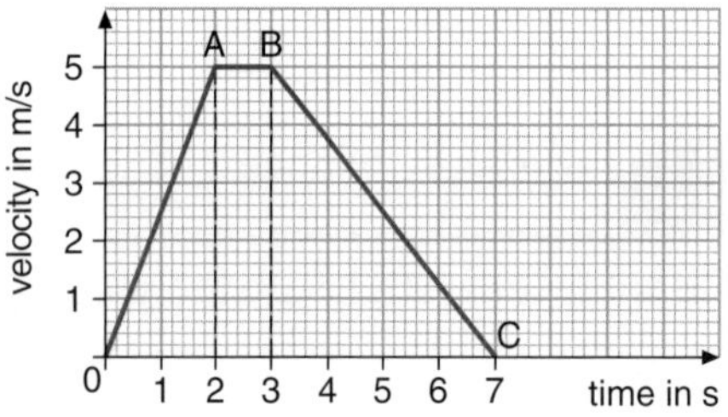

a) Briefly describe the motion represented by (i) OA, (ii) AB, (iii) BC.
b) Use the graph to calculate:
  (i) The initial acceleration of the lift.
  (ii) The total distance travelled by the lift.
  (iii) The average speed of the lift for the whole journey.

Use a graphical method or formula to answer questions 5–11.

14 A car accelerates at 3 m/s^2 for 10 seconds. If it started with a velocity of 20 m/s, calculate its final velocity.

15 An ice-skater moves off from rest (this means that $u = 0$ m/s) with a uniform acceleration of 0.3 m/s^2. What is her speed and distance travelled after 10 s?

16 A stone is thrown vertically upwards with a velocity of 20 m/s. Find how high it will go and the time taken to reach this height (assume $g =$ 10 m/s^2). Ignore air resistance.

(Hint: g is acting in the opposite direction to the velocity so it must be given a negative sign.)

17 A stone is dropped down an empty mine shaft, taking 3 seconds to reach the bottom. Assuming that the stone falls from rest and accelerates at 10 m/s^2, calculate:

a) the maximum speed reached by the stone before hitting the bottom
b) the average speed of the stone in flight
c) the depth of the mine shaft.

18 A helicopter at a height of 500 m drops a package which falls to the ground without its parachute opening. Neglecting air resistance and assuming the acceleration is constant and equal to 10 m/s^2, calculate:

a) the time taken for the package to reach the ground
b) the velocity with which it hits the ground.

19 A ball is thrown vertically upwards into the air with a velocity of 50 m/s. Neglecting air resistance and assuming the acceleration is constant and equal to 10 m/s^2, calculate:

a) the time taken to reach maximum height
b) the maximum height reached by the ball.

20 A cyclist accelerates at 3 m/s^2.

a) What is his speed after 5 s?

He then decelerates at 0.5 m/s^2.

b) How long will it take for his speed to reach zero and how far will he have travelled?
c) Draw a velocity–time graph for this motion.

Friction and motion

A car engine produces the forwards force necessary to keep a car moving. If a car is not accelerating, but is moving at a steady speed, the forwards force from the engine must be balanced by an equal backwards force. This force, called **air resistance** or **drag**, is a force of **friction**.

Figure 14 For this car, the forwards force is the engine and the backwards force is friction

In many instances it is important to maximise the amount of friction between two surfaces in order to increase the amount of grip available. Car brakes and tyres are designed with this in mind. Pushing the brake pedal causes friction between the brake pads and the tyres. This friction slows the wheels and stops the car.

The total stopping distance of a car is made up of two parts:

- the **thinking distance**
- the **braking distance**.

The thinking distance is how far the car travels in the time that the driver reacts to an emergency and hits the brakes. The braking distance is how far the car travels once the brakes have been applied. The larger the braking force, the shorter will be the braking distance.

In icy or wet conditions, the friction between the car tyres and the road is reduced, which reduces the grip and thus increases the braking distance. Under these conditions a car will not only need a greater stopping distance, but something to prevent it skidding out of control. The tread pattern on car tyres is designed to remove excess water on the road, providing better grip. The thinking distance can be affected if the driver is tired or distracted or if they have been drinking alcohol or taking drugs.

Speed affects both the thinking distance and the braking distance. The faster the car is travelling, the greater the total stopping distance.

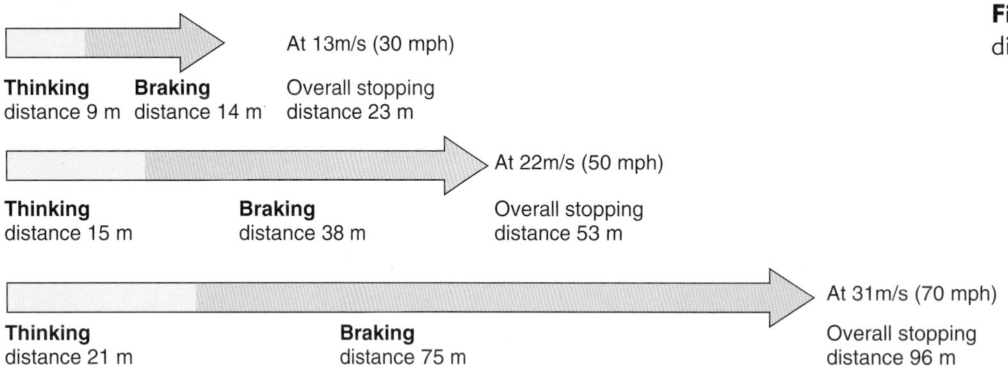

Figure 15 Stopping distances

Drag

When an object moves through a fluid (liquid or gas), the opposing frictional forces are usually called drag. The amount of drag depends on the shape of the object, and so can be reduced by good design.

Circular motion

There are many examples of circular motion:

- planets going round the Sun
- the Moon orbiting the Earth
- clothes in a tumble drier
- a car turning a corner, the shape of which may follow an arc of a circle.

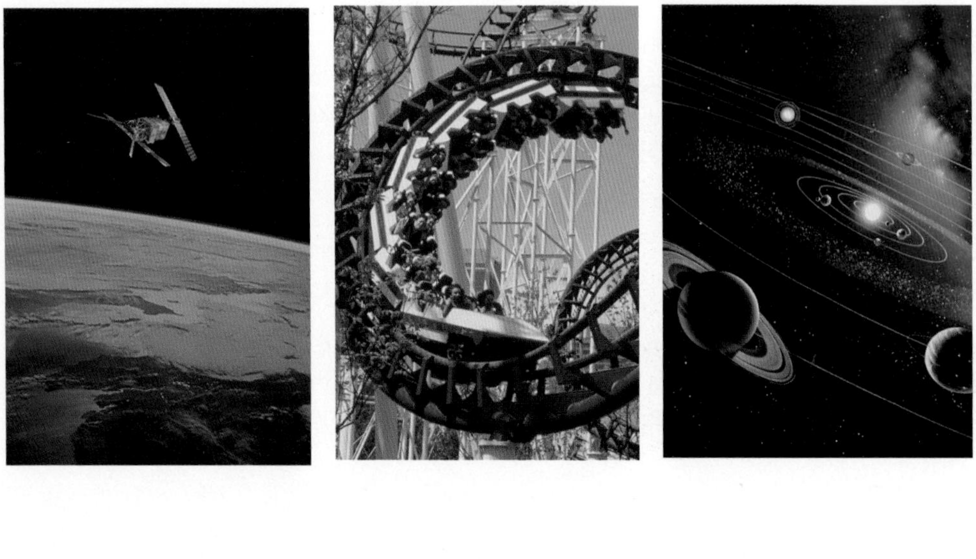

Figure 16 These are all examples of circular motion

Why do bodies move in a circular path?

Consider a ball attached to a string being whirled round in a horizontal circle, as in Figure 17.

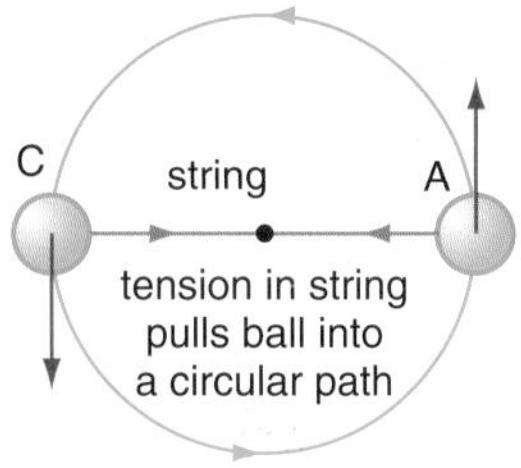

Figure 17 This ball is moving in a circular path, but what would happen if the string broke?

It is clear that the direction of motion is constantly changing. At A it points along the tangent at A up the page, whereas at C it points along the tangent down the page.

As we learned earlier in this chapter, velocity has both size and direction but speed has only size. Velocity is speed in a specified direction and if the direction of a moving body changes, even if its speed does not, then its velocity has changed.

According to its definition, acceleration is a change of velocity in unit time and so during its whirling motion, the ball is accelerating.

It follows from Newton's First Law of Motion (see Chapter 2) that if we consider a body moving in a circle to be accelerating, then there must be a force acting on it to cause the acceleration. In the case of the whirling ball it must be the tension in the string pulling inwards on the ball which causes the velocity of the ball to change its direction at every point in its path.

A larger force is needed if:

1 the speed of the ball is increased
2 the radius of the circle is decreased
3 the mass of the ball is increased.

The first two points follow directly from Newton's Second Law: $F = ma$ (Force = Mass × Acceleration).

If the force is greater than the string can bear, the string breaks, so what will happen to the ball?

According to Newton's First Law, 'the body will continue in its state of uniform motion', i.e. the ball will fly off in a tangent at the point where the ball is when the string breaks. It will not fly radially outwards, which is a common misconception.

The force which acts towards the centre and keeps a body in a circular path is called the **centripetal** (centre-seeking) **force**. We say that the tension in the string provides the centripetal force.

In Figure 18, gravitational attraction between the Earth and Moon provides the centripetal force.

Figure 18

In Figure 19, the electrostatic force of attraction between the proton and the electron in the hydrogen atom provides the centripetal force.

In Figure 20, the friction force between the tyres of a car and the road provide the centripetal force.

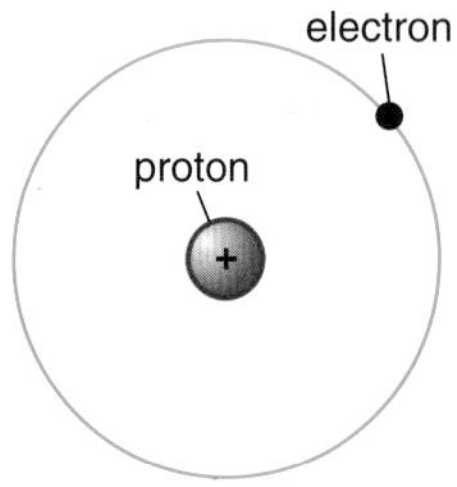

Figure 19

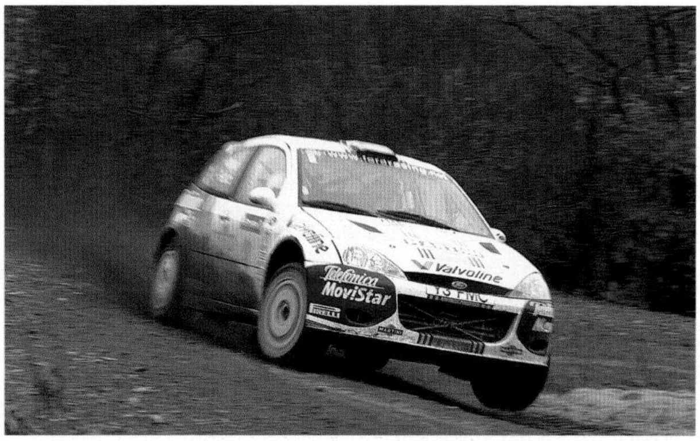

Figure 20

Websites

Use your favourite search engine (such as **www.goggle.com** or **www.excite.com**) and search using the keywords:

Braking distances

Friction

Circular motion

Exam questions

1 a) A taxi makes a journey of 3.0 km in 5 minutes. What is its average speed in m/s?
Show clearly how you get your answer. *(6 marks)*

b) The velocity–time graph for the return journey is shown below.

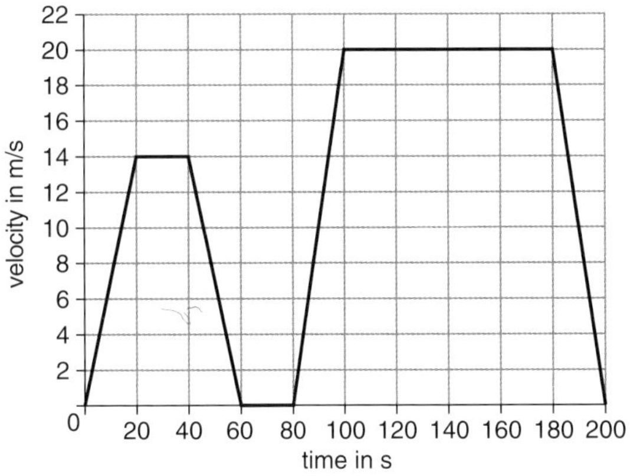

(i) What is the acceleration of the taxi during the first 20 seconds?
Show clearly how you get your answer. *(5 marks)*

(ii) The mass of the taxi and its passengers is 1500 kg. The driving force acting on the taxi for the first 20 s is 3000 N.

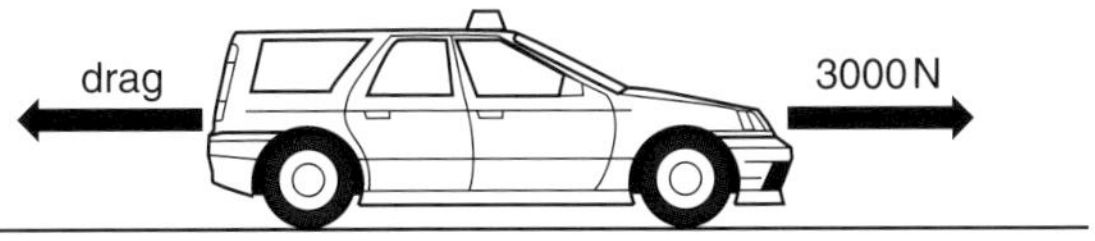

Calculate the average drag (frictional) force acting on the taxi during this time in Newtons.
Show clearly how you get your answer. *(7 marks)*

(iii) What is the distance travelled from the time of 80 s to the end of the journey?
Show clearly how you get your answer. *(6 marks)*

(iv) Describe the movement of the taxi during the times indicated below.
A) 20 s to 40 s
B) 40 s to 60 s
C) 60s to 80s *(3 marks)*

(v) The mass of the taxi and its passengers is 1500 kg. Calculate the momentum of the taxi and its occupants at a time of 20 s.
Show clearly how you get your answer. *(5 marks)*

2 a) A hovercraft has a mass of 10 000 kg. It hovers at a constant height above the surface of the sea.

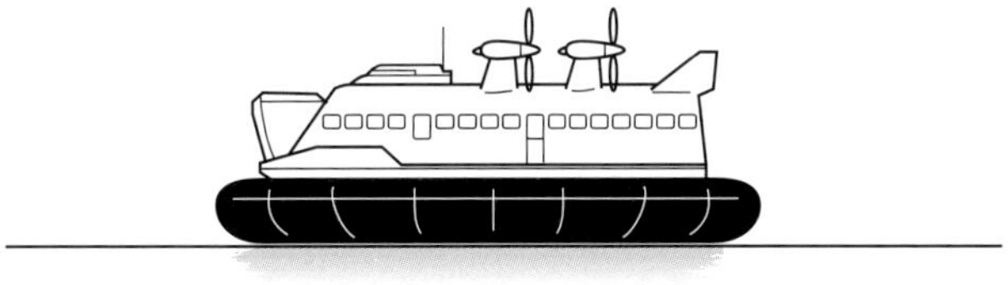

(i) Calculate the weight of the hovercraft in Newtons. *(2 marks)*

(ii) Write down the size in Newtons of the upward force exerted by the air cushion below the hovercraft. *(1 mark)*

(iii) The base of the hovercraft is a rectangle measuring 20 m by 5 m. Use your answer to part (ii) to calculate the upward pressure on the base of the hovercraft in Pascals.
Show clearly how you get your answer. *(4 marks)*

The hovercraft now moves to the left at a steady speed as shown in the diagram below.

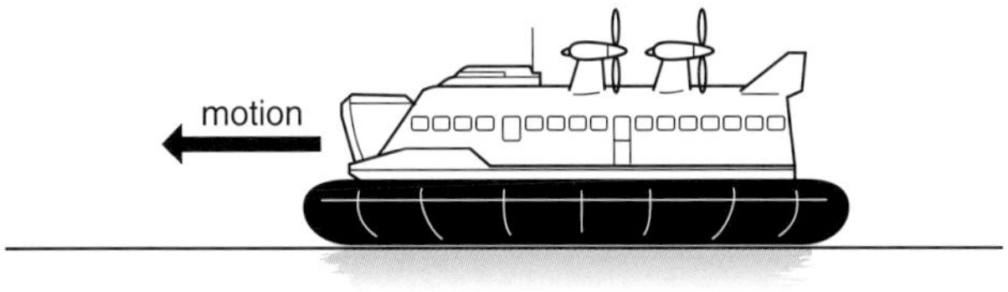

(iv) Copy the diagram above and draw an arrow to show the direction of the frictional force on the hovercraft. *(1 mark)*

When the forward force is 15 000 N, the hovercraft moves at a steady speed. The forward force is now increased to 20 000 N but the size of the frictional force remains unchanged.

(v) Calculate the acceleration of the hovercraft when the forward force is 20 000 N. Remember the mass of the hovercraft is 10 000 kg.
Show clearly how you get your answer. *(4 marks)*

(b) Below is a velocity–time graph showing the motion of a train.

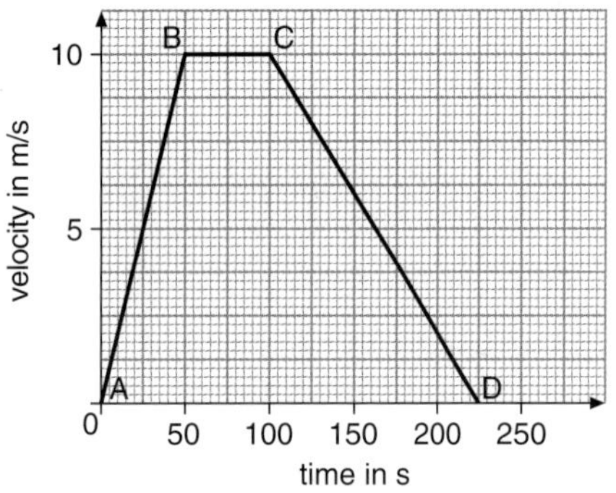

(i) How can you tell from the graph that the train is always travelling in the same direction? *(1 mark)*

(ii) Calculate the acceleration of the train represented by the line AB on the graph.
Show clearly how you get your answer. *(3 marks)*

(iii) At what time does the train driver first apply the brakes? *(1 mark)*

(iv) Calculate the distance travelled by the train on each of the two stages of the journey, BC and CD.
Show clearly how you get your answer.

A) Distance travelled on BC *(2 marks)*

B) Distance travelled on CD *(3 marks)*

(v) The distance travelled by the train in the first 50 s of its motion is 250 m. Calculate the average speed of the train during the 225 seconds of its journey.
Show clearly how you get your answer. *(3 marks)*

(vi) During the part of the journey marked BC, the force opposing the motion of the train is 5000 N. Calculate the work done in Joules against this force during this part of the journey.
Show clearly how you get your answer. *(3 marks)*

3 Last year the Tour de France cycle race started in Dublin. Cyclists A and B start the race at the same time.

a) The graph of distance travelled against time for cyclist A is shown below.

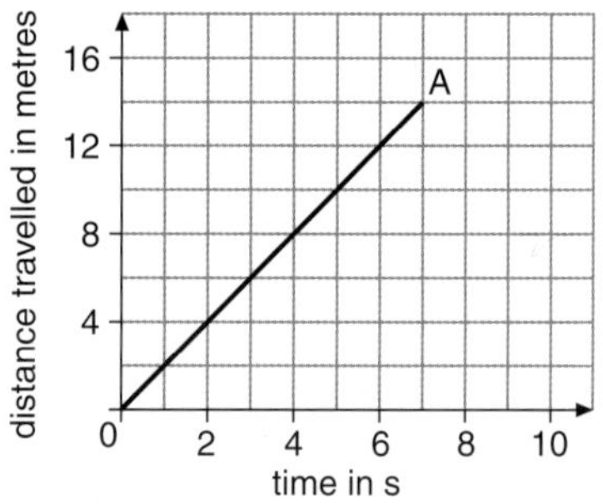

(i) What is the speed of cyclist A?
Show clearly how you get your answer. *(2 marks)*

(ii) For the first 4 seconds, cyclist B has a steady speed of 4 m/s. Copy the grid and draw the graph for cyclist B. Label it B. *(2 marks)*

b) Part of the race takes place in the Wicklow Mountains where riders climb to a height *h*.

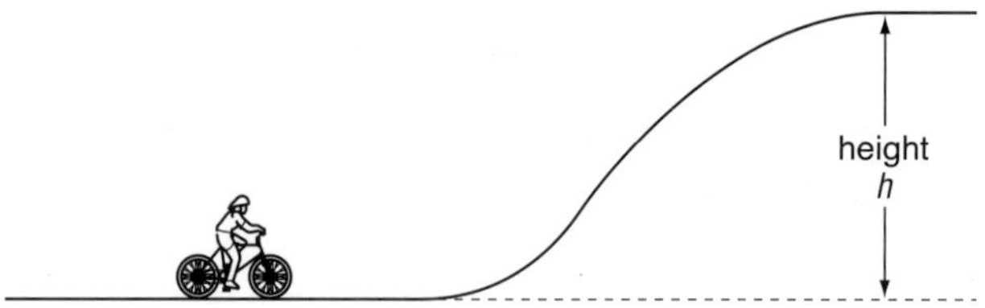

(i) The total mass of a cyclist and his bike is 80 kg. The gain in potential energy of a cyclist (man and bike) at a height *h* is 320 000 J. Calculate the height *h*. ($g = 10\ m/s^2$)
Show clearly how you get your answer. *(3 marks)*

(ii) Near the finish the speed of the cyclist is 14 m/s. Calculate the kinetic energy of the cyclist.
Show clearly how you get your answer. *(3 marks)*

Chapter 4

Waves

Learning objectives

By the end of this chapter you should know:

- How to distinguish between longitudinal and transverse waves
- The meaning of frequency, wavelength and amplitude as applied to waves
- The wave equation and how to use it
- How to use wavefront diagrams to describe reflection and refraction
- That waves can be represented on a CRO display
- Some experiments which demonstrate that sound travels through different materials at different speeds
- How to explain ultrasound and its applications to industry and medicine
- Some calculations on the echo principle
- How to draw ray diagrams to describe the formation of shadows
- How light is dispersed by prisms
- How to explain total internal reflection and its applications
- How images are formed and some applications of convex lenses
- The major parts of the electromagnetic spectrum and their applications

Types of waves

Waves transfer energy and information from one point to another but they do not, in general, transfer matter. Radio waves, for example, carry energy from a radio transmitter to your home, but no matter moves in the air as a result.

All waves are produced as a result of **vibrations** and can be classified as **longitudinal** or **transverse**. A vibration is a movement first in one direction and then in the opposite direction.

Longitudinal waves

A longitudinal wave is one in which the particles vibrate *parallel* to the direction in which the wave is travelling. Some examples of longitudinal waves are:

- sound waves
- slinky spring waves.

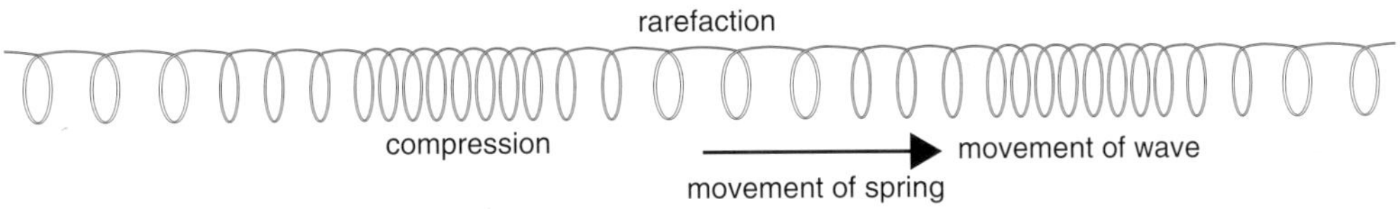

Figure 1 A longitudinal wave moving along a slinky spring

It is easy to demonstrate longitudinal waves by moving your hand back and forth parallel to the axis of a stretched slinky spring. **Compressions** are places where the coils or particles bunch together. **Rarefactions** are places where the coils or particles are furthest apart.

All longitudinal waves are made up of compressions and rarefactions. In the case of sound waves, the particles are the molecules of the material through which the sound is travelling. These molecules bunch together and separate just as they do in a longitudinal wave on a slinky spring.

Transverse waves

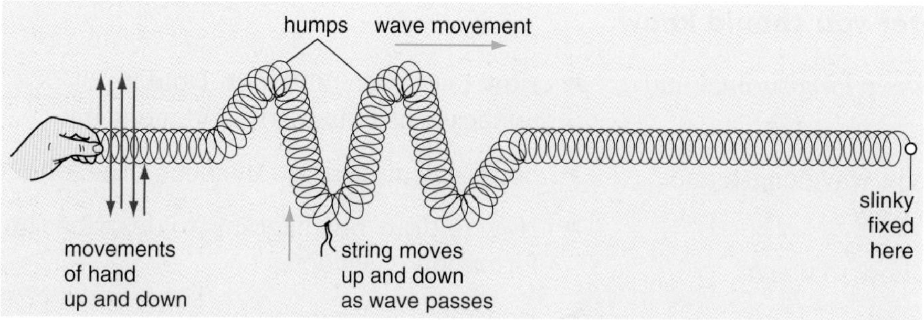

Figure 2 A transverse wave moving along a slinky spring

A transverse wave is one in which the particles vibrate at 90° to the direction in which the wave is travelling. Most waves in nature are transverse. Some examples of transverse waves are:

- water waves
- waves on strings and ropes
- slinky spring waves
- electromagnetic waves.

A transverse wave pulse can be created by shaking one end of a rope. The pulse moves along the rope, but the final position of the rope is exactly the same as it was at the beginning. None of the material of the rope has moved permanently. But the wave pulse has carried energy from one point to another.

There are many other examples to show that waves carry energy:

- Visible light, infrared radiation and microwaves all make things heat up.
- X-rays and γ-waves can damage cells by disrupting DNA.
- Loud sound waves can cause objects to vibrate (even if that is only your eardrum).
- Water waves can be used to generate electricity.

Describing waves

There are a number of important definitions relating to waves that must be learned.

1 The **frequency** of a wave is the *number of complete waves passing a fixed point in a second*. Frequency is given the symbol, f, and is measured in units called **Hertz** (abbreviation Hz).
2 The **wavelength** of a wave is the *distance between two consecutive crests or troughs*. Wavelength is given the symbol λ, and is measured in metres. λ is the Greek letter 'l' and is pronounced *lamda*.
3 The **amplitude** of a wave is the *greatest displacement of the wave from its undisturbed position*. Amplitude is measured in metres.

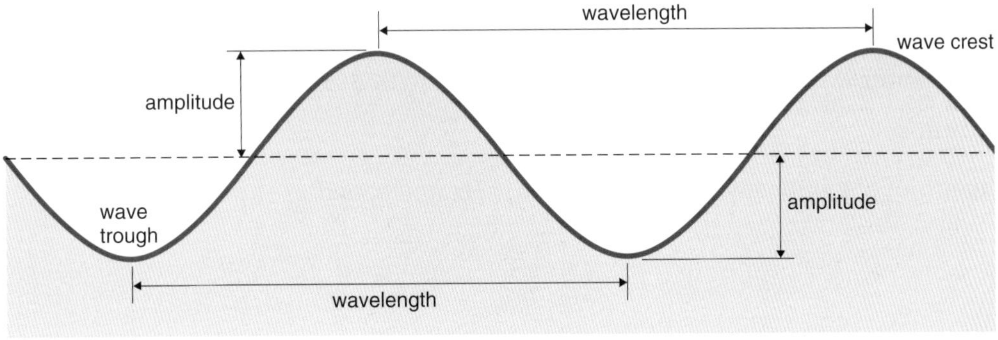

Figure 3 A transverse wave in water showing the wavelength and amplitude

Did you know?

The sea wave with the largest amplitude was measured in the Pacific Ocean in the 1990s at over 35 metres. Tsunami, often wrongly called tidal waves, can have amplitudes greater than 70 metres.

Wavelength and amplitude of longitudinal waves

It is much easier to visualise wavelength and amplitude for transverse waves than longitudinal waves. For a longitudinal wave, the wavelength is the distance between the centre of one compression and the next.

But what is the amplitude of a longitudinal wave? Remember that the particles in a longitudinal wave vibrate back and forth parallel to the direction in which the wave is moving. The amplitude is the maximum distance the particle moves from the centre of this motion.

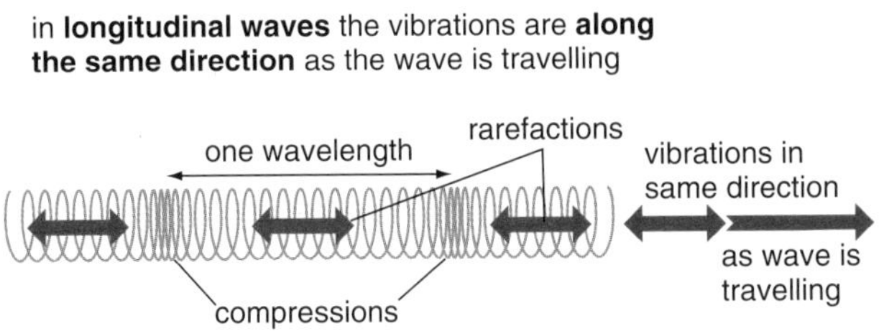

Figure 4

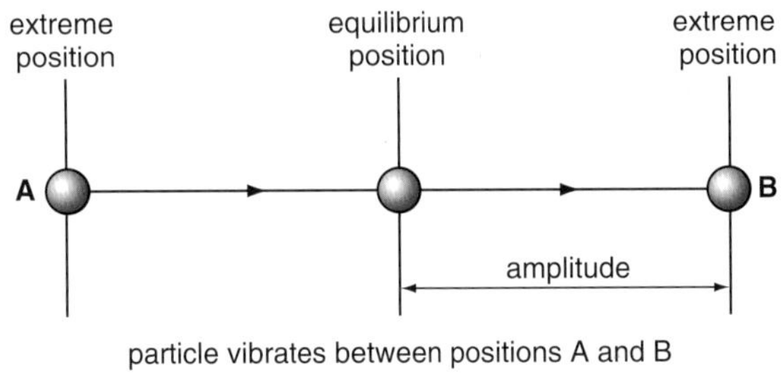

Figure 5 Determining the amplitude of a longitudinal wave

The wave equation

Imagine a wave with wavelength λ (metres) and frequency f (Hertz).

From the definition of frequency, in 1 second f waves pass a fixed point.

But each wave has a length λ.

So, the total distance travelled every second is $f \times \lambda$.

But the distance travelled in a second is the speed.

So,

$$\text{Wavespeed} = \text{Frequency} \times \text{Wavelength}$$

Or

$$v = f\lambda$$

This important equation must be learned for the GCSE examination.

Note that the units used in the wave equation must be consistent as shown in Table 1.

Table 1

Frequency	Wavelength	Speed
Always in Hertz	cm	cm/s
	m	m/s
	km	km/s

Examples

1 What is the speed of a water wave of frequency 4 Hz and wavelength 3 cm?

$v = f\lambda = 4 \times 3 =$ **12 cm/s**

2 What is the wavelength of a sound wave of frequency 264 Hz and speed 330 m/s?

$v = f\lambda$

$330 = 264 \times \lambda$

$\lambda = 330/264 =$ **1.25 m**

3 Find the frequency of radio waves of wavelength 1500 m if their speed is 300 Mm/s.

First note that 300 Mm/s = 300 million metres per second = 300 000 000 m/s. Then apply the wave equation

$v = f\lambda$

$300\,000\,000 = f \times 1500$

$f = 300\,000\,000/1500 =$ **200 000 H_z**

4 The vertical distance between a crest and a trough is 24 cm and the horizontal distance between the first and fifth wavecrest is 40 cm. If 30 such waves pass a fixed point every minute, find the amplitude, frequency, wavelength and speed of these waves.

Amplitude $= \frac{1}{2} \times$ Distance between crest and trough $= \frac{1}{2} \times 24 = 12$ cm

Frequency = No. of waves passing in 1 s = 30 waves/60 seconds = 0.5 Hz

Wavelength = Distance between consecutive crests $= \frac{1}{4} \times 40 = 10$ cm

Speed $= f\lambda = 0.5 \times 10 =$ **5 cm/s**

Plane wavefronts

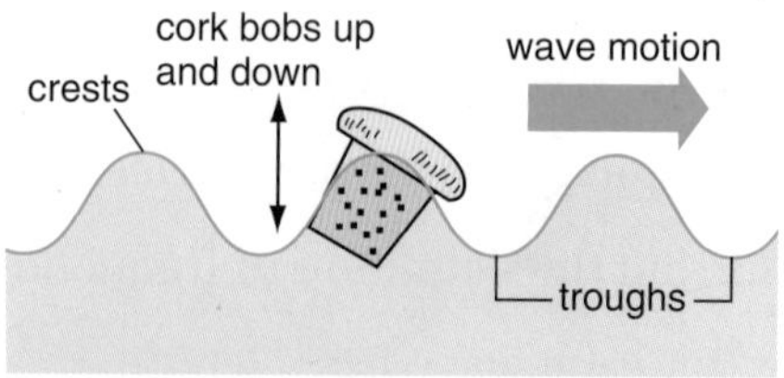

Figure 6 Ripples on water are transverse waves

We can learn much about the behaviour of waves using a ripple tank as shown in Figure 7. A motor makes a straight dipper vibrate up and down continuously. This produces straight water waves or **plane waves**. By shining a light from above the tank, we can see bright and dark patches on the white screen below. These patches show the wave crests and troughs. The direction of movement of the water waves is always at right angles to the wavefronts.

Water waves move quite quickly and it can sometimes be hard to see what is happening. Looking through a **rotating stroboscope** can make the waves appear to be standing still.

Suppose the stroboscope had 12 slits and rotated twice every second. Then the tank would be seen 24 times a second. If the waves had a frequency of 24 Hz, then every $\frac{1}{24}$th of a second, each wave would have moved forward by exactly one wavelength. So the wave pattern when viewed through the stroboscope would appear to be stationary.

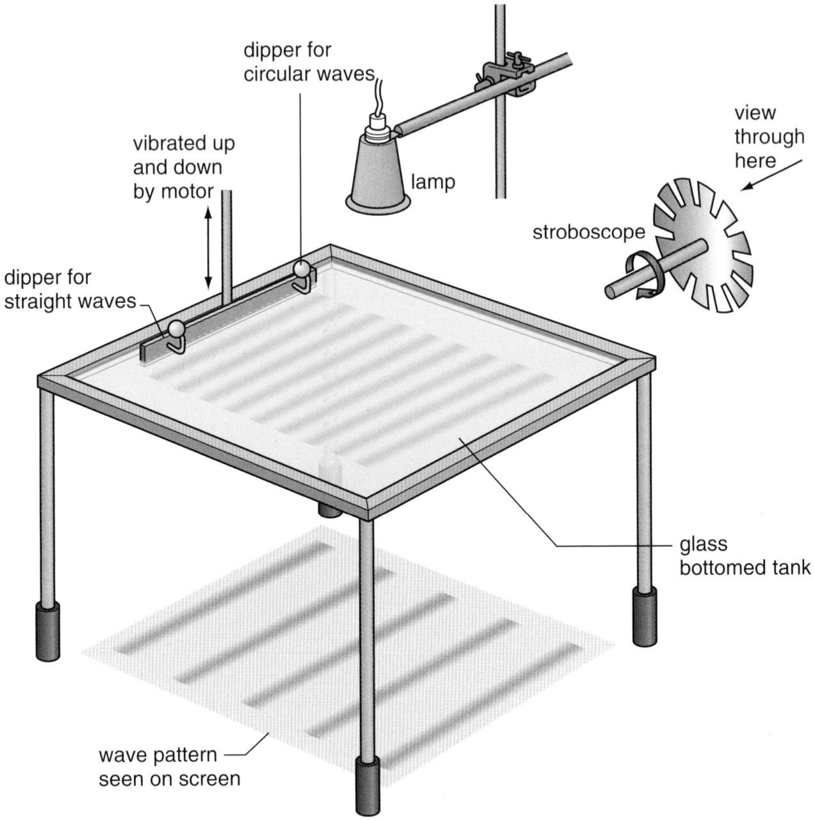

Figure 7 Viewing the wave pattern using a ripple tank and a stroboscope

Reflection

Figure 8 shows plane waves approaching a straight metal barrier. The barrier is big enough to prevent waves going 'over the top'. The incident waves are reflected from the barrier.

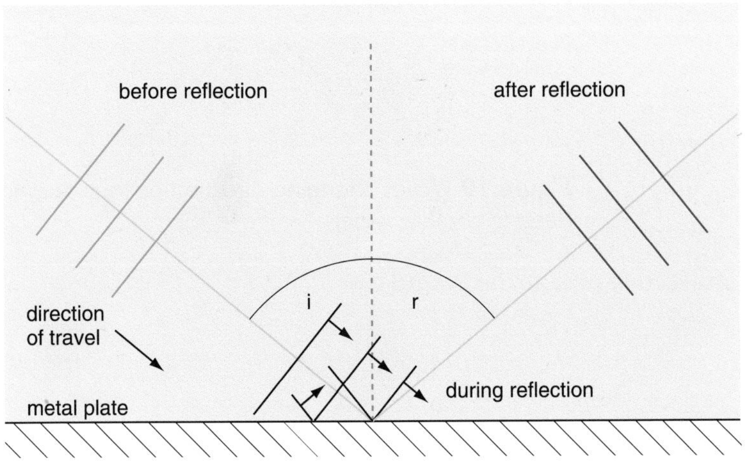

Figure 8 The reflection of waves off a plane surface.
The angle of incidence = i,
the angle of reflection = r

Note carefully:

- the **angle of incidence** always equals the **angle of reflection**
- the wavelengths of incident and reflected waves are equal
- there is continuity of incident and reflected waves at the barrier.

The behaviour of water waves at a boundary is very similar to that of light at a mirror. However, water waves can easily be observed because they have a wavelength of many centimetres. Light waves have a wavelength typically around half a millionth of a metre, so their wave behaviour is a little more difficult to demonstrate.

Refraction

In Figure 9, water waves are travelling from deep water to shallow water. A region of shallow water in a ripple tank can be made by immersing a rectangular glass block. The block displaces the water so that the water directly above it is shallow while the surrounding water is deeper.

Waves travel *slower* in shallow water than they do in deep water. Since the same number of waves leave the deep water as enter the shallow water every second, the frequency in both deep and shallow regions must be the same. This in turn means that the waves in shallow water must have a shorter wavelength than those in deep water.

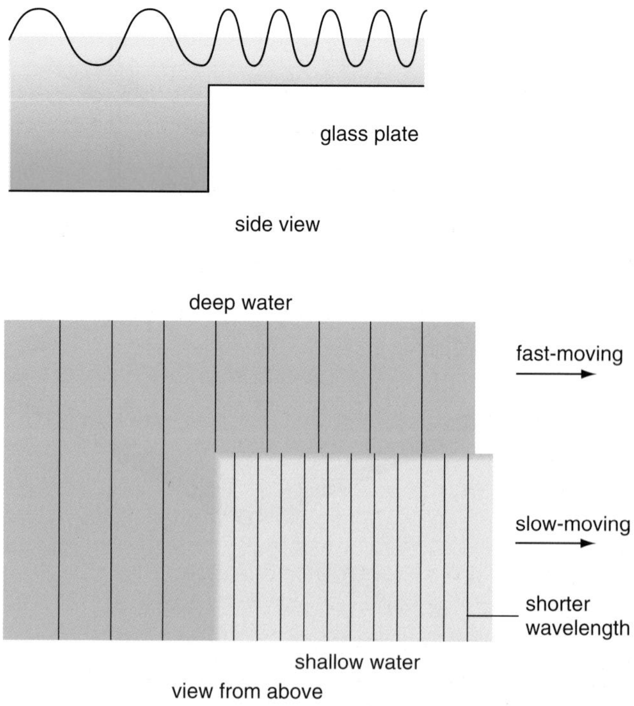

Figure 9 a) Side view and b) aerial view of waves going from a deep water area to a shallow water area

If the water waves enter the shallow region obliquely (at an angle), they not only slow down but will also change direction as shown in Figure 10.

Note carefully:

- the angle of incidence in deep water is always greater than the angle of refraction in shallow water
- the wavelength and speed of waves in deep water are greater than that in shallow water
- the frequencies of waves in both deep and shallow water are the same
- there is continuity of incident and refracted waves at the boundary.

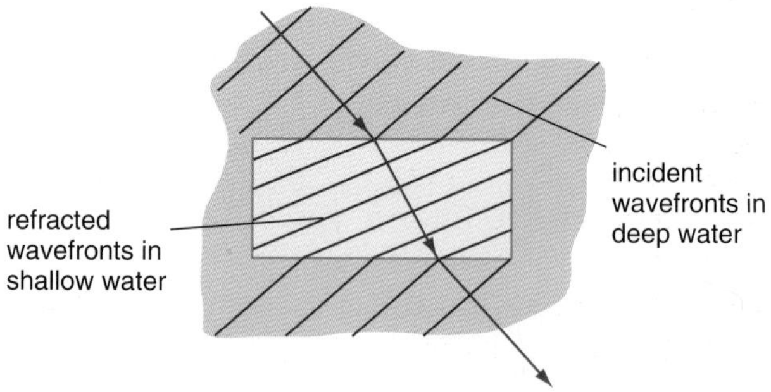

Figure 10 Waves changing direction as they pass from deep to shallow water

Example

A deep water wave of wavelength 12 cm and speed 36 cm/s enters a shallow region where the wavelength is 8 cm. Find the wave speed in shallow water.

Frequency in deep water = $v/\lambda = 36/12 = 3$ Hz

Frequency in shallow water = Frequency in deep water = 3 Hz

Speed in shallow water = $f\lambda = 3 \times 8 =$ **24 cm/s**

Sound

Sound waves are produced when an object vibrates at a frequency that the human ear can detect. The range of human hearing is around 20 Hz to 20 000 Hz (20 kHz). Sound at frequencies above 20 kHz cannot be heard by humans and is called **ultrasound**.

The vibrating object causes small changes in air pressure that are passed from molecule to molecule as a longitudinal wave. In this way energy passes from particle to particle by collisions, which explains why sound cannot travel through a vacuum, where there are no particles.

Figure 11 shows an important experiment to demonstrate that sound needs a medium (material) to pass through. The ringing electric bell is seen and heard from within the bell jar. The pump is switched on and slowly the air is pumped out of the jar. As the air is removed, the sound becomes fainter and fainter until all the air has been removed, when it can scarcely be heard at all. Some sound will always be heard but this is the sound that travels through the elastic cords and outwards through the glass jar.

Table 2 gives some examples of what is vibrating when certain sounds are made.

In every case the vibrating object causes the surrounding air to vibrate. This in turn causes sound to pass through the air to your ear. But without some medium such as the air, sound cannot reach your ear.

Did you know?

Although the normal outdoor range of the human voice is 200 metres, the whistled language of the Spanish-speaking Canary Island of La Gomera can be heard more than 3 kilometres away.

Although for most people the upper frequency limit of the human voice is 20 kHz, a tiny number of children suffering from asthma can hear sound at frequencies approaching 30 kHz.

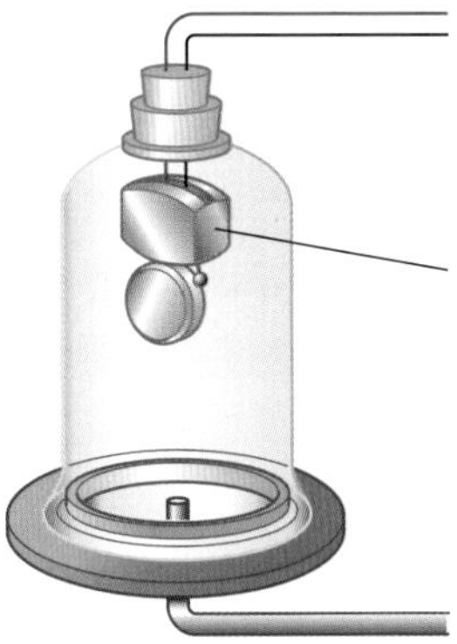

Figure 11 This experiment shows that sound cannot travel through a vacuum

Table 2

Sound coming from ...	What is vibrating?
Drum	Drumskin
Loudspeaker	Cone of the speaker
Human voice	Vocal cords in the larynx
Guitar	Strings
Clarinet	Reed
Bell	Gong

Pitch, loudness and waveform

Musicians use the word **pitch** to describe a sound or musical note. Bass notes are low pitch, treble notes are high pitch. The pitch of a note is directly related to its frequency. The higher-pitched notes are those with higher frequency.

Loudness is linked to the energy of the sound wave reaching your ears. The louder the sound, the greater is its energy. We can relate the loudness of a sound wave to its amplitude.

But why does the same note sound different on two different pianos? The answer is that the notes are of different **quality**. They may have a very similar waveform, but one will have more **overtones** than the other. A pure note has no overtones. A rich note from a high-quality instrument will have many overtones and will be pleasant to listen to.

Displaying waves on a CRO

The easiest way to display the waveform of a sound is to use a microphone with a **CRO (cathode ray oscilloscope)**. The microphone converts the sound into electrical energy, while the CRO gives a visual representation of the sound.

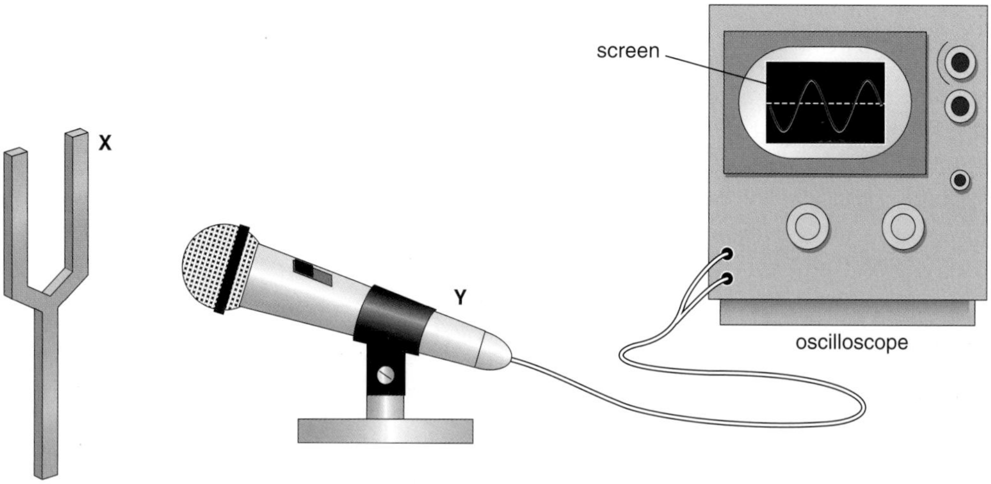

Figure 12 Displaying sound waves on a CRO screen

Figure 13 shows the effects of changing the loudness and pitch of a sound wave.

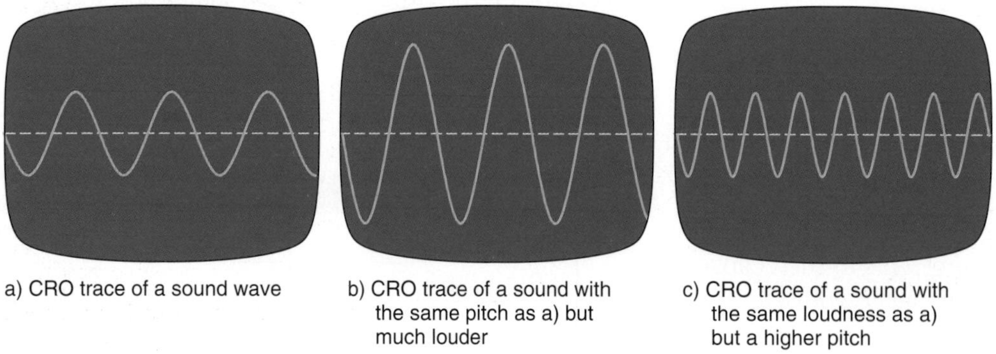

a) CRO trace of a sound wave
b) CRO trace of a sound with the same pitch as a) but much louder
c) CRO trace of a sound with the same loudness as a) but a higher pitch

Figure 13 Sound waves on oscilloscope screens

Note that:

- increasing the loudness makes the peaks higher (showing increased amplitude)
- increasing the pitch makes the peaks closer together (showing increased frequency).

Table 3 summarises the various terms used.

Table 3

When musicians say ...	Physicists think of ...
Loudness	Amplitude
Pitch	Frequency
Quality or timbre	Overtones

Sound pollution

Excessive sound can be very damaging to our hearing. Its effects can be temporary (as in the case of a disco dancer standing too close to the loudspeakers) or permanent (as in the case of a person using a pneumatic road drill who becomes deaf because he failed to take the correct precautions).

Sources of noise pollution include:

- car and lorry engines, particularly near busy roads
- mowers, diggers, pneumatic drills
- factory equipment
- neighbours with loud stereo systems and barking dogs.

Steps that can be taken to reduce sound pollution and its effects include:

- fitting silencers and mufflers to engines and machinery
- building sound-absorbing walls near motorways
- insulating homes against noise pollution with acoustic tiles, carpets, curtains and double glazing.

It is important to recognise that sound pollution can have serious effects on a person's health and well-being by:

- increasing stress
- causing distractions from work
- causing damage to hearing.

Sound reflection

Like all waves, sound and ultrasound can be made to reflect. This happens in a way that is similar to the reflection of water waves discussed earlier. It is important to remember that whenever waves reflect, the angle of incidence is equal to the angle of reflection.

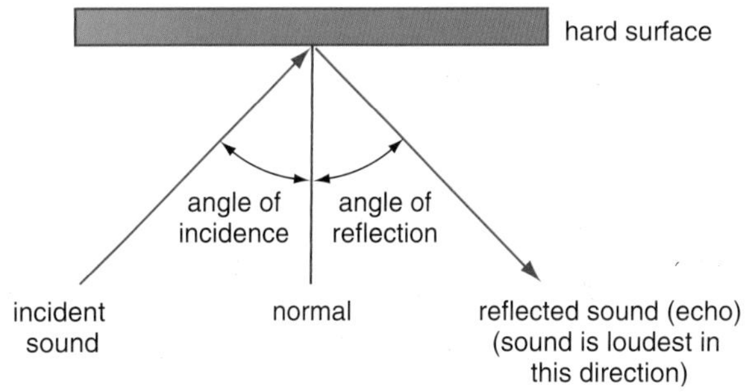

Figure 14 The reflection of sound waves from a surface

Ultrasound

Everybody knows that dogs can hear sounds from dog whistles that humans cannot detect. Bats too have the ability to hear very high-pitched sound. This type of sound is called ultrasound because it is above the upper limit of human hearing. That means it is above 20 000 Hz or 20 kHz.

Interestingly whales, dolphins, sharks and many other creatures living in the sea are well-adapted to hearing both sound and ultrasound. The audible clicks which whales produce pass easily through the water from animal to animal. But many sea creatures can also produce and hear ultrasound, and can use it for locating their prey.

In the past few years biologists have discovered that elephants emit sounds which can travel incredible distances, especially at night. It is believed the elephants use this sound to communicate with each other, over distances of many kilometres. This sound has a frequency *below* that of human hearing and is called **infrasound**.

Did you know?

Whales are not only the largest mammals in the oceans – they are also the noisiest. They give out low-frequency sounds that can be detected by other whales thousands of kilometres away.

Man has found many applications for ultrasound:

- scanning metal castings for faults or cracks (e.g. in rail tracks)
- scanning a woman's womb to check on the development of the foetus
- scanning soft tissues to diagnose cancers
- fish location by sea-going trawlers
- mapping the surface of the ocean floor in oceanography
- cleaning sensitive electronic equipment
- removing harmful tartar from teeth.

In an ultrasound scan of an unborn baby, a probe is moved across the mother's abdomen. The probe sends out ultrasound waves and also detects the reflections. The low wavelength of the ultrasound waves means that, unlike audible sound waves, ultrasound can be sent out in a very narrow beam and can be focused easily on the unborn baby. The other end of the probe is connected to a computer. By examining the reflected waves from the womb, the computer builds up a picture of the foetus like that in Figure 15. Unlike X-rays, ultrasound is now known to be quite safe for this purpose.

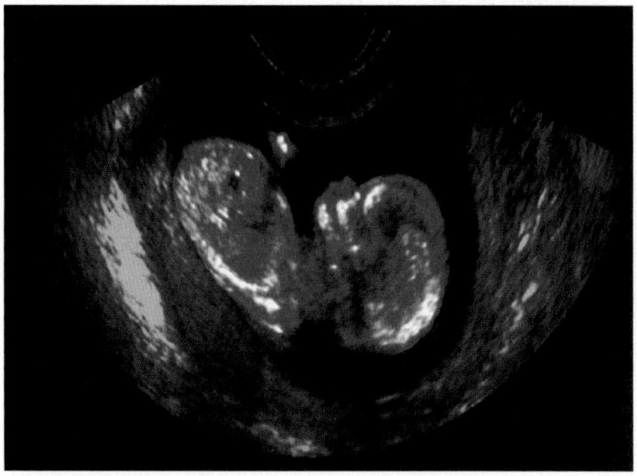

Figure 15 This ultrasound scan shows an unborn baby in its mother's womb at 35 weeks

Speed of sound

The speed of sound depends on the material it is travelling through. Since sound waves are transmitted by vibrating molecules, the closer together the molecules, the faster the sound travels. Sound, therefore, travels slowest in gases (like air) where the molecules are far apart and fastest in heavy metals where the molecules are much closer together. The position is illustrated in Table 4.

The figures in the table are approximate as the speed of sound depends on the temperature of the material through which the sound is travelling.

Table 4

Material	Approximate speed of sound in m/s
Air	330
Water	1500
Steel	5000

Measuring the speed of sound in air

It is possible to get a rough idea of the speed of sound in air using an echo method. Stand a known distance (say 100 m) from a high wall and clap your hands. The sound produced travels in all directions, but some will travel to the wall and be reflected from the wall back towards you. When you hear the echo, clap again, so that you clap in time with the echo. While you continue to clap, a friend uses a stopwatch to time how long you take to make 30 claps (say 18 seconds). This means that the time between one clap and the next is 18/30 = 0.6 s.

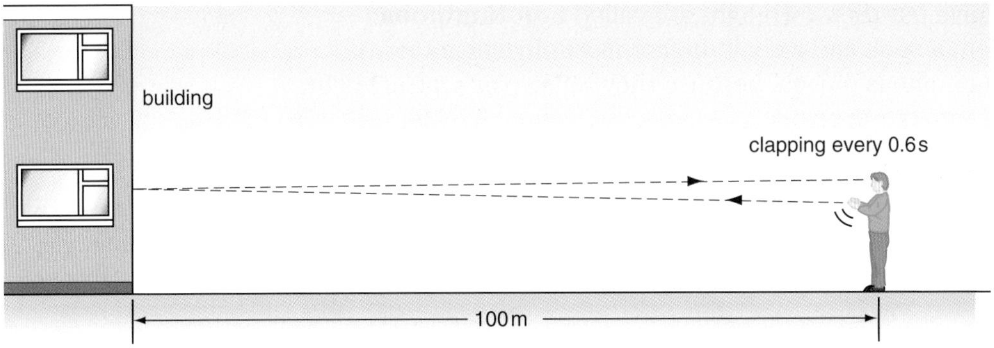

Figure 16 Measuring the speed of sound in air

In the time between each clap, the sound travels a total distance of 200 m (100 m from you to the wall and then the echo travels 100 m from the wall back to you).

So, Speed of sound in air = Distance travelled/Time taken = 200 m/0.6 s = **330 m/s**

Measuring the speed of sound in steel

A CRO and two microphones can be used to measure the speed of sound in steel. The small microphones are attached to a long steel rod with the microphones about 1 m apart. The microphones are then connected to the CRO so that when sound reaches the first microphone, the CRO trace begins and when sound reaches the second microphone, the CRO trace stops. When one end of the rod is struck with a hammer, a trace can be seen on the CRO screen.

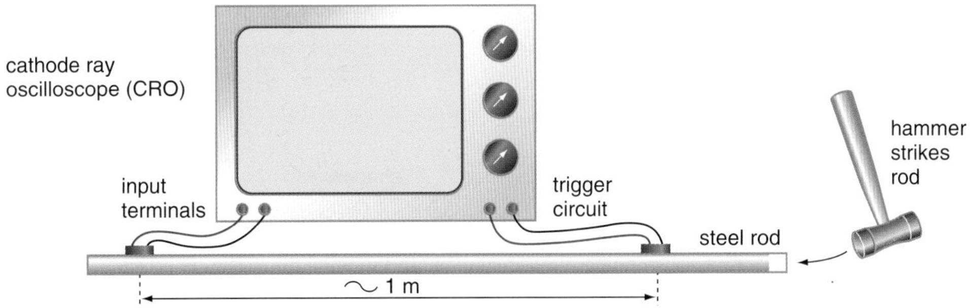

Figure 17 Measuring the speed of sound in steel

By adjusting the CRO controls, it is possible to see two separate spikes which correspond to the sound wave reaching the two microphones. By measuring the distance between the spikes on the CRO screen and reading the time setting, a figure for the time taken for the sound to travel between the two microphones along the steel rod can be obtained.

So, Speed of sound in rod = Distance between microphones/Time taken
= 1.0 m/0.0002 s = **5000 m/s**

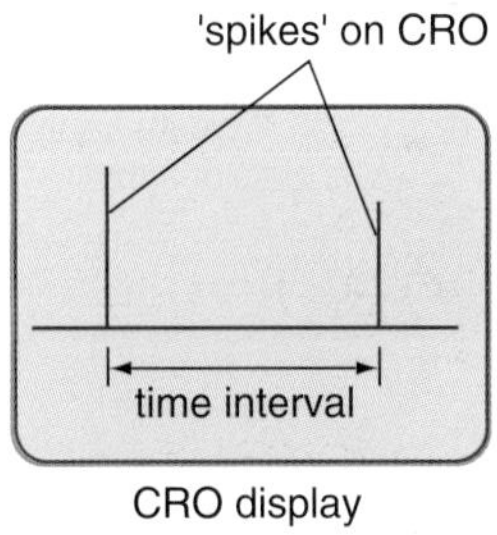

Figure 18 Spikes on the screen correspond to the sound of the hammer strike

Light

Luminous and non-luminous

Objects which produce light are called **luminous**. Examples of luminous objects include the Sun, a candle flame and the red ring on an electric cooker. We can see such objects because the light from them travels directly to our eyes.

Objects which do not give out their own light are called **non-luminous**. Examples include a pen, a book and a chair. In fact most objects are non-luminous. We see non-luminous objects because they reflect (or scatter) light from luminous objects into our eyes.

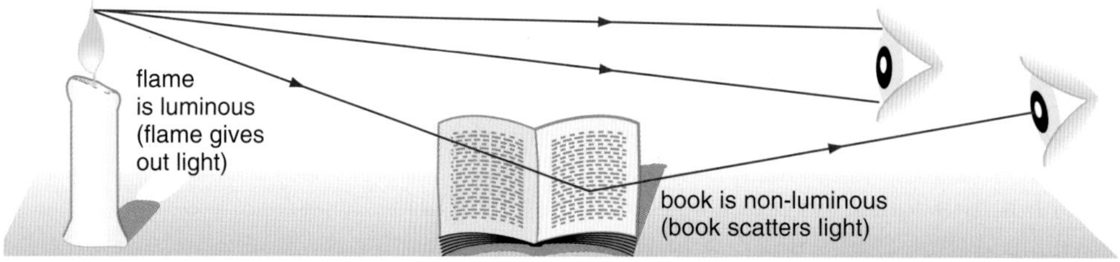

Figure 19 The difference between luminous and non-luminous objects

Transparent and opaque

Light can travel readily through materials which are **transparent**, such as air, glass and water. If light cannot travel through a material, it is called **opaque**. Examples include wood, coal, cardboard and metals.

If opaque objects are placed in the way of a beam of light, a **shadow** is created. In Figure 20, a piece of card is held in front of a point source of light. Some light misses the card and passes on, in a straight line, to the screen. This produces a shadow which

- is called an **umbra**
- is uniformly dark
- has sharp edges.

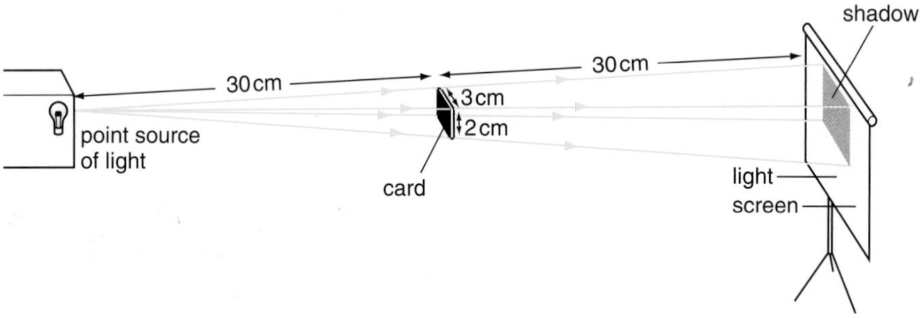

Figure 20 Creating a shadow using a point source of light

What happens if the light is not a point source? If the experiment is repeated with an extended source, like a candle flame, we get two different types of shadow on the screen. Surrounding the uniformly dark umbra, there is a lighter region which

- is called a **penumbra**
- gets darker as you get closer to the umbra
- has fuzzy edges.

An umbra is totally dark because no light from the source can reach it. A penumbra is not uniformly dark because light from some parts of the source can reach it, but light from other parts cannot. Figure 21 shows how a shadow is formed using an extended source of light.

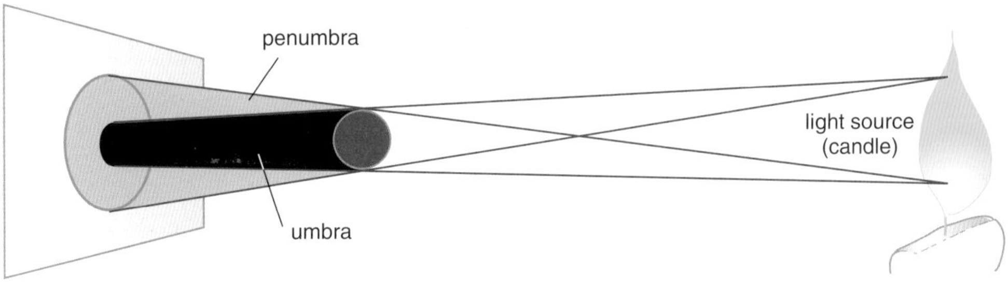

Figure 21 Creating a shadow using an extended source of light

Reflection of light

All of us are familiar with the way light reflects from a straight (plane) mirror. Figure 22 shows an arrangement for investigating what happens when a beam of light strikes a mirror.

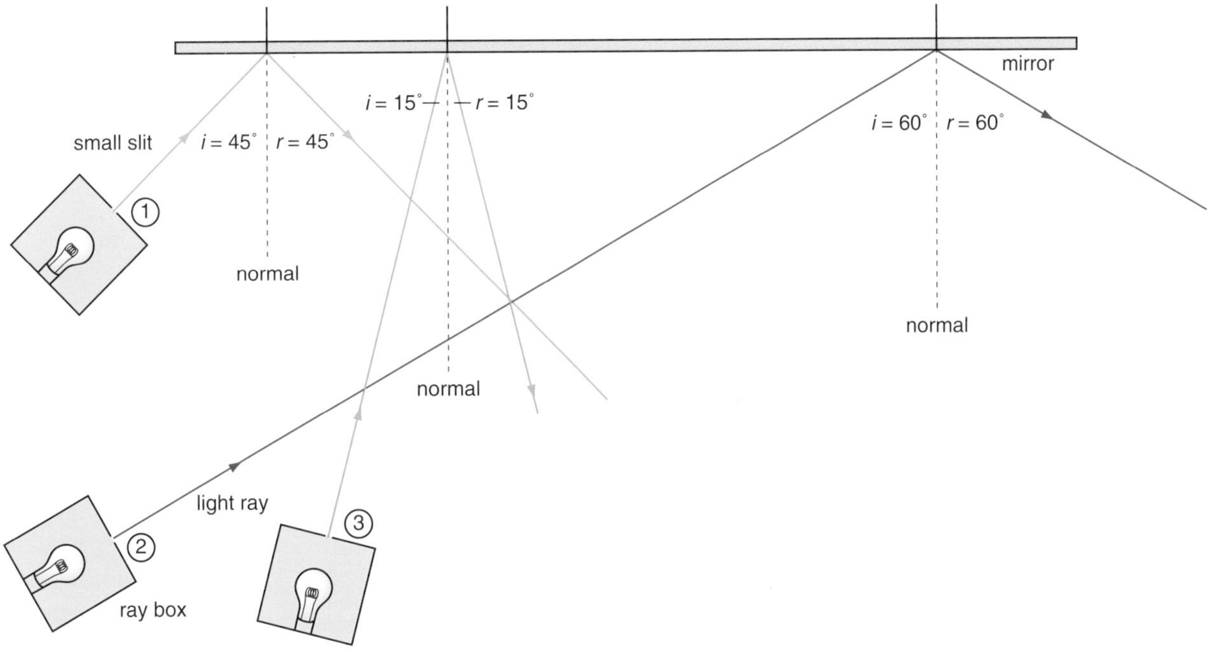

Figure 22 Investigating the reflection of light rays from a mirror

The light ray which strikes the mirror is called the **incident ray**. The **normal** is an imaginary line which meets the mirror at right angles to the point of incidence. The ray which travels away from the mirror is called the **reflected ray**.

- The angle between the incident ray and the normal is called the angle of incidence.
- The angle between the reflected ray and the normal is called the angle of reflection.

Did you know?

The human eye can detect light passing through a hole only three thousandths of a millimetre in diameter. But, that is nothing compared with some of the most powerful telescopes. They can detect the light from a candle at a distance of over 100 000 km!

Experiments show that the angle of incidence is always equal to the angle of reflection. This is known as the **Law of Reflection**.

Note that when light is reflected from a rough surface, the Law of Reflection still applies. But since the surface is rough, the light is reflected in many different directions and cannot produce a clear image. The word **scattering** is used to describe such reflections.

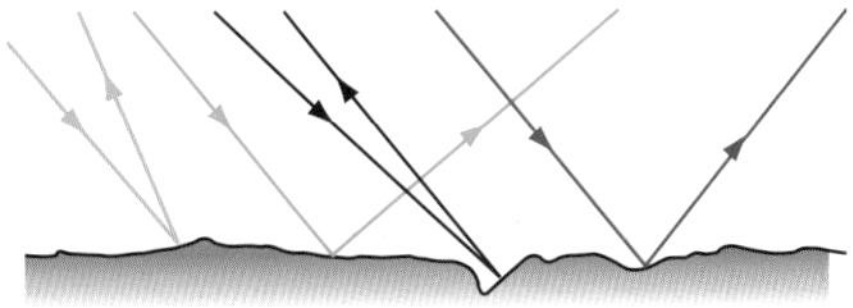

Figure 23 Light is scattered in all directions from a rough surface

Questions

1 What size is the angle of incidence when the incident ray strikes a plane mirror at 90°?

2 The angle between a plane mirror and the incident ray is 40°. What size is the angle of reflection?

3 The angle between the incident ray and the reflected ray is 130°. What size is the angle of incidence?

The image in a plane mirror

Figure 24 shows what happens when light from a point object strikes a mirror. The reflected rays get further apart (diverge) and enter the eye. But the eye follows the rays back in a straight line. The rays entering the eye appear to come from a point behind the mirror. This point is the **image**.

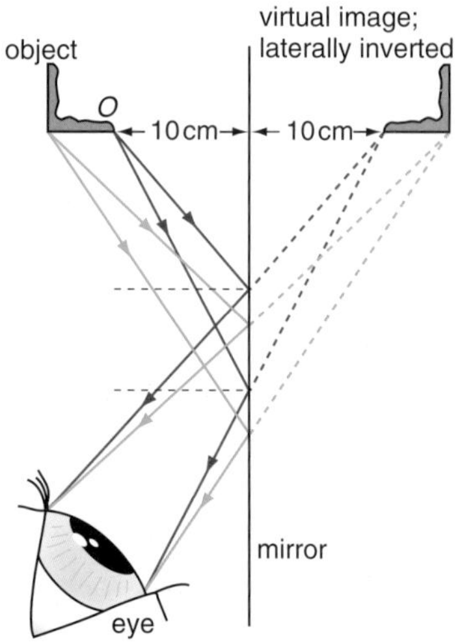

Figure 24 Seeing an image in a plane mirror

Note that the image in a plane mirror is not caused by real rays of light coming to a focus, as happens on a cinema screen. A mirror image is therefore called a **virtual image**.

A mirror image is also 'back-to-front'. If we hold a left-handed glove in front of a mirror, its image looks like a right-handed glove and vice versa. The image is said to be **laterally inverted**.

The image in a plane mirror is

- virtual
- the same size as the object
- laterally inverted
- the same distance behind the mirror as the object is in front of the mirror.

Refraction of light

Refraction is the change in direction of a beam of light as it travels from one material to another. It occurs because light travels at different speeds in different materials. Table 5 shows the speed of light in various media.

Table 5

Material	Speed of light in m/s
Air (or vacuum)	300 000 000
Water	225 000 000
Glass	200 000 000

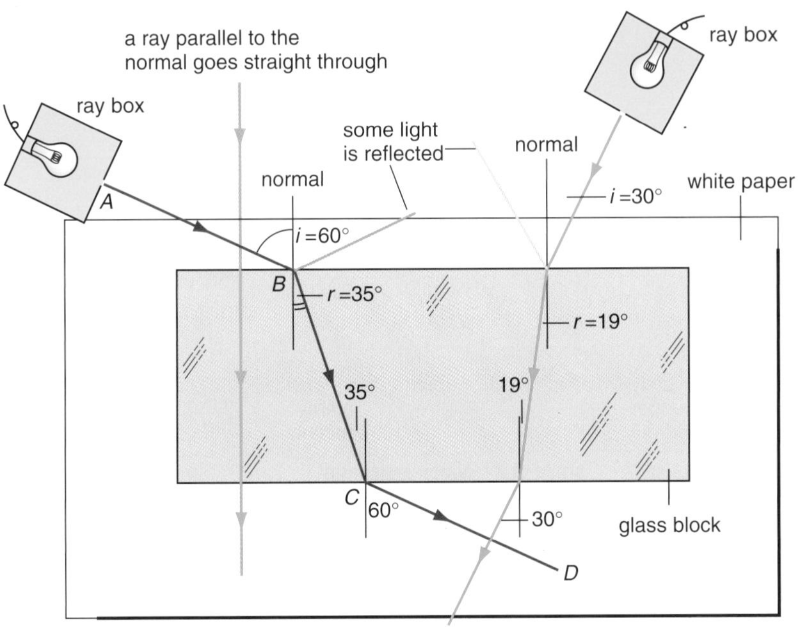

Figure 25 Refraction of light rays by a glass prism

The angle between the normal and the

- incident ray is called the angle of incidence
- refracted ray is called the angle of refraction
- emergent ray is called the **angle of emergence**.

Experiments show that when light speeds up, it bends away from the normal and when it slows down, it bends towards the normal. This is also what happens when water waves travel from deep water into shallow water.

Note that if the glass block has parallel sides, the angle of incidence is equal to the angle of emergence.

Sound waves, like light waves, also refract when they pass from one material into another. But sound waves, unlike light waves, travel faster in solids and liquids than they do in air. So, sound waves refract towards the normal as they pass from water into air, while light waves travelling in the same direction refract away from the normal.

Dispersion

All colours of light travel at the same speed in air. But different colours of light travel at different speeds in glass. This means that different colours bend by different amounts when they pass from air into glass. When light is passed through a triangular glass block called a **prism**,the effect is called **dispersion** and results in a **spectrum** showing all the colours of the rainbow. Red light is bent (refracted) the least because it travels fastest in glass. Violet light bends the most because it is slowest in glass.

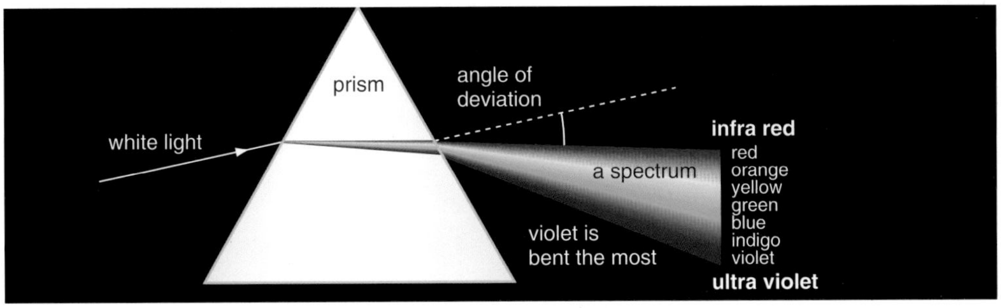

Figure 26 Dispersion of light through a prism

Total internal reflection

Figure 27 shows what happens when light travels through glass and emerges into the air. When the angle of incidence in glass is small enough, most of the light refracts into the air, but a little light is internally reflected.

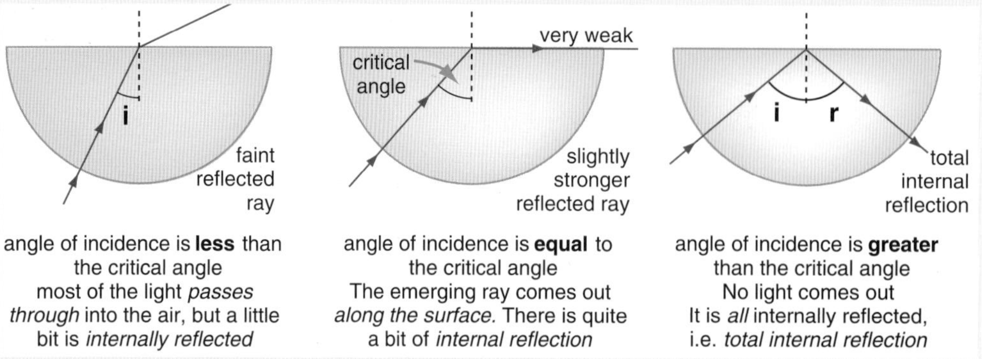

i
faint reflected ray
angle of incidence is **less** than the critical angle
most of the light *passes through* into the air, but a little bit is *internally reflected*
critical angle
very weak
slightly stronger reflected ray
angle of incidence is **equal** to the critical angle
The emerging ray comes out *along the surface.* There is quite a bit of *internal reflection*
i
r
total internal reflection
angle of incidence is **greater** than the critical angle
No light comes out
It is *all* internally reflected, i.e. *total internal reflection*

Figure 27 Total internal reflection of light

As the angle of incidence increases, the refracted ray bends closer and closer to the glass and becomes weaker and weaker. At the same time, the light being internally reflected into the glass becomes stronger. Eventually, at a certain angle of incidence called the critical angle, the light is refracted at an angle of refraction of 90°. At this point the refracted ray is very weak and the internally reflected ray is quite strong.

The critical angle for glass is about 42°. At angles above the critical angle, there is no refraction at all. All the light is reflected back into the glass. This is called total internal reflection.

You should remember:

- the critical angle is the angle of incidence in a material for which the angle of refraction in air is 90°
- at angles of incidence less than the critical angle, both reflection and refraction occur
- at angles of incidence greater than the critical angle, no refraction occurs and the light is totally internally reflected.

Uses of total internal reflection

Total internal reflection in 45° glass prisms is used in

- binoculars
- periscopes
- bicycle reflectors
- optical fibres for communications
- endoscopes.

In binoculars and periscopes, the light is totally internally reflected at two triangular glass prisms as shown in Figure 28. By using prisms instead of mirrors, less light is lost so the image is of superior quality.

In the bicycle reflector, the light is bent through 180° so it returns parallel to its original path. This means any light from a car headlamp is reflected back towards the car allowing the motorist to see the rear of the bicycle easily.

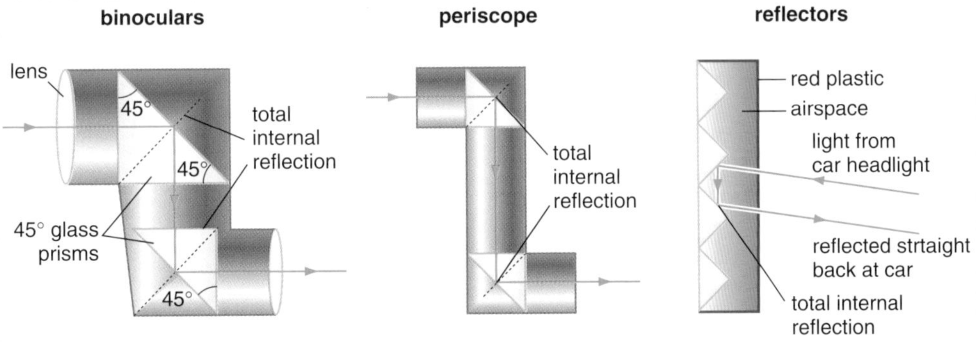

Figure 28 How total internal reflection is used in a) binoculars, b) a periscope and c) a bicycle reflector

Optical fibres are lengths of solid glass core with an outer plastic sheath. Provided the fibre is not too tightly bent, light will strike the core-cladding boundary at an angle greater than the critical angle and be totally internally reflected at the surface of the glass core. However, every optical fibre has some imperfections at its reflecting surface and this means that the signal must be boosted every kilometre or so. Optical fibres are used to transmit both telephone and video signals.

The big advantage of an optical fibre is that it can carry much, much more information than a copper cable of the same diameter. It has been estimated that the optical fibres in a sheath no thicker than a man's arm could carry all the telephone conversations taking place at any one time, all over the world.

What happens if the optical fibre is too tightly bent? If this happens, the angle of incidence at the core-cladding boundary may become less than the critical angle and light will be lost by refraction into the cladding.

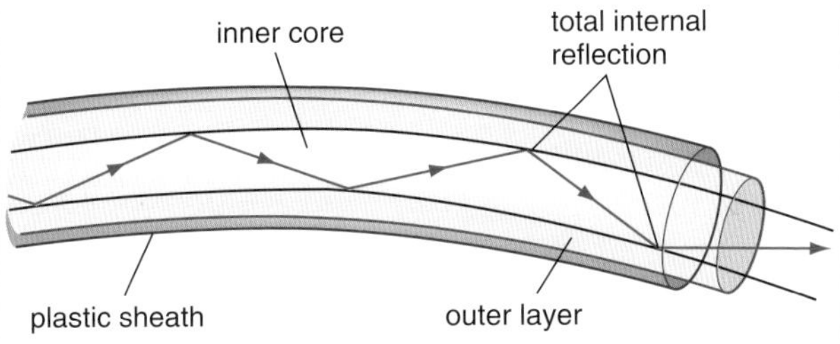

Figure 29 Passage of light through an optical fibre

Endoscopes are used by surgeons to see inside a patient's body without needing to cut a large hole. They consist of bundles of optical fibres which allow light to travel into the body and image information to pass out of the body. The surgeon can therefore see on a monitor what is happening inside the body, as it happens. The endoscope kit also carries tools for cutting, snaring, water irrigation and retrieval of tissue. It is the use of optical fibres that makes keyhole surgery possible.

Lenses

Lenses are specially shaped pieces of glass or plastic. There are two main types of lens:

- **converging** (or **convex**) lenses
- **diverging** (or **concave**) lenses.

Light refracts at each surface as it enters and leaves the lens. Figure 30 shows how a ray of light is refracted at a converging lens and at a diverging lens.

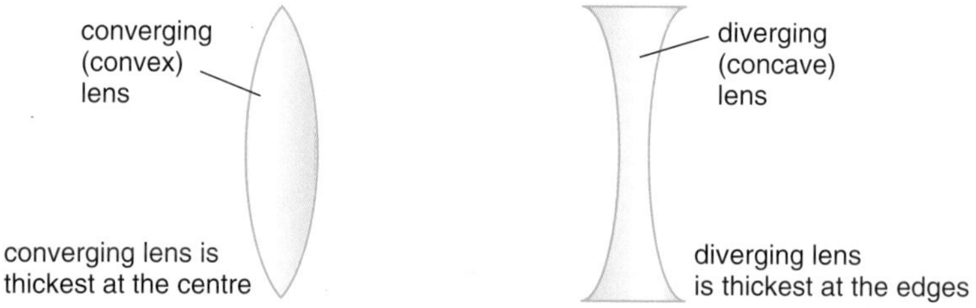

Figure 30 How light is refracted through a converging and a diverging lens

There are two features of a converging lens which need to be defined.

- Rays of light parallel to the principal axis of a convex lens all converge at the same point on the opposite side of the lens. This point lies on the principal axis and is called the **principal focus**.
- The distance between the principal focus and the optical centre of a lens is called the **focal length**.

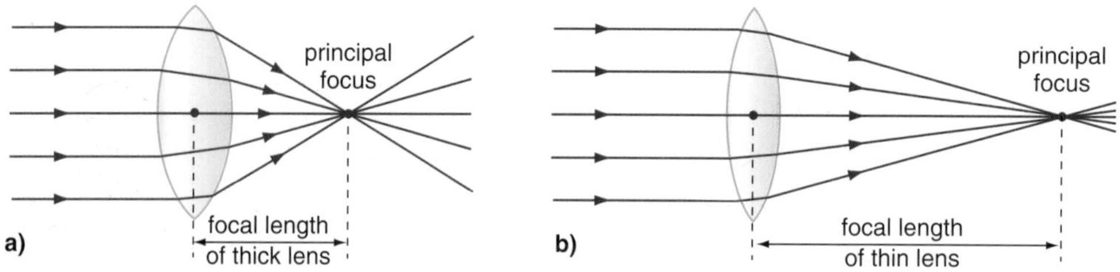

Figure 31 The focal length of a thin lens is much longer than that of a thick lens

Figure 31 shows that:

- a thick lens is strong and has a short focal length
- a thin lens is weak and has a long focal length.

Since light can pass through a lens from left to right or from right to left, every convex lens has two principal focuses and two focal lengths. However, the only lenses necessary to learn at GCSE are **equiconvex**. This means that the principal focuses on each side of the lens are the same distance from the optical centre. This becomes important when drawing ray diagrams to scale to find the position of the image.

Did you know?

Probably the greatest scientist of the seventeenth century was Isaac Newton. But Newton was so frightened that his notes might fall into the hands of his rivals, he wrote them in code. Then, to make doubly sure, they were laterally inverted, as in a mirror.

If you know the focal length of a lens and the position and height of an object, it is easy to draw a ray diagram to scale on graph paper to find the position and size of the image. To construct such a ray diagram you will need to draw at least two of the following three rays:

- a ray parallel to the principal axis refracted through the principal focus
- a ray through the optical centre of the lens that does not change its direction
- a ray through the principal focus on one side of the lens emerges that is parallel to the principal axis on the other side of the lens.

When drawing a ray diagram, it is important to:

- draw a horizontal line to represent the principal axis and a vertical line for the lens
- mark the position of the principal focus with a letter F, the same distance from the optical centre on each side of the lens
- draw a vertical line touching the principal axis at the correct distance from the lens to represent the object
- draw at least two of the three construction rays, starting from the top of the object
- draw arrows on all rays to show the direction in which the light is travelling

The point where the construction rays meet is the top of the image. The bottom of the image lies on the principal axis.

To illustrate the process, consider the following example. An object 5 cm tall is placed 6 cm away from a converging lens of focal length 4 cm. Find the position and height of the image.

In the solution in Figure 32, circled numbers have been added to show the order in which the lines or rays have been drawn. These are drawn for illustration only and are normally omitted from such ray diagrams.

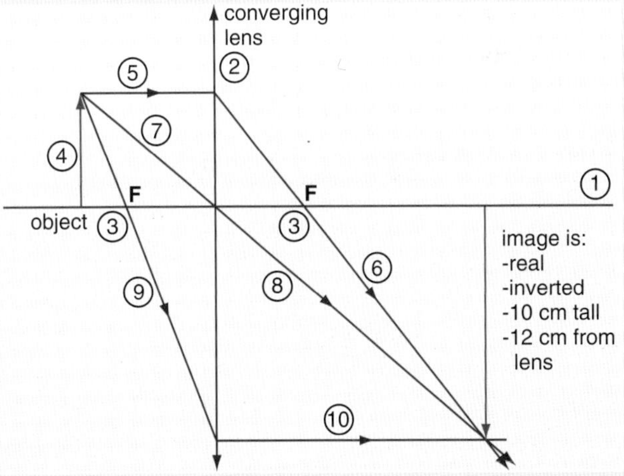

Figure 32 To calculate the position and height of an image

If the rays of light converge, the image is real and can be projected onto a screen. In a converging lens it is useful to remember that:

- all real images are also inverted – this means that if the object is drawn above the principal axis, the image will appear below the axis
- if the object is further away from the lens than the principal focus, the image will be real

But what happens if the rays which pass through the lens diverge? This happens when the object is placed closer to the lens than the principal focus. To locate the image we trace the refracted rays backwards, in straight lines, to find the point where the refracted rays appear to come from. This point is the top of the image. It is conventional not to draw arrows on such construction lines as they are not rays at all but simply lines drawn to locate the image. Such an image is virtual, so it cannot appear on a screen. It is useful to remember that all virtual images in a converging lens are erect. This is the principle of the magnifying glass or simple microscope.

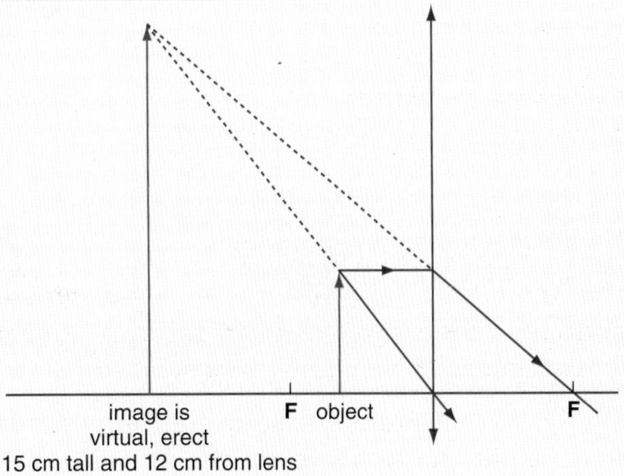

Figure 33 How a simple microscope works

Image properties

Table 6 illustrates the kind of image which can be obtained using a converging lens for different positions of the object. All the information can be obtained by drawing the appropriate ray diagram.

Table 6

Position of object	Location of image	Properties of image				
		Nature	Erect or inverted	Larger or smaller than object	Application
Between lens and F	On same side of lens as object, but further away from lens	Virtual	Erect	Larger	Magnifying glass
At F	At infinity	Real	Inverted	Larger	Searchlight
Between F and 2F	Beyond 2F	Real	Inverted	Larger	Cinema projector
At 2F	At 2F	Real	Inverted	Same size	Telescope – erecting lens
Just beyond 2F	Between F and 2F	Real	Inverted	Smaller	Camera
Very far away from lens	At F	Real	Inverted	Smaller	Astronomical telescope

The camera

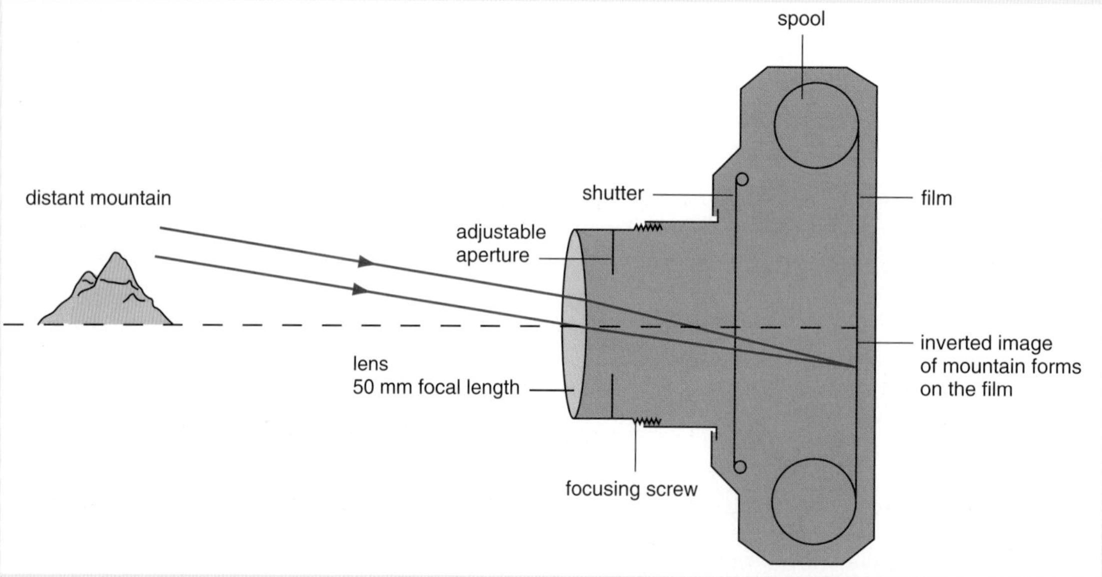

Figure 34 How a camera focuses light rays to produce an image

Figure 34 is a diagram of a simple camera. The purpose of the lens is to project an image of a distant object onto a light-sensitive film.

Focusing is achieved by changing the distance between the lens and the film. This is done by moving the lens backwards or forwards using the focusing screw.

Shutter speed can also be set by the photographer. A very fast speed (typically $\frac{1}{250}$th of a second) needs to be set by a sports photographer if the action of a goalkeeper making a save is to be captured without blurring. On the other hand, the photographer may set a much slower speed (about $\frac{1}{60}$th of a second) when taking a posed shot of a wedding.

The **f-number** refers to the aperture setting. f/16 means that the diameter of the aperture is $\frac{1}{16}$th of the focal length of the lens. So the bigger the f-number, the smaller the aperture. Increasing the aperture lets more light into the camera to allow photographs to be taken in dull conditions. Reducing the aperture lets less light into the camera. This might be done to prevent over-exposure of the film in very bright conditions. Setting a high f-number also increases the depth of focus so that more of the foreground and background are sharply focused than would otherwise be the case.

The projector

Since a projector produces an enlarged image on a screen, the film or slide must be placed between one and two focal lengths away from the lens. If the image on the screen is to be the right way up, the slide must be upside down when placed in front of the lens. Much of the design of a projector relates to the problem of getting rid of the heat coming from the projector's powerful lamp.

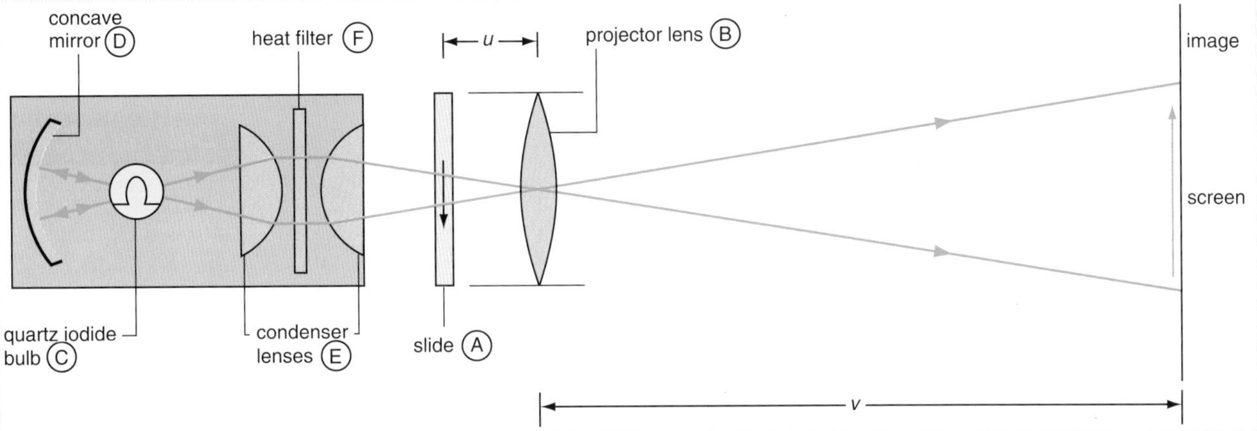

Figure 35 The principle of the slide projector

Measuring the focal length of a convex lens experimentally

To carry out this experiment you need a metre rule, a white screen and a convex lens in a suitable holder.

- Tape the rule to the bench and place the screen at the zero mark.
- Place the lens in its holder as close as possible to the screen.
- Slowly move the lens away from the screen until the image of some distant object is as sharp as possible.
- Using the metre rule, measure the distance from the centre of the lens and the screen This distance is the focal length.

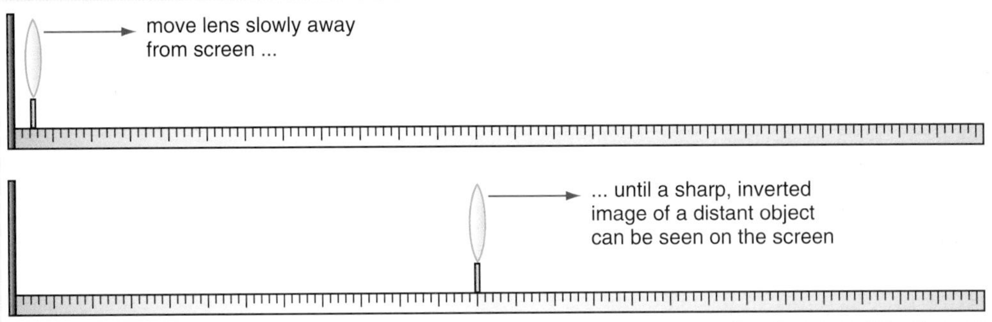

Figure 36 To measure the focal length of a convex lens

Explanation

Rays of light from any point on a distant object arrive at the lens as a parallel beam. Such rays will be brought to a focus in the focal plane. This is the plane at right angles to the principal axis and containing the principal focus.

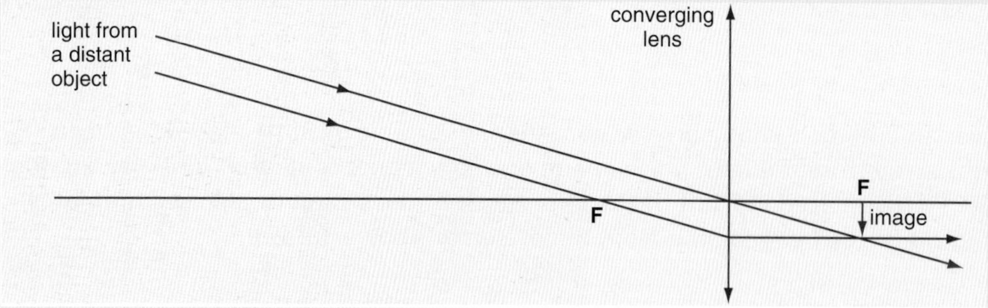

Figure 37

Electromagnetic waves

Electromagnetic waves are members of a family with common properties called the **electromagnetic spectrum**. Every one of them

- can travel in a vacuum
- travels at exactly the same speed in a vacuum
- are transverse waves.

Electromagnetic waves also show properties common to all types of wave. They

- carry energy
- can be reflected
- can be refracted.

Did you know?

The brightest known star is S-Doradus in the Magellan Clouds. It is thought to be about 50 times more massive than our Sun and about 1 million times brighter.

There are seven members of the electromagnetic family. The properties of electromagnetic waves depend very much on their wavelength. In Table 7 they are arranged in order of increasing wavelength (or decreasing frequency).

Table 7 The electromagnetic spectrum

Electromagnetic wave	Typical wavelength
Gamma (γ) rays	0.01 nm
X-rays	0.1 nm
Ultraviolet light	10 nm
Visible light	0.5 μm
Infrared light	0.01 mm
Microwaves or radar waves	3 cm
Radio waves	1000 m

Uses and dangers of electromagnetic waves

Gamma rays

Generally, waves with the shortest wavelengths (like γ waves) can destroy viruses and bacteria, disrupt the DNA in cells and cause cancers. These are also among the most penetrating radiations. They are therefore used in the treatment of tumours and in sterilising medical equipment like plastic syringes and surgical dressings.

Gamma rays are also used in industry to detect leaks from underground pipes and to monitor the wear of machine parts like the piston rings in prototype car engines.

In the food industry, gamma rays are used to kill the surface fungi and bacteria which are present on fresh fruit and vegetables. This prolongs their shelf-life considerably and thus reduces costs and minimises waste.

X-rays

These too can cause cancers, so exposure to **X-rays** is always carefully controlled. They are widely used in medicine for diagnosis (finding out what is wrong) and for therapy (treatment). Although X-rays can pass through soft tissue like skin and muscle, most short wavelength X-rays are stopped by bone. This enables doctors to use them to take a photograph to check whether a patient has a broken bone.

Slightly longer wavelength X-rays are used in body scanning. This enables the doctor to build up a picture of a section of the body. Here the X-rays are not allowed to strike a photographic film. Instead they hit special sensors which pass their information to a computer so that the picture, or scan, is built up bit by bit. This type of scan is often used to investigate whether a patient has cancer.

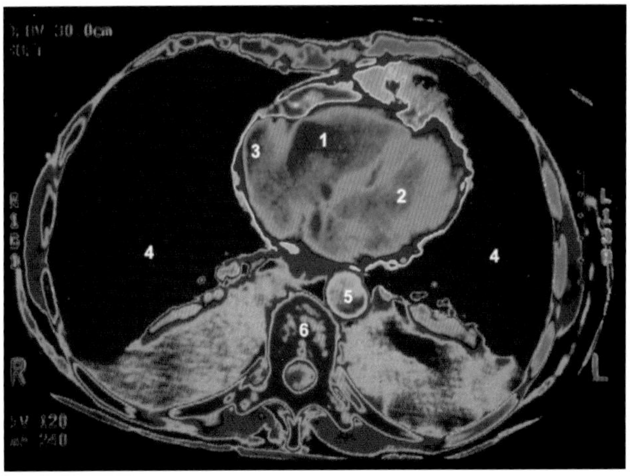

Figure 38 Longer wavelength X-rays are used to create an image of a complete scan through a person's body (1, 2 and 3 – heart, 4 – lungs, 5 – aorta, and 6 – spine)

Ultraviolet light

Objects which are extremely hot (above 4000 °C) emit **ultraviolet light**. For people on Earth, the Sun is a major source of ultraviolet light. Prolonged exposure to ultraviolet light can cause skin cancer and damage to eyes. Sensible people always use a very high SPF (sun protection factor) cream when they are exposed to sunlight in the summer. Better still, they minimise exposure by spending more time in the shade.

Fortunately, much of the ultraviolet light from the Sun is absorbed by the **ozone layer** high above the Earth's surface. However, recent studies have shown that some pollutants are causing this layer to become very thin, particularly at high latitudes. Care will have to be taken if this effect is to be stopped and then reversed.

Ultraviolet light can be used to detect forgeries of banknotes. Special marks on banknotes are made with security ink and these only show up in ultraviolet light.

Water chillers also use an ultraviolet lamp to destroy the bacteria which might otherwise build up. Without this precaution, disease might spread in a contaminated water supply.

Visible light

Humans use **visible light** for vision and photography. However, probably the most important chemical reaction on Earth takes place as a result of the absorption of visible light. That reaction is **photosynthesis**. Photosynthesis is the process that takes place in the leaves of green plants and causes the light energy to be converted into chemical energy in the form of starches and sugars.

Infrared radiation

All hot objects give out **infrared radiation**. Skin feels it as radiant heat. Infrared radiation is readily absorbed by objects, causing their temperature to rise. This makes it useful for toasters, grills, ovens and stoves.

Over-exposure to infrared radiation causes damage to cells. Infrared radiation causes sunburn but ultraviolet light causes skin cancer.

Infrared is used in night-vision equipment by detecting the radiation given off by living creatures or by engines. The hotter the object is, the brighter it appears in a night-vision scope. Night-vision scopes are mainly used by security forces and scientists interested in the behaviour of animals which are most active at night, such as badgers.

Figure 39 A night-vision scope detects infrared radiation given off by living creatures like these soldiers

Infrared is also used for the remote controls of televisions, videos and car security systems. It is suitable for this purpose because it does not interfere with radio and television

Microwaves and radar waves

Microwaves and **radar waves** are essentially the same thing, but we give them different names to describe their use.

Microwaves of an appropriate wavelength are used for mobile phone and satellite transmissions because they readily pass through the Earth's atmosphere, including clouds. But the most common domestic use is the microwave oven. The microwaves pass easily into the food and are quickly absorbed by water molecules inside. Since our bodies contain a great deal of water, microwaves are a potential hazard. To minimise the risks, safety interlocks are fitted to the oven to prevent the production of microwaves when the door is open.

Air traffic controllers, pilots and the masters of large ships also use microwaves, as radar waves, for navigation. Increasingly too, motorists are making use of Global Positioning Satellites (GPS) to find the best route around and between large cities.

Radio waves

Radio waves are used extensively for communication. Television and FM radio use short wavelength radio signals, typically about 1 m long. This is why your television set can be tuned to receive some radio programmes. Radio communication is also important for pilots, seafarers, policemen and the military.

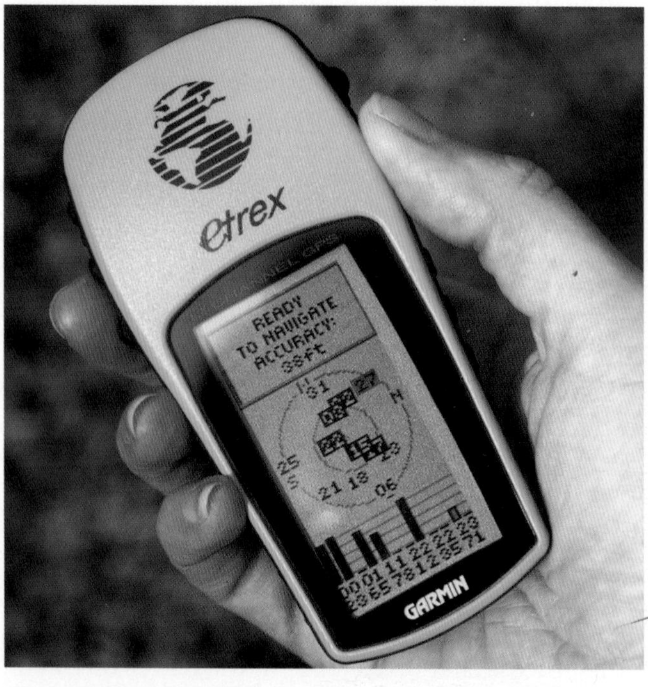

Figure 40 Increasingly, people are using Global Positioning Satellites to find their way around

Websites

Use your favourite search engine (such as **www.google.com** or **www.excite.com**) and search using the keywords:

dispersion + light	reflection
electromagnetic + wave	refraction
light	sound
longitudinal	transverse
pitch + sound	ultrasound
rarefaction	waves

http://library.thinkquest.org/10796/ch8/ch8.htm

http://member.aol.com/nicholash/waves/waves.htm

http://www.physics.nwu.edu/ugrad/vpl/waves/wavetypes.html

http://www.physics.nwu.edu/ugrad/vpl/waves/superpositionl.html

http://www.purchon.com/physics/e1ectromagnetic.htm

http://www.explorescience.com/activities/activity_list.cfm?categoryID=10

http://www.soton.ac.uk/~irc3/chudler/retina.html

Exam questions

1 a) The diagram below shows two buoys, 60 m apart, floating on the sea.

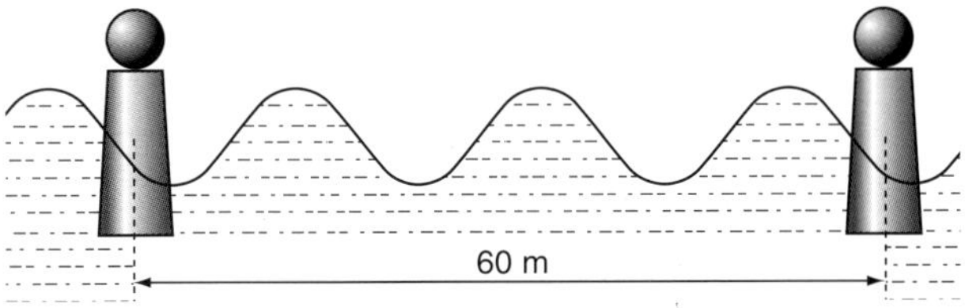

(i) Use the diagram to determine the wavelength of the sea waves. *(1 mark)*

(ii) Explain the meaning of the term frequency. *(1 mark)*

(iii) Ten complete waves pass the buoy in 25 seconds. Calculate the frequency of the waves. *(1 mark)*

(iv) Calculate the speed of the waves across the sea. *(1 mark)*

b) Waves approaching a sea wall are shown below.

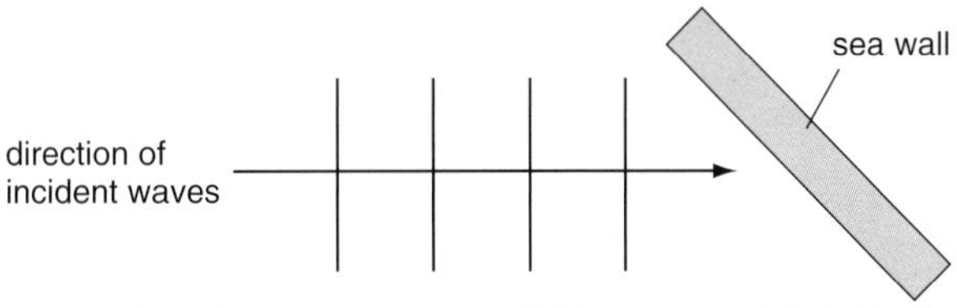

The arrow showing the direction of the incident waves is shown.

(i) Copy the diagram and draw another arrow showing the direction of the reflected waves. *(1 mark)*

(ii) On your diagram draw three waves which have been reflected from the sea wall. *(2 marks)*

(iii) Some distance from the sea wall the waves come closer together. Explain. *(2 marks)*

2 a) The following objects are all producing sound.

(i) What are all of the objects doing to produce sound? *(1 mark)*

(ii) The drum is hit harder and this produces louder sound. What is happening to the drumskin to make the sound louder? *(1 mark)*

(iii) The loudspeaker is made to produce a higher-pitched sound. What is happening to the loudspeaker cone to make the pitch higher? *(1 mark)*

b) At an airport the ground control officer wears ear protectors to protect his ears when he is near to the aircraft.

(i) What damage could be caused to his ears if he did not wear the ear protectors? *(1 mark)*

(ii) Suggest one measure which could reduce the effects of noise pollution for people living in houses close to the airport. *(1 mark)*

c) Brian's driveway leads on to a main road It has high walls on either side.

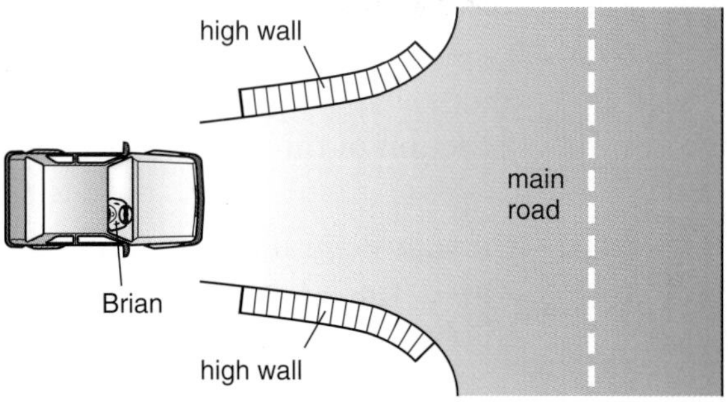

(i) Copy the diagram and shade the part of the main road Brian cannot see from this position. *(2 marks)*

He then places a plane (flat) mirror on the post at A and positions it as shown in the diagram below.

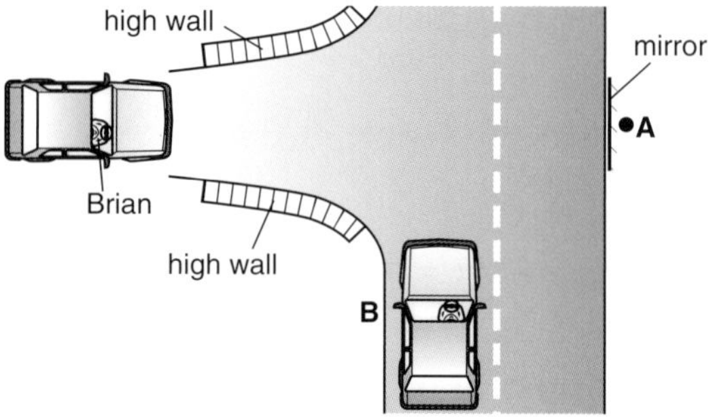

(ii) Can Brian now see the car at B? Explain your answer by drawing a ray of light on your diagram. *(2 marks)*

d) Two light rays pass through a perspex block.

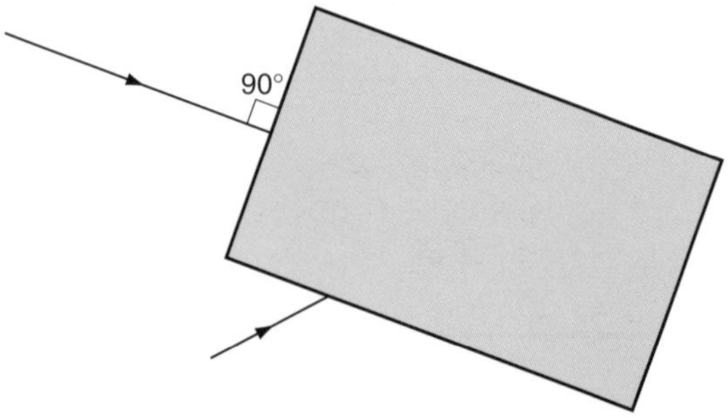

Copy the diagram and complete the paths of both light rays through the block and out into the air on the opposite side. *(1 mark)*

e) Different waves form the electromagnetic spectrum.

Radio waves   Visible light   Microwaves
Ultraviolet waves   Infrared waves
X-rays   Gamma waves

Copy and complete the table by matching the statements to the correct waves above.

Statement	Waves
These waves can cause sunburn and skin cancer	
These waves can heat food	
These waves have the greatest wavelength	

(3 marks)

3 a) The diagram shows a ray of white light incident on a glass prism. The prism breaks the white light up into a spectrum.

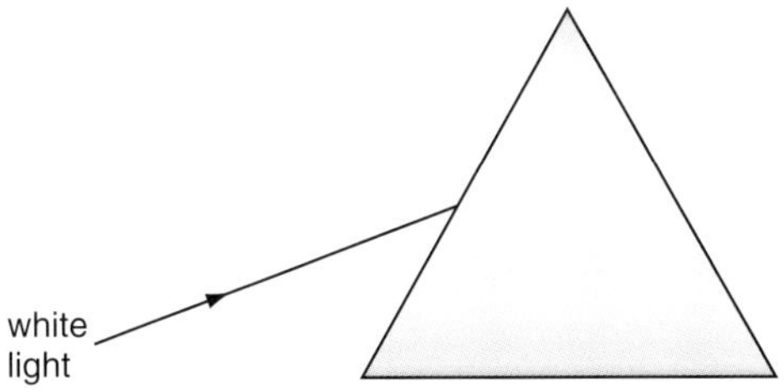

(i) What name is given to the breaking up of white light into different colours?

(1 mark)

(ii) Copy and complete the ray diagram to show the paths taken by a ray of red light and a ray of violet light that result from the break up of the white light as it enters the prism.

(2 marks)

(iii) Explain what causes the glass prism to break white light up into its many colours.

(2 marks)

b) In a camera, a lens is used to form an image of a film. The diagram below is full scale and represents the lens of the camera and the film. The diagram shows an object in front of the camera lens. The lens is correctly adjusted so that a sharp image is formed on the film.

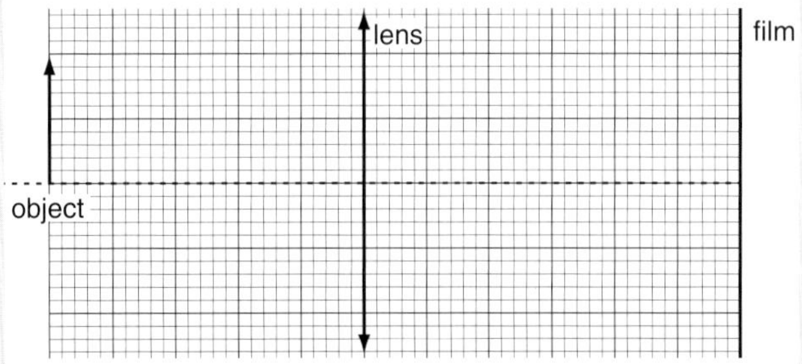

(i) Copy the diagram and draw two rays of light from the top of the object to show how the image is formed on the film.

(2 marks)

(ii) Mark carefully and accurately the principal focus of this lens

(1 mark)

(iii) Measure the focal length of the lens.

(1 mark)

(iv) Below is a list of properties of an image. Tick (3) those that apply to the image formed on the film of this camera.

Magnified	
Diminished	
Same size as object	
Same way up as object	
Upside down	

(3 marks)

Chapter 5

Electricity

Learning objectives

By the end of this chapter you should know:

- That insulating materials can be charged by friction and explain this in terms of transfer of charge
- That positively-charged objects have a deficiency of electrons and negatively-charged objects have a surplus of electrons
- How to describe the dangers and use of electrostatic charge generated in everyday contexts
- The difference between conductors and insulators in terms of free electrons
- That an electric current is a flow of electrons and that it is in the opposite direction to that of conventional current
- The quantitative relationship between current, charge and time
- That charge is measured in coulombs
- How to describe the effects of varying the current on bulb brightness and motor speed
- How to explain potential difference
- That EMF is the energy per unit charge supplied by a battery
- That voltage is the energy transferred per unit charge
- The rule for PDs around a circuit
- How to perform calculations using the formula: Energy = Voltage × Charge
- That in a series circuit the current is the same everywhere
- That in a series circuit the sum of the voltages is equal to the voltage across the whole circuit
- That in a parallel circuit the sum of the currents in the branches is equal to the current entering the parallel section
- That voltages across components in parallel circuits are equal
- How the resistance of a thermistor varies with temperature
- How the resistance of a light dependent resistor (LDR) varies with light level
- How to explain resistance and list the factors that affect resistance
- Several different types of resistor, how they work and a practical application of each
- The relationship between voltage, current and resistance of a conductor and be able to use the equation $V = I \times R$
- How to describe some experiments to obtain current–voltage characteristics for the filament bulb and diode
- How to plot and interpret voltage–current graphs for the filament bulb and diode
- Ohm's Law in the form $V/I = R$, where R is the resistance, measured in ohms
- How to calculate the total resistance of resistors in series
- How to calculate the resistance of two equal resistors in parallel
- How to calculate the combined resistance of any number of resistors in parallel
- How to calculate the combined resistance of circuits with series and parallel sections
- How to recall and use the quantitative relationships between power, energy, current, voltage and time
- How to define the volt
- The difference between a.c. and d.c.
- The difference between one-way and two-way switching
- That fuses and earth wires protect the user
- How to wire a three pin plug
- The function of live and neutral wires
- How double insulation protects the user
- The positioning of switches and fuses on the live side of appliances
- How to calculate the costs of using electricity from meter readings

Electricity is an extremely versatile and useful form of energy. Many of our everyday activities depend on the use of electricity. Living in society today would be unimaginable without it. Simple activities such as entertainment, communications, transport and industry would simply grind to a halt if electricity ceased to exist.

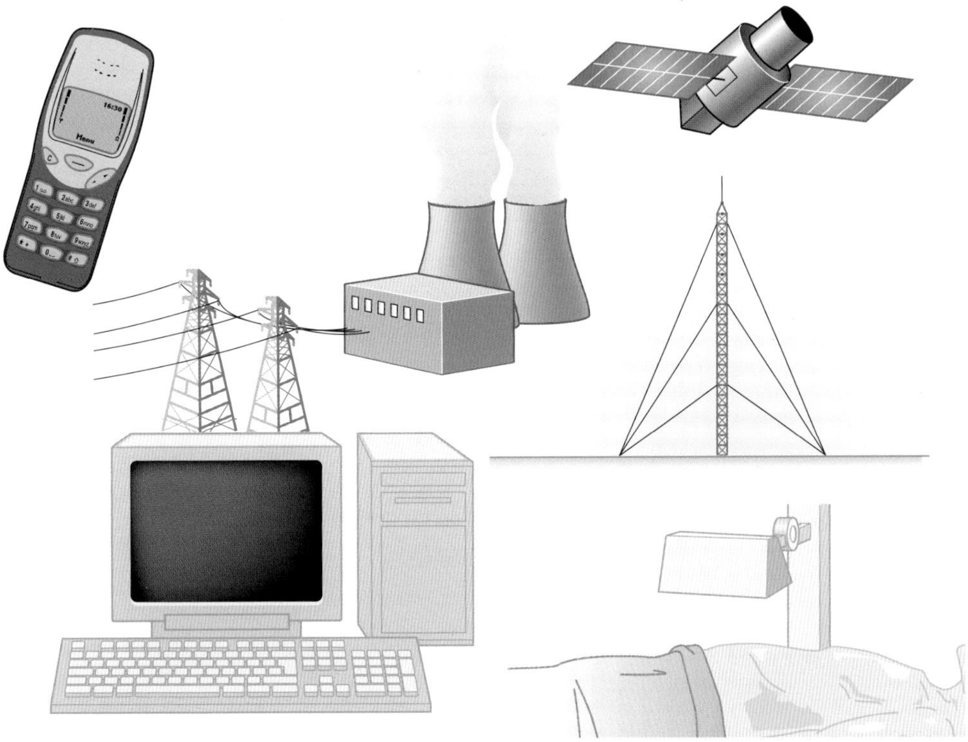

Figure 1 Without electricity, our life would be unimaginable

Electrostatistics

When a woollen jumper is taken off over a nylon shirt in the dark, it is possible to hear crackles and see tiny blue electric sparks. The nylon shirt has become charged with **static electricity**.

Nature provides much more spectacular electrical discharges in the form of lightning.

There are two types of charge which can be demonstrated by the simple experiments shown in Figure 2.

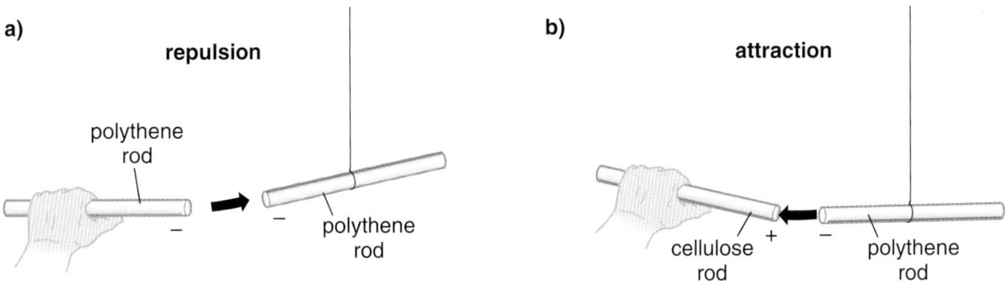

Figure 2 These two experiments demonstrate the existence of positive and negative charges

When the polythene rod is rubbed with the cloth, electrons are taken off the cloth (which now has a shortage of electrons and is therefore positively charged) and transferred to the polythene rod (which now has a surplus of electrons and is therefore negatively charged).

In Figure 2a, the polythene rod has been rubbed with a cloth and suspended. When a second similarly charged polythene rod is brought up to the first one, the two rods repel each other.

In Figure 2b, a rubbed cellulose acetate rod is brought close to the polythene rod. This time attraction occurs between the two rods.

These simple experiments show that:

1 There must be two types of charges – positive and negative – since there are two types of force.
2 Bodies may be charged by **friction**.

The charge on cellulose acetate is taken as **positive** (+) and that on polythene is **negative** (−).

From the experiment we can see that similar charges (i.e. + and + or − and −) repel, while opposite charges (+ and −) attract. This can be summarised as:

LIKE charges REPEL UNLIKE charges ATTRACT

So where do these charges come from and why can the rods become oppositely charged? Scientists believe that atoms consist of a tiny positively-charged nucleus surrounded by orbiting electrons, which are negatively charged.

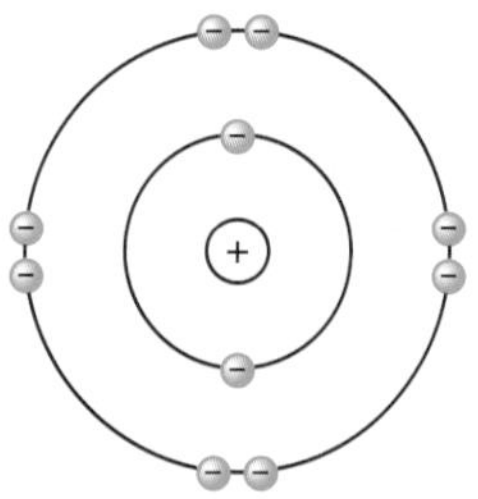

Figure 3 The'satellite' model of an atom, with a central nucleus and orbiting electrons

Something similar happens when the cellulose acetate rod is rubbed with a cloth. Electrons move from the cellulose acetate rod, leaving it positively charged, while the cloth gains electrons making it negatively charged.

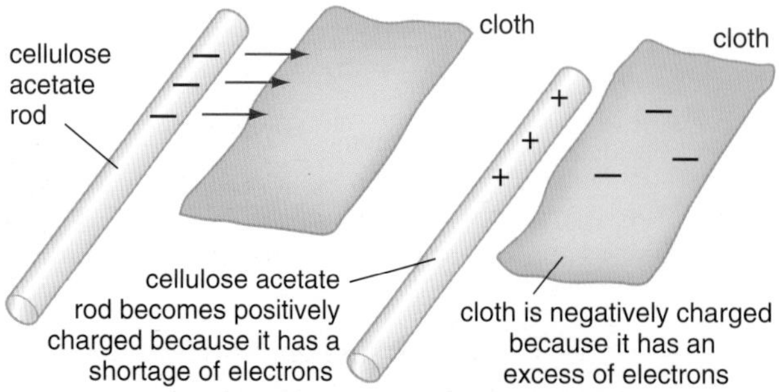
cellulose acetate rod
cloth
cloth
cellulose acetate rod becomes positively charged because it has a shortage of electrons
cloth is negatively charged because it has an excess of electrons

Figure 4 The rod has lost electrons and become positively charged. The cloth has gained the electrons and become negatively charged

It is important to remember that an object becomes negatively charged when it *gains* electrons and positively charged when it *loses* electrons.

Did you know?

The static build-up in the home can lead to shocks of 50 000 V. However very little harm is done because very few electrons flow.

Useful applications of static electricity

Dust precipitators in power stations

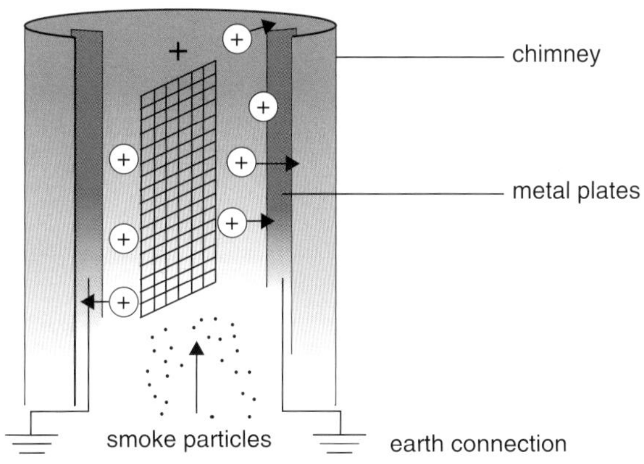

Figure 5 A dust precipitator in a fossil fuel power station

When fosssil fuels are burned in power stations, vast quantities of smoke are emitted into the atmosphere along with the waste gases. Because the smoke consists of lots of tiny particles of solid matter, it can be removed from the chimneys before it passes out into the air using the principle of electrostatics. In a device called a smoke precipitator, like that shown in Figure 5, the smoke particles pass up through the chimney, where they pass a negatively-charged grid. As they pass the grid, they become negatively charged and so are repelled by it. The chimney is lined with large positively-charged collecting plates which are connected to earth. The negatively-charged smoke particles are attracted to the oppositely-charged plates, and as they touch them, they lose their charge and fall to the bottom of the chimney, from where they can be collected.

Photocopiers

Certain substances are electrical insulators in the dark, but become electrical conductors when exposed to light. These substances are called **photoconductors** and include selenium, arsenic and tellurium. Use is made of photoconductors in photocopiers, as shown in Figure 6.

1 In a photocopier, there is a plate consisting of a layer of photoconducting material on a thin metal sheet. When a piece of paper is put into the machine to be copied, this plate is given a positive charge.

2 A strong light is shone on the page to be copied, which results in an image of the page forming on the surface of the charged plate. The white areas of the page light up the layer of photoconducting material, making it an electrical conductor. This charge leaks away to the metal backing. The areas of page covered in text are black and are left as an image in the positive charges on the belt.

3 At the next stage, toner is spread onto the plate. The toner is negatively charged, so is attracted to the positively-charged parts of the plate – those parts which were dark on the original copy.

4 A blank sheet of paper is given a positive charge and rolled over the belt, where it attracts the negatively-charged toner.

5 At the final stage, heat and pressure are applied to the paper by rollers to fix the toner to the page.

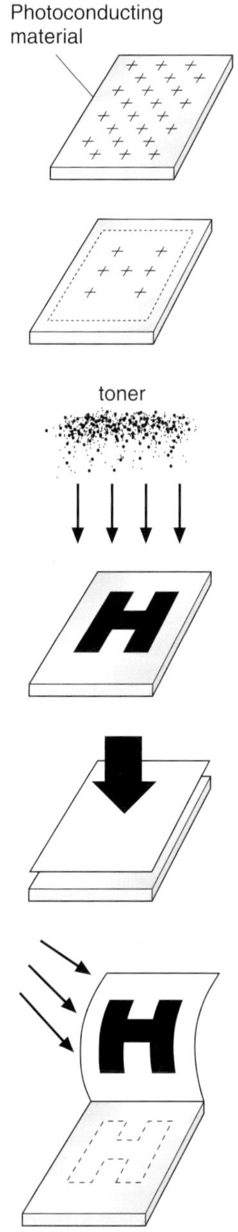

Figure 6 How static electricity is used in a photocopier

Paint spraying

In an electrostatic paint spray gun, like that shown in Figure 7, the droplets of paint become charged as they leave the gun. As they are all given the same charge, they repel each other, forming a fine mist of paint. This results in an even coating for the object. The process is made more efficient if the object being sprayed is given an opposite charge to that of the paint droplets.

Figure 7 An electrostatic paint spray gun

Dangers of static electricity

Fuelling aircraft

When large petrol tankers are used to refuel aircraft, friction from the movement of the petrol through the pipe results in a charge on the pipe. If this charge was allowed to develop, it could be hazardous due to the flammable nature of the liquid. To prevent this, a wire connects the pipe nozzle to the ground, enabling the charges to leak away to earth.

Figure 8 Refuelling an aircraft

Lightning

In a storm, if a cloud with a large charge comes close to a tall object on the ground – such as a building or a tree – the charge can run to earth, resulting in a lightning strike. The air particles between the cloud and the tree become ionised. Some lose their electrons to become positive ions while others gain electrons to become negative ions. These ionised air particles allow the electrons to move quickly from the charged cloud to the tree during the discharge. The lightning flash is created when the air particles rejoin their missing charge.

Figure 9a Lightning between oppositely-charged clouds

Figure 9b A lightning strike between a charged cloud and a tree

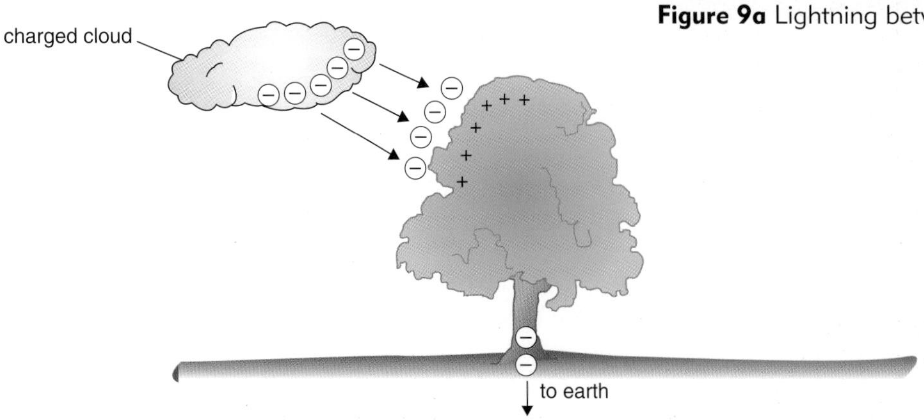

Overhead power cables

The overhead power cables which carry electricity around the country consist of insulated metal wires held high above the ground by insulated pylons. If a kite was flown too close to these uninsulated wires, an electric circuit would be completed, enabling the current to flow from the wires down to earth through the person. The charge can be so great that it can easily kill the person holding the kite.

Figure 10 The insulated supports are clearly visible on these pylons

Static electricity as a nuisance

Static electricity can cause:

- clothes to stick together when removed from a tumble drier
- the moving black plastic handrails on an escalator to provide nasty 'shocks'
- 'shocks' from walking across a nylon carpet and then touching a door handle
- a need for the smart card in the satellite receiver to be 'discharged' occasionally due to the build up of static charge
- TV screens and computer monitors to develop a build up of static charge. They need to be cleaned frequently with anti-static cloths.

Questions

1 a) What is static electricity?
b) Name the two types of charge.
c) Write down the laws of forces between charged bodies.

2 a) Explain in terms of electron movement what happens when a polythene rod becomes negatively-charged when rubbed with a cloth.
b) What is the name of the process you have described in part a)?

3 A small positively-charged polystyrene bead hangs on a nylon thread. Different rods charged by friction are brought near the bead. The movement of the bead is recorded in a table. Copy the table and tick each charge present on the rod.

Material of rod	Bead movement	Charge on rod		
		Positive	Negative	Uncharged
Perspex	Repelled			
Cellulose acetate	Repelled			
Polythene	Attracted			
Steel	None			

4 Describe two examples where:
a) static electricity is useful
b) static electricity is a nuisance
c) static electricity is dangerous.

Current electricity

An electric current is a flow of electric charges. When a Van der Graaf generator is connected to Earth via a sensitive current meter, a current is detected by the meter.

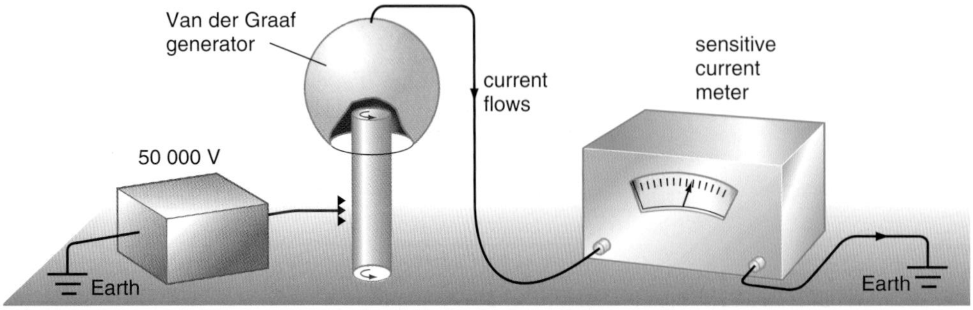

Figure 11

In metals the charge is carried by electrons. Most materials conduct electricity to a greater or lesser extent.

Table 1 Classiifying some common materials in terms of electrical conduction

Very good conductors (plenty of free electrons)	Semi-conductors	Poor conductors (insulators) (very few free electrons)
Silver	Silicon	Plastic
Copper	Germanium	Wood
Steel		Rubber
Aluminium		Cork

Current in a simple circuit

An electric **cell** (commonly called a **battery**) can make electrons move, but only if there is a conductor connecting its two terminals, making a complete circuit. Chemical reactions inside the cell push electrons from the negative (−) terminal round to the positive (+) terminal. Figure 12 shows how an electric current would flow in a wire connected across a cell.

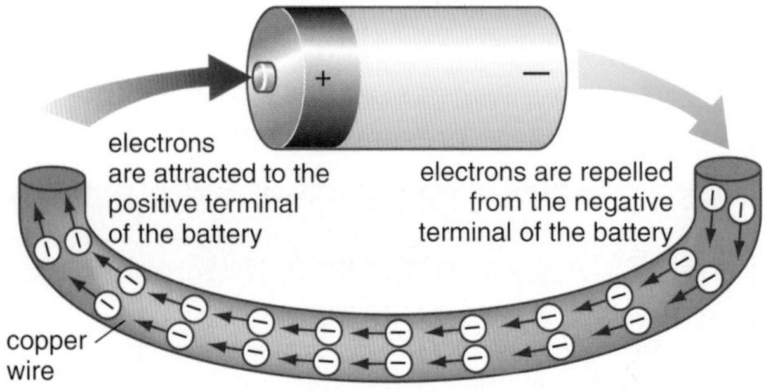

Figure 12 The flow of electrons in a simple cell

The electrons are repelled from the negative terminal of the cell, since like charges repel, and are attracted to the positive terminal, since unlike charges attract. The electrons therefore flow from the negative terminal to the positive terminal.

Scientists in the nineteenth century thought that an electric current consisted of a flow of positive charge from the positive terminal of the cell to the negative terminal. Unfortunately, although this idea is now known to be incorrect, this is still known as the direction of **conventional current**.

Circuit diagrams and symbols

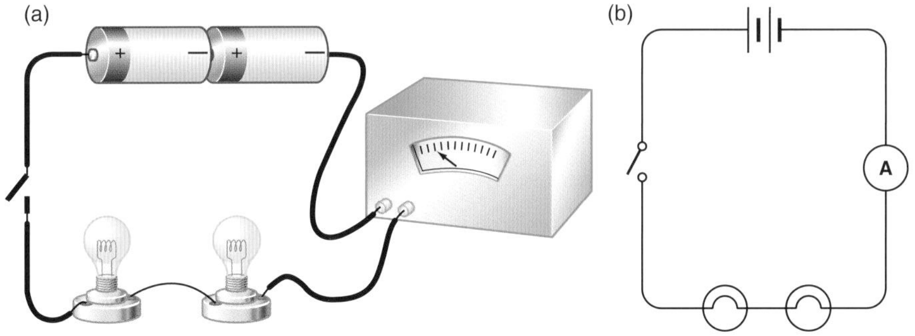

Figure 13 This circuit can be represented as a simple circuit diagram, using symbols for the different components

An electrical circuit may be represented by a **circuit diagram** with symbols for components. Circuit diagrams are easy to draw and are universally understood.

Table 2 Circuit diagram of components and their symbols

Component	Symbol	Component	Symbol
cell	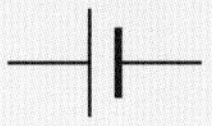	ammeter	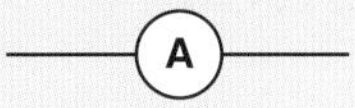
battery	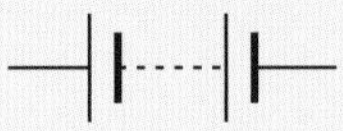	voltmeter	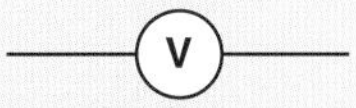
wire		diode	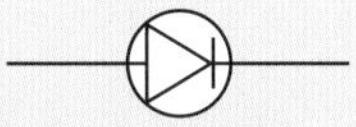
switch		variable resistor	
amp		thermistor	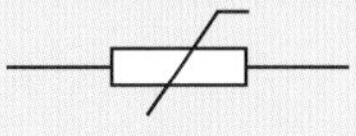
resistor		light dependent resistor (LDR)	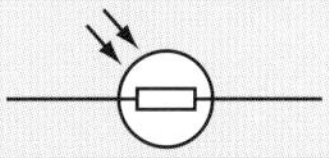
bell		buzzer	

Measuring current

Figure 14a An analogue and a digital ammeter

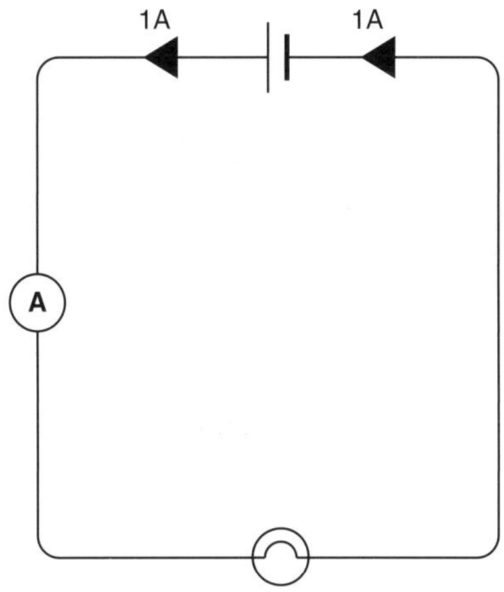

Figure 14b An ammeter connected into a simple circuit

Ammeters, like that shown in Figure 14, are connected into circuits to measure current. An ammeter must be connected the correct way round. The red (+) terminal should be on the same side of the circuit as the positive (+) terminal of the battery. Putting an ammeter into a circuit has almost no effect on the current.

The effects of a current

An electric current is difficult to 'see' directly, but there are three effects, which show when a current is flowing:

1 Heating and lighting – bulb lights when a tiny wire inside it (the filament) is made white hot by the current.
2 The needle in a plotting compass is deflected when placed in the magnetic field produced around any wire carrying a current.
3 Bubbles of gas are given off at the wires in the acid because of the chemical action of the current.

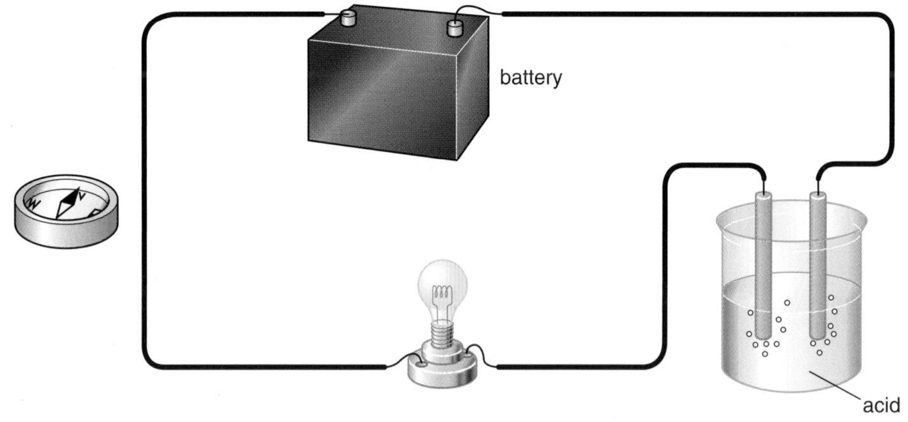

Figure 15 Some of the things that can be seen when a current is flowing

The effect of increasing current through various devices

Increasing the current through a filament bulb has the effect of increasing the brightness of the bulb.

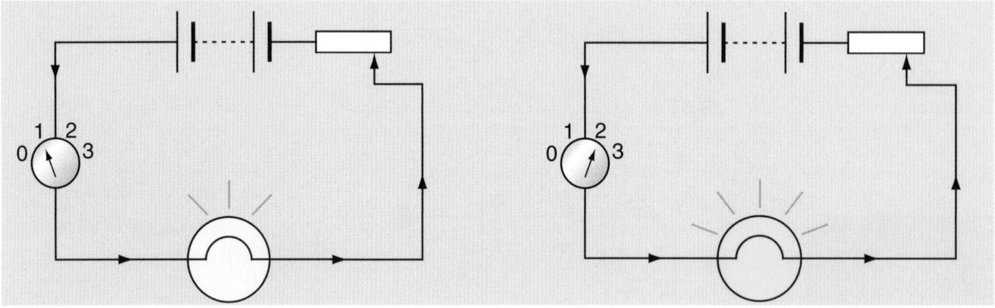

Figure 16 When the current is increased, the bulb glows brighter

Similarly, increasing the current through an electric motor has the effect of increasing the speed of rotation of the spindle of the motor.

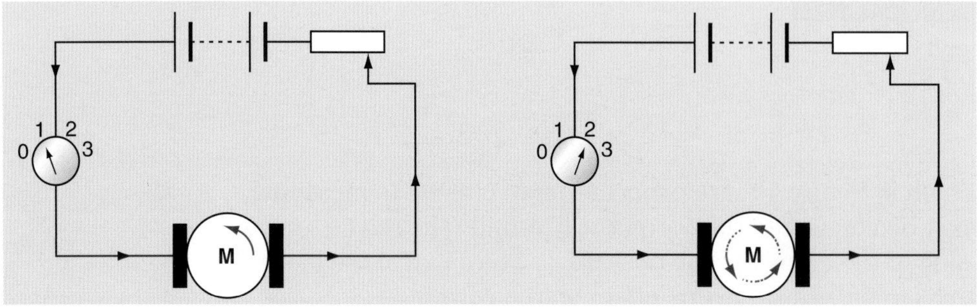

Figure 17 The motor rotates slowly when the current is small. When the current is increased, the motor rotates more quickly

The relationship between charge and current

The unit of charge is the **coulomb** (C). If it was posssible to see a coulomb of charge, it would look like a very large assembly of electrons – about six million million million electrons.

The unit of current is the **ampere** (A). Currents of over around one ampere can be measured by connecting an ammeter into the circuit. For smaller currents, a **milliammeter** is used. The unit in this case is the milliampere (mA). (1000 mA = 1 A.) An even smaller unit of current is the **microampere** (μA). (1 000 000 μA = 1 A.)

The relationship between charge and current can be stated as follows:

> A current of 1 ampere is flowing when 1 coulomb of charge flows past a point in a circuit in 1 second. This is given by the formula:
>
> $$\underset{(C)}{\text{Charge}} = \underset{(A)}{\text{Current}} \times \underset{(s)}{\text{Time}}$$

For example, if a current of 5 A is flowing, then 5 C of charge passes a point in a circuit in 1 second.

In general, if a steady current 'I' (amperes) flows for time 't' (seconds), the charge 'Q' (coulombs) passing any point is given by the formula below:

$$Q = I \times t$$

Example

A current of 150 mA flows around a circuit for 1 minute. How much electrical charge flows past a point in the circuit in this time?

Solution:

$I = 150\text{ mA} = 0.15\text{ A}$

$t = 1\text{ minute} = 60\text{ s}$

$Q = ?$

Substituting into $Q = I \times t$

gives $Q = 0.15\text{ A} \times 60\text{ s}$

$= \mathbf{12\ C}$

There are two conditions which *must* be met before an electric current will flow:

1 There must be a *complete circuit*, i.e. there must not be any gaps in the circuit.

2 There must be a *source of energy* so that the charge may move. This source of energy may be a cell, a battery or the mains power supply.

Questions

5 Convert the following currents into milliamperes:

a) 3.0 A b) 0.2 A.

6 Convert the following currents into amperes:

a) 400 mA b) 1500 mA.

7 What charge is delivered if

a) a current of 6 A flows for 10 seconds,
b) a current of 300 mA flows for 1 minute.

8 Calculate the currents which flow when the following charges pass a point in the following times.

a) 100 C, time = 5 s
b) 500 mC, time = 50 s
c) 60 μC (0.000 06 C), time = 200 s.

Potential difference, electromotive force and voltage

The battery or cell gives energy to the charge which passes through it. The ability of the cell or battery to fulfil this function is called the **potential difference** (PD), usually referred to as **voltage**. The unit for PD and voltage is the **volt** (V).

A single AA cell has a PD of 1.5 V. This means that each coulomb of charge that leaves the cell receives 1.5 joules of electrical energy. A PP3 battery with a PD of 9 V will give 9 joules of energy to each coulomb of charge that leaves it. In other words, the bigger the PD of the cell, the more energy is given to each coulomb of charge.

What does the charge do with this energy?

Example 1 – The charge deposits this energy in the light bulb which then converts the energy to light and heat.

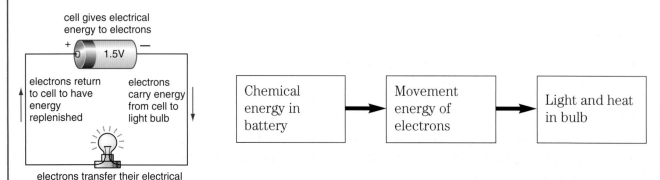

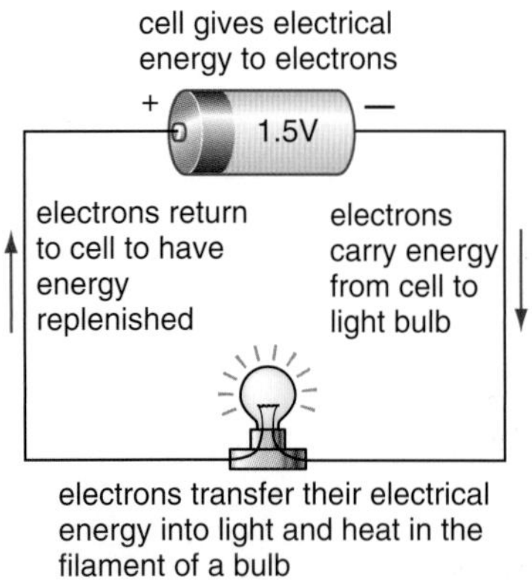

cell gives electrical energy to electrons
+
–
1.5V
electrons return to cell to have energy replenished
electrons carry energy from cell to light bulb
electrons transfer their electrical energy into light and heat in the filament of a bulb

Chemical energy in battery → Movement energy of electrons → Light and heat in bulb

Figure 18

Example 2 – The charge deposits this energy in the motor which then converts the energy to movement and heat.

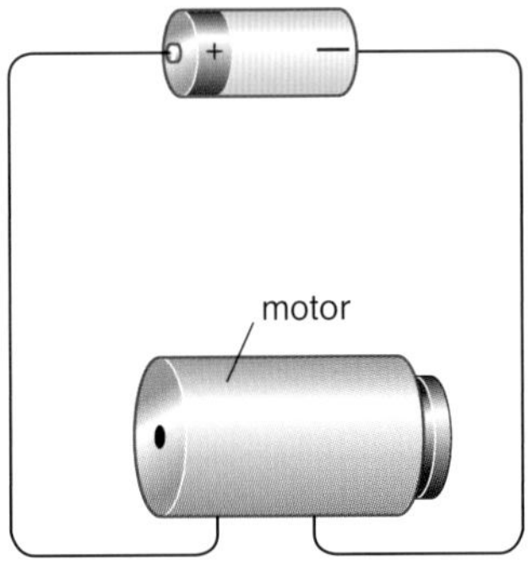

Chemical energy in battery → Movement energy of electrons → Movement and heat in motor

Figure 19

These two examples show that electric circuits behave like machines. They merely convert energy from one form to another.

A cell produces its highest PD when off-load, i.e. not supplying a current. This maximum PD is called the **electromotive force** (EMF) of the cell. However, when current is being supplied, the PD drops because of energy wastage inside the cell. For example, a car battery labelled '12 V' might only deliver 10 V when being used to turn a starter motor.

Cells in series

Portable stereo systems have a number of cells in series. The reason for this is that the system requires a high voltage to operate. So connecting cells in series to make a battery increases the voltage.

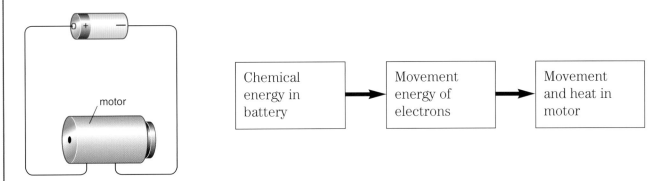

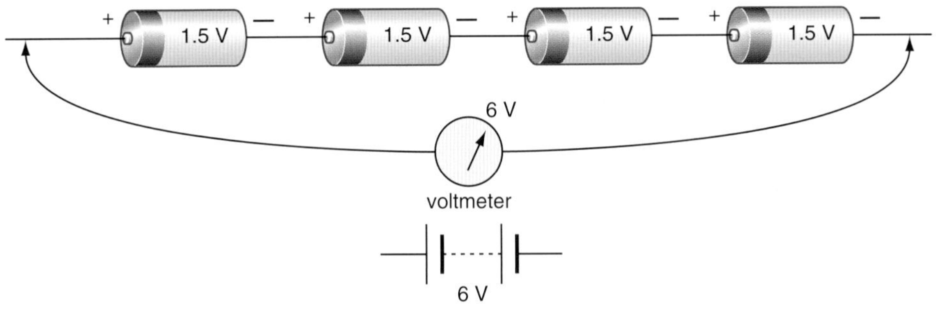

Figure 20 The voltage of a circuit can be increased by connecting cells in series to make a battery

PDs around a circuit

In Figure 21, the electrons collect energy from the battery and deposit some of this energy in the light bulb and the rest of it in the electric motor. All the energy supplied by the battery is transformed in the bulb and motor. Almost none is spent in the connecting wires.

Like the battery, the bulb and motor each have a PD across them. A PD of 2 V across the bulb means that each coulomb of charge that passes through the bulb deposits 2 joules of energy.

A PD of 4 V across the motor means that each coulomb of charge that passes through the motor deposits 4 joules of energy.

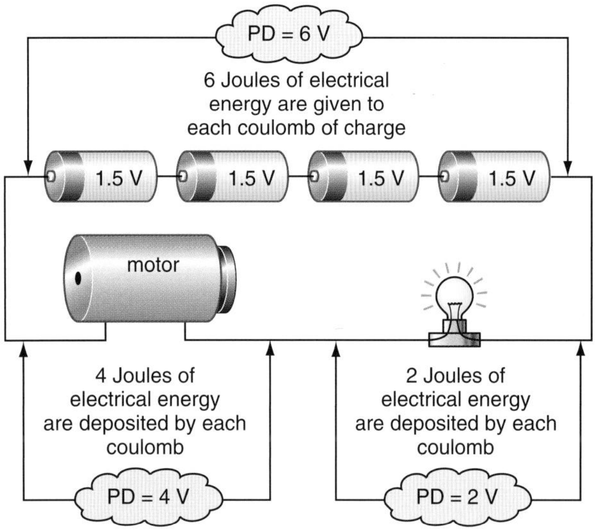

Figure 21

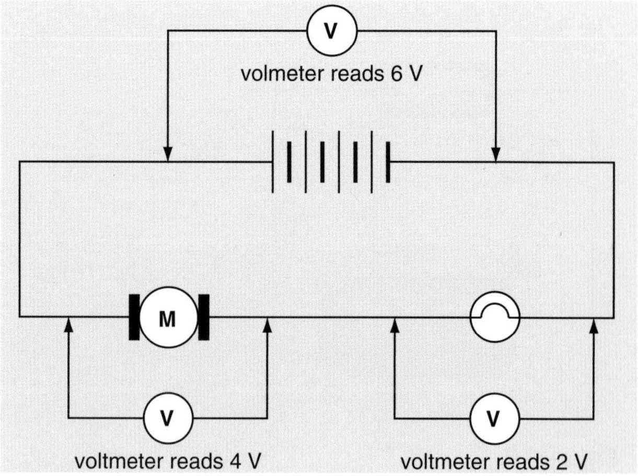

Figure 22

The battery has a PD of 6 V across it, because it supplies 6 joules of energy to each coulomb of charge that passes through it. Cells and batteries supply *energy* to the charge, they do not supply charge.

Figure 22 shows the circuit diagram for the circuit in Figure 20. Note the voltage readings. The readings illustrate an important principle which applies to any circuit.

> The sum of the PDs across the components is equal to the PD across the battery.

The relationship between charge, energy and voltage

There is a relationship between the voltage across a component and the charge flowing through it.

The voltage, measured in volts (V), is the ratio of the amount of energy, measured in joules (J), delivered by a cell/battery or deposited in a component per unit charge flowing through it.

$$\text{Voltage} = \frac{\text{Energy}}{\text{Charge}}$$

In terms of units this formula may be written as

$$\text{Volts} = \frac{\text{Joules}}{\text{Coulombs}}$$

When doing calculations, this triangle may be useful

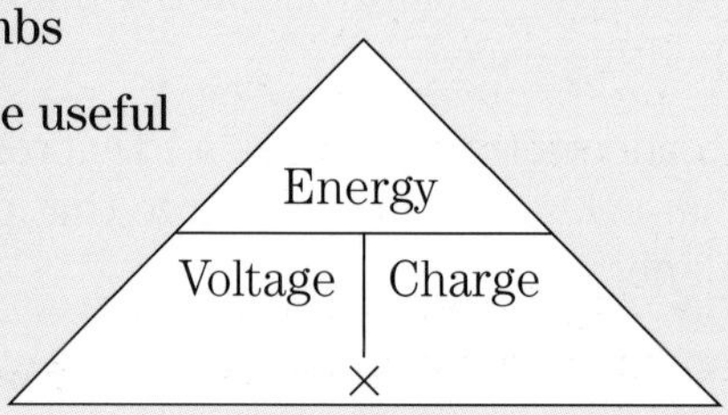

Questions

9 A cell is labelled as 2 V. How many joules of energy are supplied to each coulomb of charge that the cell supplies?

10 A cell supplies 9 joules of energy to 6 coulombs of charge. What is the voltage of the cell?

11 How many joules of energy are deposited in a light bulb which has a PD of 18 V across it when 3 coulombs of charge pass through it?

12 An electric motor consumes 150 joules of energy when 25 coulombs of charge pass through it. Find the PD across the motor.

13 The circuit contains a 12 V battery, a bulb and a motor.

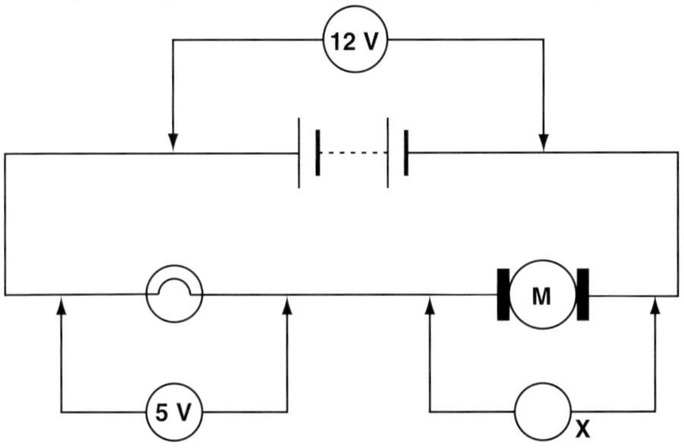

a) What type of meter is meter X?
b) What is the reading on meter X?
c) How many joules of electrical energy does each coulomb of charge possess as it leaves the battery?
d) How much electrical energy is deposited by each coulomb of charge as it passes through the motor?

Series and parallel circuits

There are two types of electric circuits **series circuits** and **parallel circuits**.

Series circuits

In a series circuit the components are connected one after the other. There is only one path for the current to follow. If we measured the current at points 1, 2 and 3 in the circuit in Figure 23, it would have the same value. It is a common misconception to think that the current is used up. This cannot happen because electrons cannot disappear.

The bulbs share the PD (voltage) from the battery. Because the PD is shared, the bulbs will not glow as brightly as they would if there was only one bulb

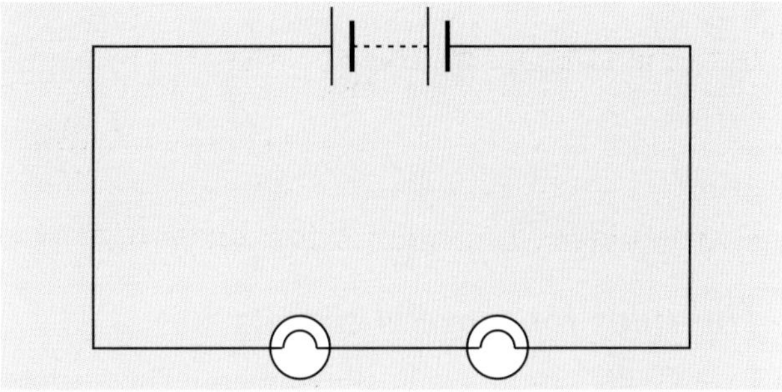

Figure 23 A series circuit

in the circuit. The important thing to remember about series circuits is that if one bulb is removed, the other bulb goes out since there is a break in the circuit, i.e. the circuit is no longer complete.

The rules for series circuits

1 The current is the same everywhere in a series circuit.
2 The components share the PD (voltage).

Parallel circuits

The lights in a house are usually connected in parallel. The reason for this is that each light requires the full mains voltage to work properly. If they were connected in series, the PD would be shared between them and they would be dim.

Parallel circuits have junctions (1 and 2 in Figure 24) where the current splits up. Each part of the current then proceeds through the corresponding bulb and joins up again before going back to the battery.

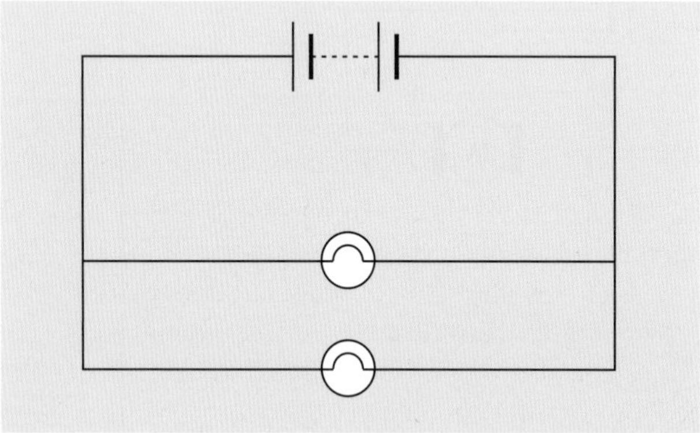

Figure 24 A parallel circuit

Because each bulb is connected directly to the battery, it receives the same PD (voltage). The bulbs therefore glow brightly. One major advantage of parallel circuits is that if one bulb is disconnected, the other bulbs in the circuit are unaffected. A second advantage of connecting bulbs in parallel is that the bulbs may be switched on and off independently.

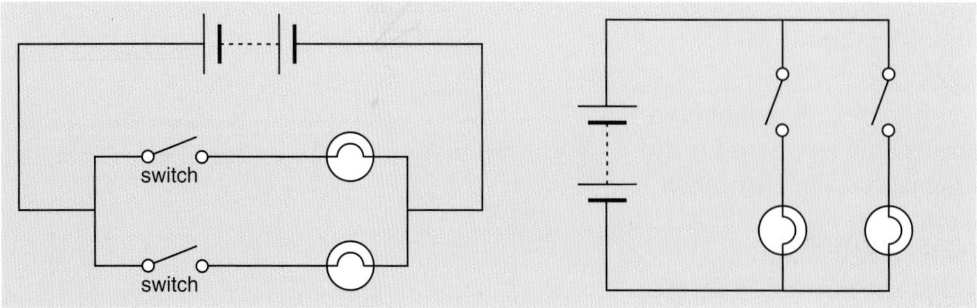

Figure 25

The rules for parallel circuits

1 Parallel circuits split the current. The sum of the currents in the branches of a parallel circuit equals the current entering or leaving the junctions.
2 The PD (voltage) across each component is the same.

Resistance

Resistance is the opposition of a conductor to current. A good conductor has a low resistance and a poor conductor has a high resistance. Copper connecting wire is a good conductor and a current passes through it easily. However, a similar piece of nichrome wire is not so good and less current flows for the same PD. The nichrome wire has more resistance than the copper.

Factors affecting resistance

The resistance of a conductor depends on several factors:

- **Length** – increasing the length of a wire increases its resistance.
- **Cross-sectional area** – increasing the thickness of a wire decreases its resistance. Conversely, decreasing the thickness of a wire increases its resistance.
- **Material** – a nichrome wire has more resistance than a copper wire of the same dimensions.
- **Temperature** – for metal conductors, resistance increases with temperature. For semiconductors, it decreases with temperature.

Resistance and heating effect

Whenever a current flows through a resistance, there is a heating effect. The heating effect occurs because electrons collide with the atoms as they pass through the conductor. The electrons may lose energy. The atoms gain energy and vibrate faster. Faster vibrations mean a higher temperature. This heating effect is put to good use in devices such as hair-driers and toasters which contain heating elements usually made from nichrome wire.

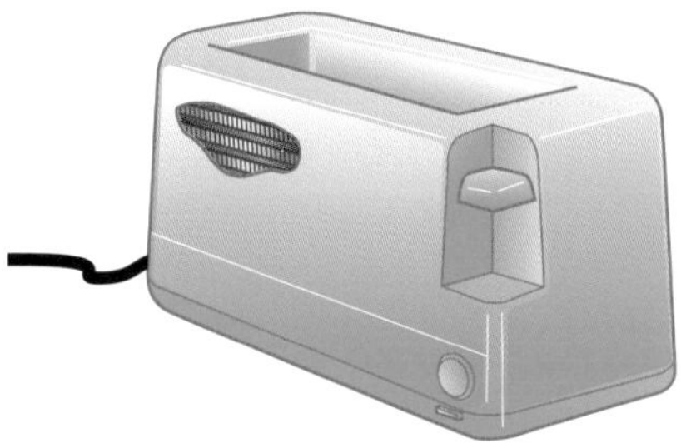

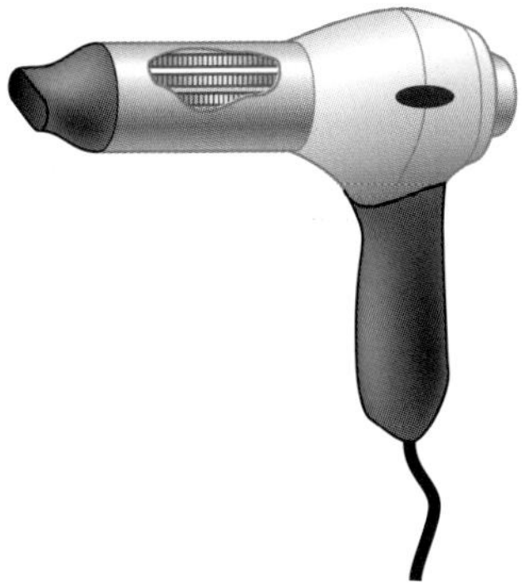

Figure 26

Types of resistive components

Resistors are specially made to provide resistance. In simple circuits they are used to limit the size of current flowing through various components.

The unit of resistance is the **ohm** (Ω). Resistors can have values ranging from a few ohms to several million ohms. The following units are used:

$$1 \text{ kilohm (k}\Omega) = 1000\ \Omega \qquad 1 \text{ megohm} = 1\,000\,000\ \Omega$$

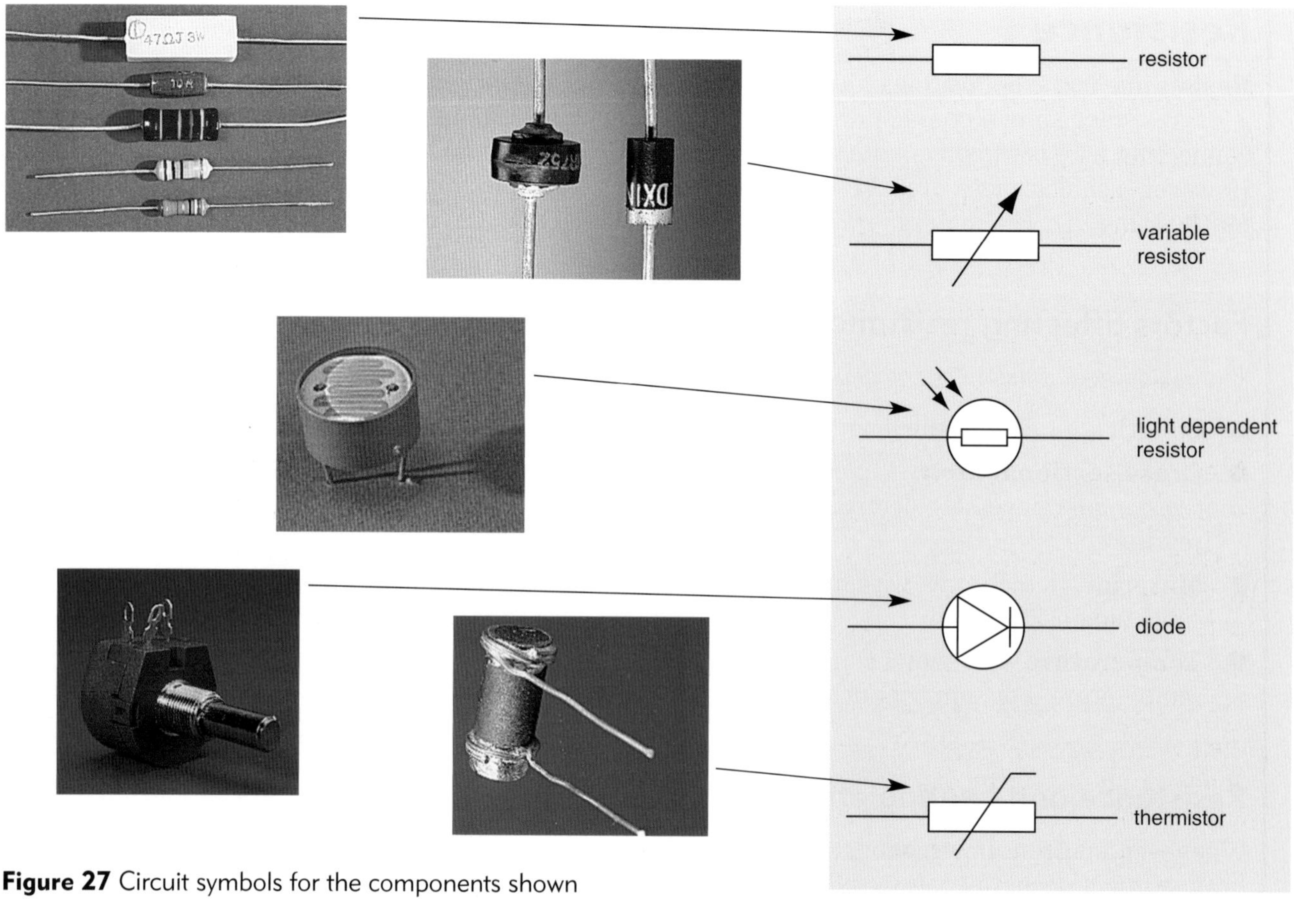

Figure 27 Circuit symbols for the components shown

There are several types of resistors:

1 **Variable resistors** (also known as **rheostats**) are used for controlling and varying current. The variable resistor shown in Figure 28 is used to control the current through a bulb which in turn controls the brightness of the bulb. In radios and hi-fis, variable resistors such as this are used as volume controls.

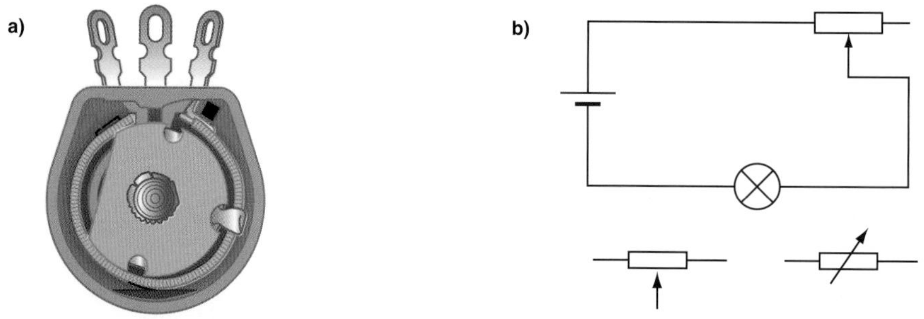

Figure 28

2 **Light-dependent resistors** (LDRs) have a high resistance in the dark but a low resistance in bright conditions. There are used in electronic circuits which switch lights on and off automatically.

3 **Diodes** have an extremely high resistance in one direction but a low resistance in the other. In effect, they allow current to flow in one direction only. They are sometimes referred to as rectifiers when they are used to convert alternating current into direct current.

4 **Thermistors** have a high resistance when cold but a much lower resistance when hot. They contain semiconductor materials. Thermistors are used in electrical thermometers to detect temperature changes.

Questions

14 Draw circuit symbols for a) a resistor and b) a variable resistor.

15 a) What does LDR stand for?
b) Draw its circuit symbol.
c) What happens to the resistance of an LDR when light is shone on it?

16 a) Draw the circuit symbol for a thermistor.
b) Give one use for a thermistor.

Measuring resistance

To measure the resistance of a component we pass various currents through it and measure the corresponding voltages across it. This is referred to as the ammeter–voltmeter method. The reason for this is clearly seen in Figure 29.

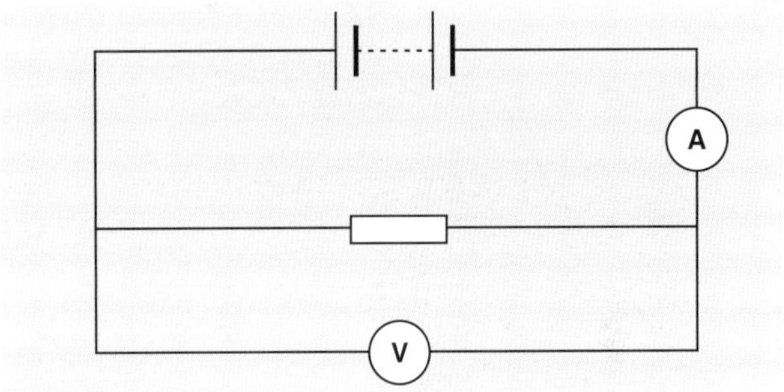

Figure 29 An ammeter–voltmeter circuit

The variable resistor is used to control the size of the current through the component under test, the ammeter measures the current through the component while the voltmeter measures the voltage across the component.

Table 2 shows that the ratio of each pair of readings of potential difference and current is a constant value (= 4). A graph of PD (in volts) versus current (in amps) shows a straight line through the origin. The slope of the graph is 4.

Table 2

Current in A	Potential difference in V	Ratio of potential difference to current in Ω
0.0	0	0
0.25	1	4
0.5	2	4
0.75	3	4
1.0	4	4

$$\frac{\text{Potential difference}}{\text{Current}} = \text{Constant}$$

The constant is the **resistance** of the component measured in ohms Ω. Another way of analysing the results in Table 2 is to say that the current is proportional to the voltage. That is, the current doubles if the voltage doubles.

The relationship between PD and current was first investigated by Georg Ohm, for whom the unit for resistance was named.

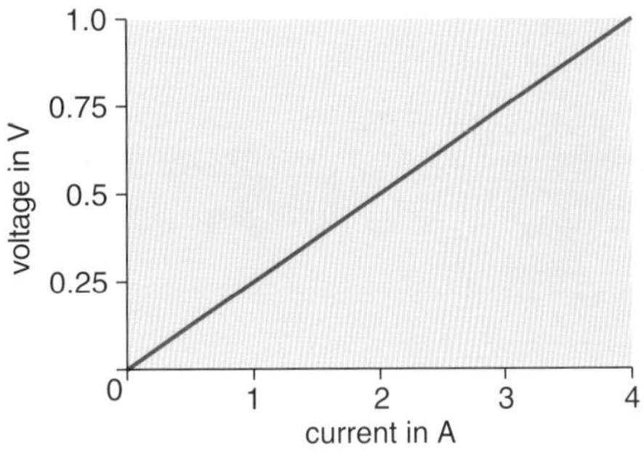

Figure 30

Ohm's Law states that the current through a wire is proportional to the PD across it, provided that the temperature of the wire remains constant.

The current, voltage and the resistance of a conductor are related by the following equation:

$$\text{Voltage (V)} = \text{Current (A)} \times \text{Resistance } (\Omega)$$

Or

$$V = I \times R$$

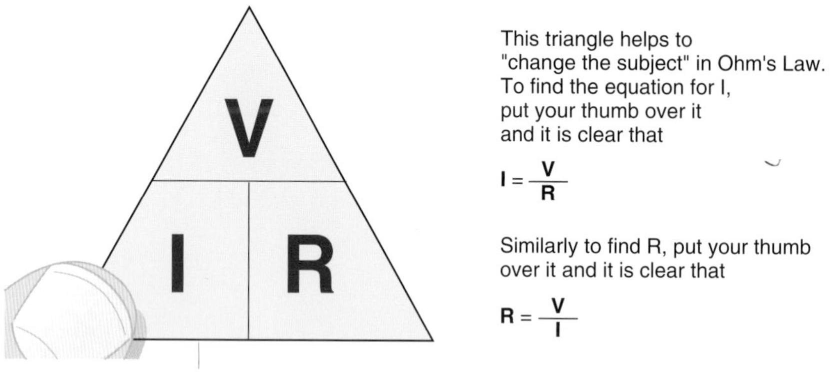

V
I
R
This triangle helps to "change the subject" in Ohm's Law. To find the equation for I, put your thumb over it and it is clear that
$I = \frac{V}{R}$
Similarly to find R, put your thumb over it and it is clear that
$R = \frac{V}{I}$

Figure 31 Remembering Ohm's law

Examples

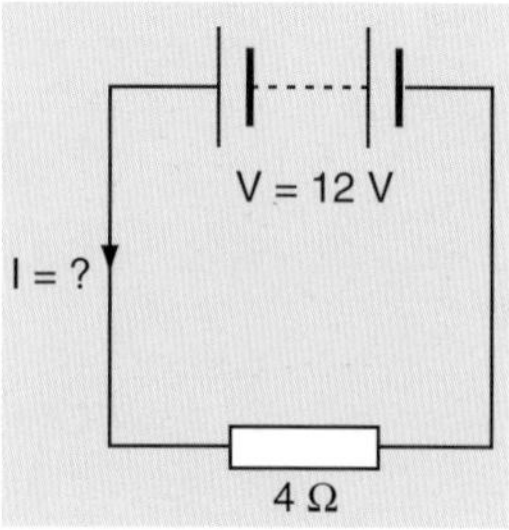

$V = 12\ V$
$R = 4\ \Omega$
$I = ?$

$$\text{Current } I = \frac{V}{R} = \frac{12\ V}{4\ \Omega} = \mathbf{3\ A}$$

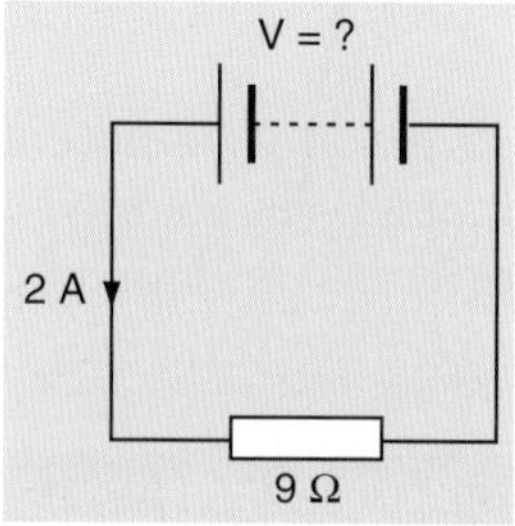

$I = 2\ A$
$R = 9\ \Omega$
$V = ?$

$$\text{Voltage } V = IR = 2\ A \times 9\ \Omega = \mathbf{18\ V}$$

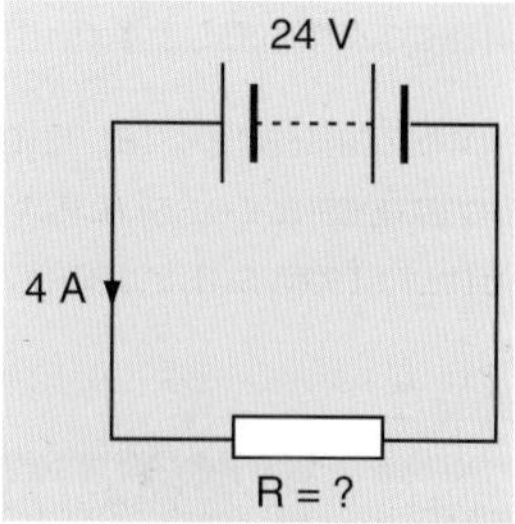

$V = 24\ V$
$I = 4\ A$
$R = ?$

$$\text{Resistance } R = \frac{V}{I} = \frac{24\ V}{4\ A} = \mathbf{6\ \Omega}$$

Questions

17 Calculate the current flowing through a 10 Ω resistor which has a PD of 20 V across it.

18 Calculate the size of a resistor which has a PD of 15 V across it, as a consequence of a current of 3 A flowing through it.

19 A current of 2 A flows through a 25 Ω resistor. Find the PD across the ressistor.

20 A PD of 15 V is needed to make a current of 2.5 A flow through a wire.

a) What is the resistance of the wire?
b) What PD is needed to make a current of 2.0 A flow through the wire?

21 There is a PD of 6.0 V across the ends of a wire of resistance 12 Ω.

a) What is current in the wire?
b) What PD is needed to make a current of 1.5 A flow through it?

22 A resistor has a PD of 6 V applied across it and the current flowing through is 100 mA. What is the resistance of the resistor?

Current–voltage graphs

Metal conductors obey Ohm's Law, provided their temperature does not change. This is not the case with other types of conductor.

Filament bulb

Using the ammeter–voltmeter method, it is also possible to investigate the variation of current with voltage for a filament bulb.

Figure 32 shows the results obtained for a filament lamp. The graph starts off from the origin a roughly straight line but it gradually curves over. The current passing through the filament causes it to get hot, and this increases its resistance. The result is that the current does not increase proportionately as it would do if its temperature remained constant. We say that the filament lamp behaves non-ohmically. The calculations on the graph show how the resistance changes.

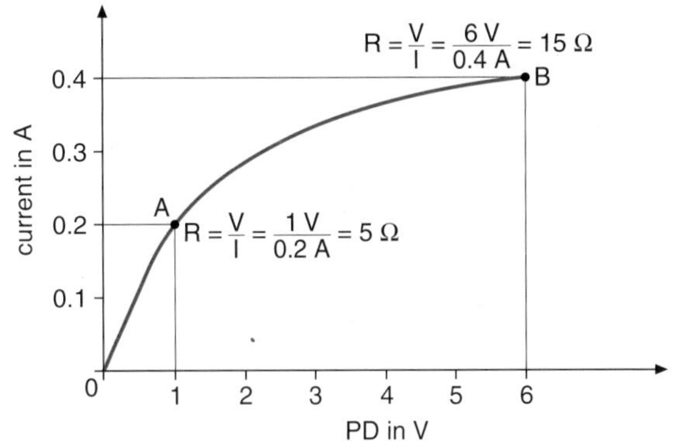

Figure 32 A current–voltage graph for a filament bulb

Diodes

It is clear from the current–voltage graph for a semiconducting diode that Ohm's Law is not obeyed. The current is not proportional to the voltage. In forward bias (voltage), the current does not begin to flow until the voltage reaches 0.6 V. Then the current increases dramatically. When the polarity of the voltage supply is reversed, virtually no current flows. In other words the diode is a unidirectional current carrier. It blocks current flow when it is in reverse bias.

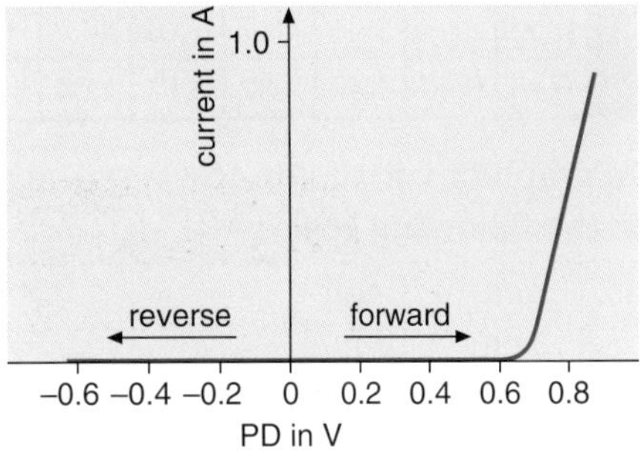

Figure 33 A current–voltage graph for a semiconductor diode

Thermistors

A thermistor is a type of resistor whose resistance depends on the temperature of its surroundings. The resistance may change by a large amount over a narrow range of temperatures.

For some thermistors, the resistance *decreases* as they are heated. The rise in temperature provides the energy needed for electrons to break free, and this makes it easier for the current to flow. These thermistors are used for temperature probes.

For other thermistors, the resistance *increases* with temperature. These are included in circuits where you want to prevent overheating.

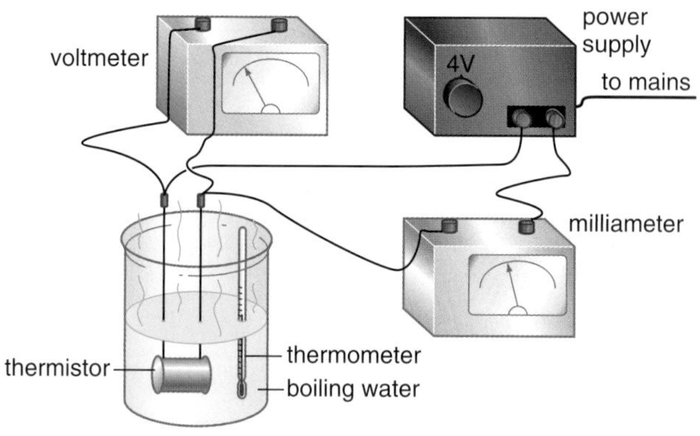

Figure 34 Investigating the behaviour of a thermistor at different temperatures

Investigation of the behaviour of a thermistor may be carried out as follows:

- Connect a thermistor into the circuit as shown in Figure 34.
- Connect the milliammeter in series and the voltmeter in parallel so that we can determine the resistance of the thermistor.
- Set the power supply to a fixed voltage.
- Add boiling water.
- As the water cools, take readings of current and voltage and temperature for convenient drops in temperature.
- Plot resistance on the y-axis versus temperature on the x-axis.

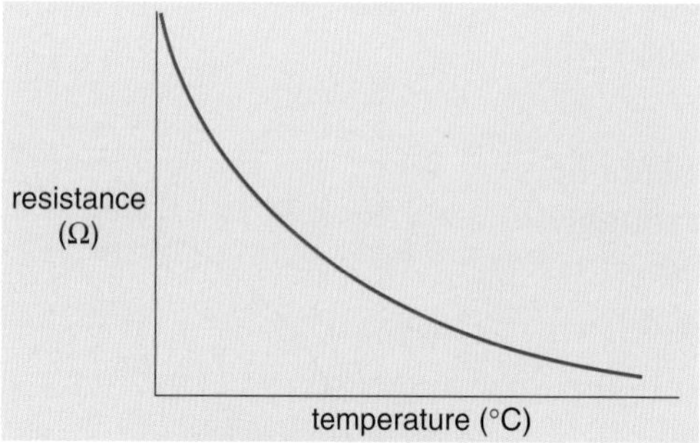

Figure 35

Questions

23 The results in the table were obtained during the investigation of a filament bulb using the ammeter–voltmeter method.

Current (mA)	4.219	27.7	36.1	43.7	50.6	56.9	63	69	74	78.6	82.3	82.3
Voltage (V)	0.43	0.69	1.49	2.32	3.17	4.04	4.92	5.81	6.7	7.56	8.42	9.3

a) Plot a graph of voltage on the y-axis against current on the x-axis, using the following scales

y-axis: 2 cm = 1 volt
x-axis: 2 cm = 10 mA

b) Draw a smooth curve through the points. Does the bulb obey Ohm's Law?

c) Explain why the graph of voltage against current is a curve.

24 The table below shows the results from an experiment which was designed to investigate the variation of resistance of a thermistor with temperature.

Temperature (°C)	23	37	47	57	65	76	85	90	100
Voltage (V)	4	4	4	4	4	4	4	4	4
Current (mA)	19	24	31	37	45	56	67	73	87
Resistance (Ω)									

a) Calculate the resistance for each temperature and plot a graph of resistance versus temperature for the thermistor.

b) Describe how the resistance of the thermistor varies with temperature.

c) When the thermistor was dipped in a cup of coffee, its resistance was found to be 100 Ω. Use your graph to estimate the temperature of the coffee.

25 The table below shows the readings obtained while investigating the behaviour of a diode.

Voltage (V)	0	0.1	0.2	0.3	0.4	0.5	0.6	0.7
Current (mA)	0	0	0	0	0	1.5	73	250
Resistance (Ω)								

a) Draw a graph of current versus voltage.

b) Does the diode obey Ohm's Law.

c) Copy and complete the table.

Summary of units used in the study of electricity

There are a bewildering number of physical quantities, units and symbols used in the study of electricity. Table 3 is a summary.

Table 3

Name of quantity	Symbol for quantity	Units for quantity	Symbol for units of quantity
Charge	Q	Coulomb	C
Current	I	Ampere	A
Resistance	R	Ohm	Ω
Voltage	V	Volt	V
Potential difference	PD	Volt	V
Electromotive force	EMF	Volt	V

Calculating the resistance of circuits

Series circuits

The total resistance of two or more resistors in series is simply the sum of the individual resistances of the resistors.

$$R_{Total} = R_1 + R_2 + R_3$$

In the above example, the three resistors may be replaced by a single resistor of (4 + 8 + 6 = 18 Ω).

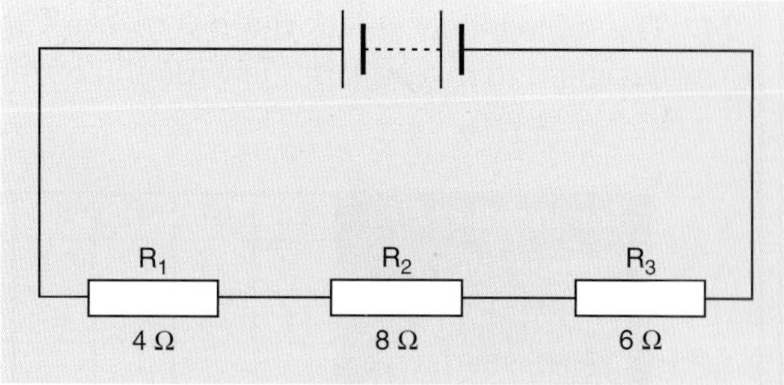

Figure 36 Calculating the total resistance of three resistors in a series circuit

Parallel circuits

The formula for calculating the combined resistance of three resistors in parallel is given by

$$\frac{1}{R_{Total}} = \frac{1}{R_1} + \frac{1}{R_2} + \frac{1}{R_3}$$

When considering two resistors in parallel, this formula is shortened to:

$$R_{Total} = \frac{R_1 \times R_2}{R_1 + R_2} = \frac{\text{Product}}{\text{Sum}}$$

Example

Find the combined resistance of two 8 Ω resistors in parallel.

In this case, the total or combined resistance is given by:

$$R_{Total} = \frac{\text{Product}}{\text{Sum}} = \frac{8 \times 8}{8 + 8}$$

$$R_{Total} = \frac{64}{16} = 4\ \Omega$$

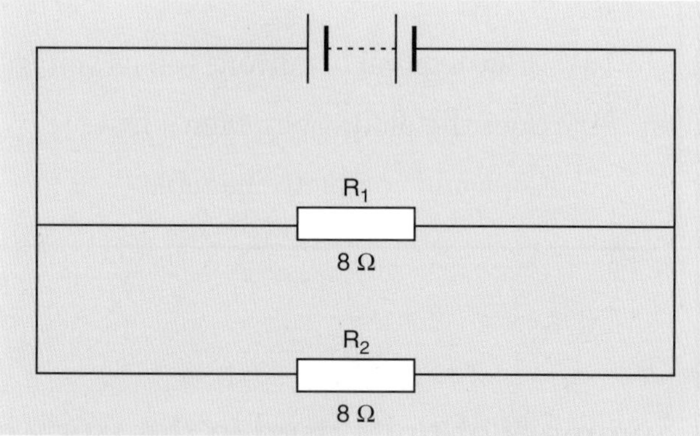

Figure 37 Calculating the total resistance of two resistors in a parallel circuit

This appears to be a surprising result. How can the combined resistance be smaller than that of either of the two resistors?

Recall that in a parallel circuit the current is split when it approaches a junction. An enlargement of junction A, as far as the current is concerned, would look like Figure 38.

The current has a choice of which path to take, i.e. the parallel arrangement makes life easier for the current, so the resistance of a parallel network of resistors is always smaller than the smallest resistor.

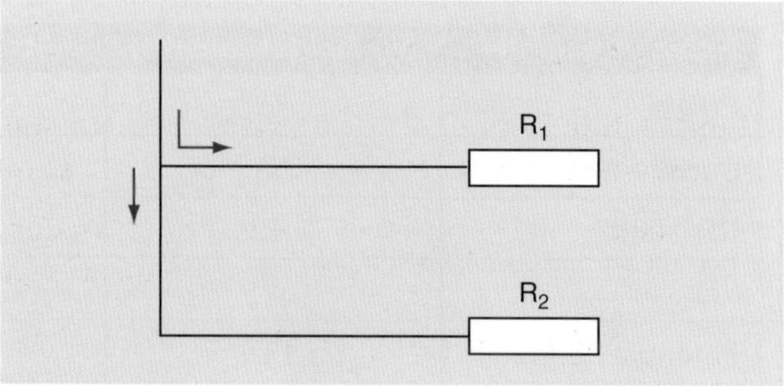

Figure 38

Questions

26 Calculate the combined resistance of the following network of resistors:

a)

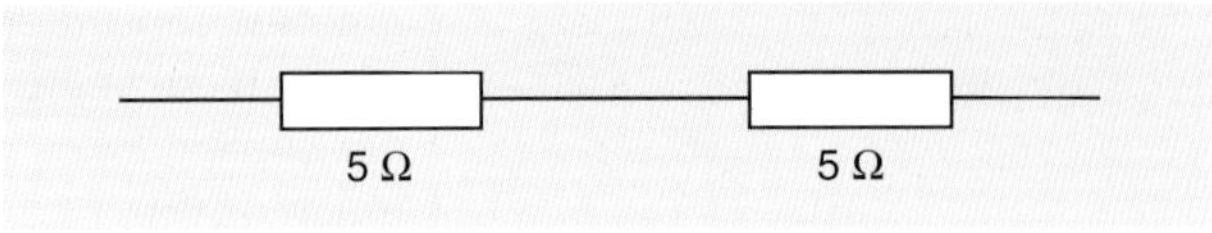

b)

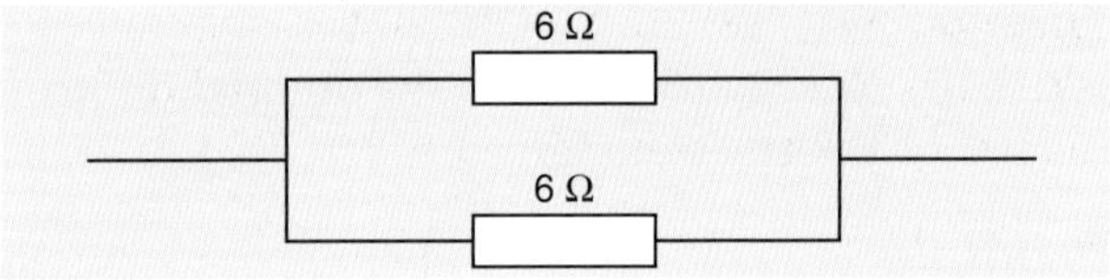

c)

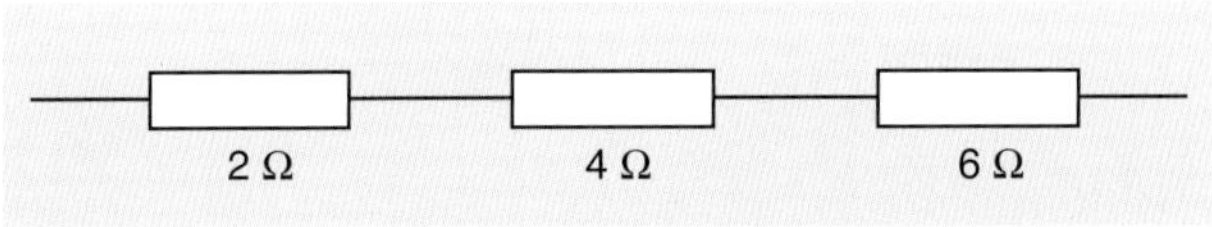

d)

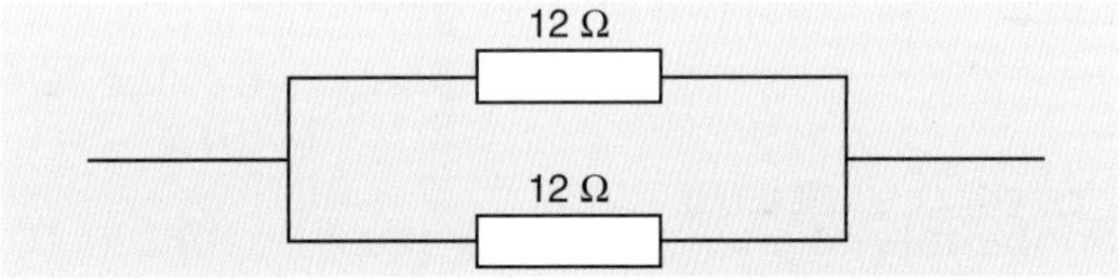

e)

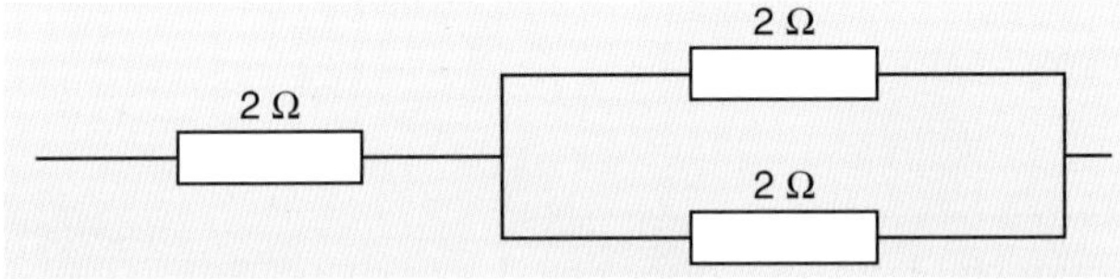

f)

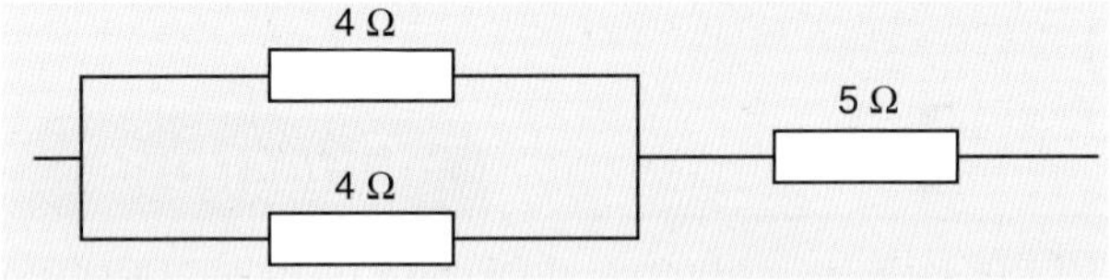

g)

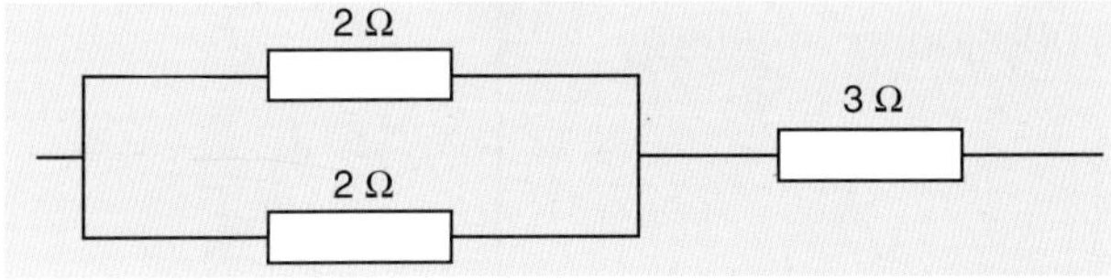

h)

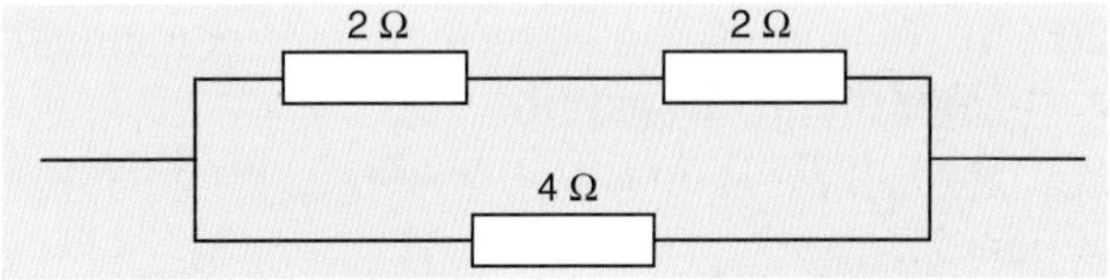

i)

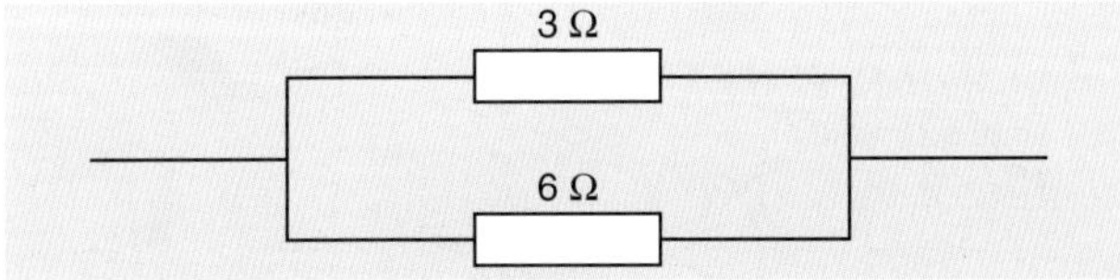

j)

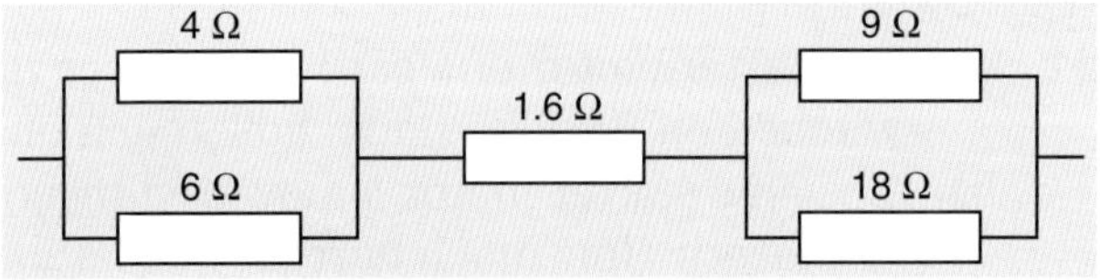

27 If you are provided with three resistors of 1 Ω, 2 Ω and 3 Ω, what different values of resistance can you get by making up different series and parallel circuits?

Electrical energy

If one coulomb of charge gains or loses one joule of energy between two points, there is a potential difference of one volt between those two points.

$$\text{PD in volts} = \frac{\text{Energy transferred in joules}}{\text{Charge in coulombs}}$$

Rearranging this formula gives us:

Energy transferred in joules = PD in volts × Charge in coulombs

It is much easier to measure current than charge, since

Charge = Current × Time

Substituting for charge, this gives a very useful formula for energy transferred in an electric circuit.

Energy transferred = Potential difference × Current × Time
Energy transferred = V × I × t

Example

If 0.5 A flows through a bulb connected across a 6 V power supply for 10 seconds, then the energy transferred is

$$\text{Energy} = 6 \times 0.5 \times 10 = \mathbf{30\ J}$$

So the rate of energy transfer must be 30 J in 10 s, i.e. 3 J per second or 3 watts.

Did you know?

In 1995, the Norwegians topped the league as the greatest consumers of electrical energy per capita. Twice as much as the average American!

Questions

28 How much electrical energy does a 1000 W convector heater consume in one hour?

29 In 10 seconds, an electric toaster consumes 15 000 joules of energy from the mains supply.
What is its power a) in watts, b) in kilowatts?

30 A study lamp draws a current of 0.25 A at 240 V from the mains supply. Calculate the amount of energy it consumes in 60 seconds.

31 a) The starter motor of a car has a power rating of 960 W. If it is switched on for 5 seconds, how much energy does it use?
b) The same starter motor is powered by connecting it to a 12 V car battery. How much current does it use?

Electrical power

On page 10 we learned that the formula for mechanical power of a machine is defined as the rate at which energy is transformed and is given by

$$\text{Power} = \frac{\text{Energy transformed}}{\text{Time}}$$

We have seen that in an electrical circuit

Energy transformed = Potential difference × Current × Time

Substituting for energy transformed

$$\text{Power} = \frac{\text{Potential difference} \times \text{Current} \times \text{Time}}{\text{Time}}$$

i.e.

Electrical power in watts = Potential difference in volts × Current in amps

Did you know?

A single lightning strike is made up of six million volts with a peak current of 20 000 amps. This corresponds to an electrical power of 12 TW, many times greater than the average coal-fired power station!

Example

A study lamp is rated at 60 W, 240 V. How much current is the bulb carrying?

$$60\text{ W} = 240\text{ V} \times \text{Current}$$

$$\text{Current} = \frac{60\text{ W}}{240\text{ V}} = 0.25\text{ A}$$

Domestic appliances such as toasters, hair-driers and TVs have a power rating marked on them in watts or in kilowatts (1 kilowatt (kW) = 1000 W).

Some typical power ratings are shown in Figure 39. Each number tells you the power the appliance will take if connected to a 240 V supply.

200 W

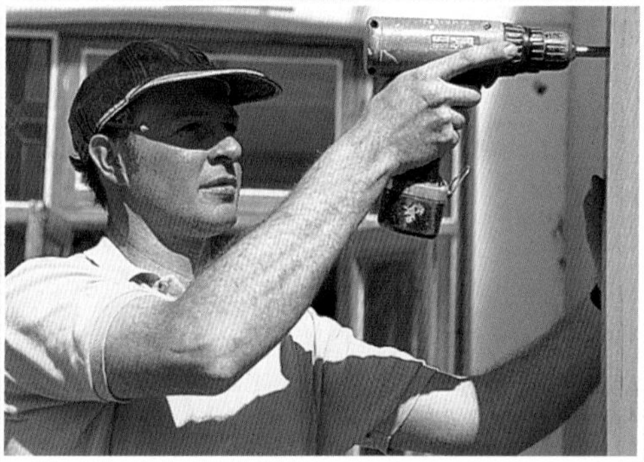

20 W

Figure 39 The typical power ratings of some household appliances

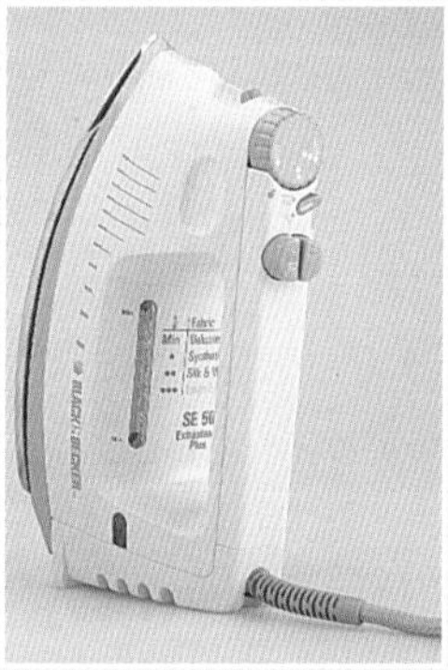

1100 W

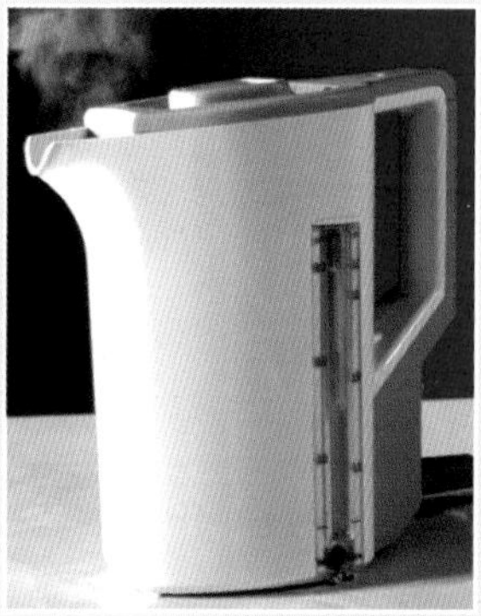

2200 W

60 W

Since Power $= \text{PD} \times \text{Current}$

and Ohm's Law $V = IR$

Power $= \dfrac{V^2}{R}$ and Power $= I^2R$

These two alternative formulae give the electrical power dissipated (converted) into heat in resistors and heating elements. The heat dissipated is sometimes referred to as Ohmic losses

Example

What power is dissipated in a 10 Ω resistor when the current through it is

a) 2 A

b) 4 A ?

a) Power = I^2R
$= 2^2 \times 10$
$= \mathbf{40\ W}$

b) Power = I^2R
$= 4^2 \times 10$
$= \mathbf{160\ W}$

This example shows that when the current is doubled, the power dissipated is quadrupled! This idea has important implications for electricity transmission (see Chapter 6).

Questions

32 If an electric heater takes a current of 4 A when connected to a 240 V supply, what is its power?

33 If a light bulb has a power of 48 W when connected to a 12 V supply, what is the current through it?

34 Copy and complete the following table for domestic appliances, all of which operate at 240 V.
Calculate a) the current drawn and b) the resistance of each appliance under normal operating conditions.

Name of appliance	Power rating	Current drawn	Resistance
Bulb of study lamp	60 W		
Colour TV	80 W		
Toaster	1200 W		
Convector heater	2 kW		
Shower	3 kW		

35 An electric kettle has an element of resistance 48 Ω. Calculate how much power it uses when it is connected to the 240 V mains supply.

Electricity in the home

Alternating current and direct current

A direct current (d.c.) always flows in the same direction, from a fixed positive terminal to the fixed negative terminal of a supply. A typical d.c. circuit is shown in Figure 40a. A cell or battery gives a constant (steady) direct current. A graph of voltage versus time for a d.c. supply is shown in Figure 40b. The current is described as being unidirectional.

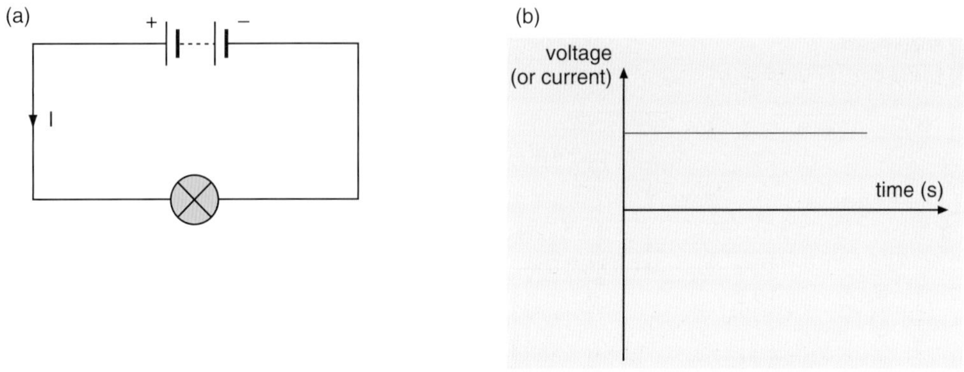

Figure 40

The electricity supply to your home is an alternating current supply (a.c.). In an a.c. supply the voltage (and hence the current) change size and direction in a regular and repetitive way, see Figure 41. In fact, the mains voltage changes from +325 V to −325 V. The average value of this voltage is 230 V. The current changes direction 100 times per second and makes 50 complete cycles per second, hence the frequency of the mains is 50 hertz (Hz).

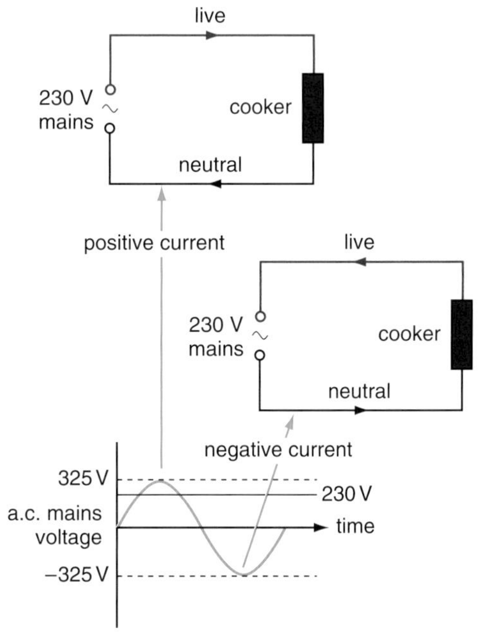

Figure 41

It is clear from Figure 41 why an a.c. supply is said to be bi-directional.

House circuits

A house circuit is shown in Figure 42. The electricity supply enters from the street by means of a two core cable. This contains two wires, the **live** (L) and the **neutral** (N). The neutral wire is earthed at the local sub-station and so there is no p.d. between it and earth. The live wire is alternately positive and negative because the supply is a.c. Both the live and neutral wires pass through a sealed container where the board's main 80 A fuse, is located. They then pass through the main switch in the consumer unit. Here the N and L wires are fed through different fuses into the main circuits of the house.

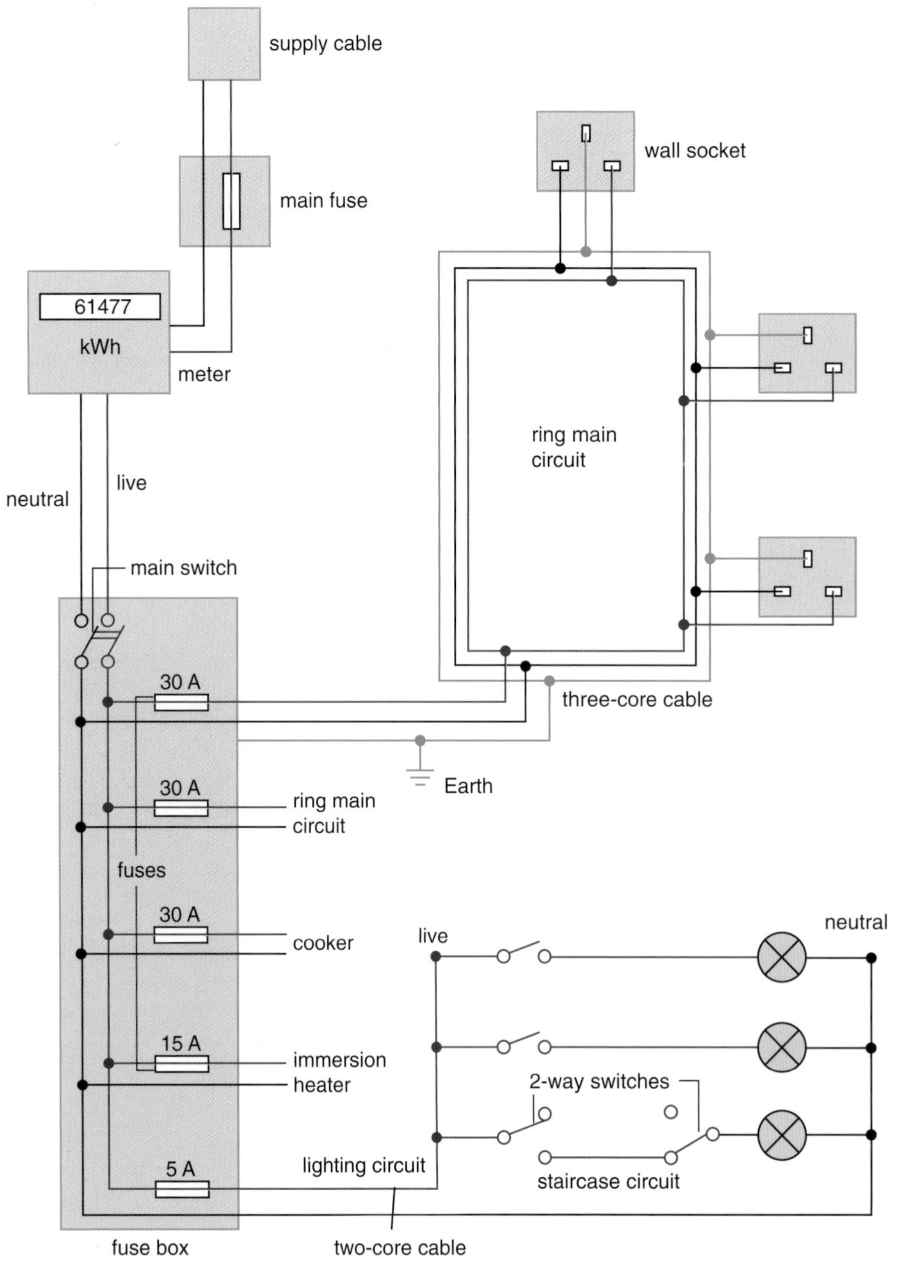

Figure 42 A house circuit

The lighting circuit supplies the light socket in each room. Each socket is wired in parallel. Two-way switches are used wherever a socket needs to be operated from more than one point. Usually a two-way switch is located at the top and bottom of a staircase. Devices such as the immersion heater and cooker are wired directly to the consumer unit. The other major circuit in the house is the ring main circuit. The live and neutral wires each run in two rings around the house and the power sockets, all rated at 13 A, are wired to them. Because current can travel in both directions around the rings, thinner wires can be used. The ring main also has a third wire that goes to the top hole of each power point. The third wire is called an **earth** and it is connected to a metal water pipe in the house.

A 40 W lamp uses a current of 0.25 A when connected to the mains. Similarly a 100 W lamp uses 0.42 A. The lighting circuit then can be fitted with a fuse rated at 5 A – that is a fuse which will melt if the current exceeds 5 A. This is perfectly reasonable since it is very unlikely that twelve 100 W lamps will all be switched on at once. It is very bad practice to connect appliances such as irons to light sockets since these use a current of about 3 A and if other light sockets are also being used, then the fuse could easily blow. The immersion heater and the cooker take large currents and are connected via 15 A and 30 A rated fuses respectively. The ring main is fitted with a 30 A fuse. This will enable a sufficient number of appliances such as irons, televisions and electric fires to be used safely without causing the fuse to blow.

Fuses and switches are always wired into the live wire. If they were in the neutral then lamp sockets and power sockets would be live, that is at a high voltage, when switches were off or fuses blown. It would then be possible, for example, to get a shock by touching the bar of an electric fire, even though it was switched off.

Two-way switches

In most two-storey houses, you can turn the landing lights on or off from upstairs or downstairs. For this, two-way switches are used:

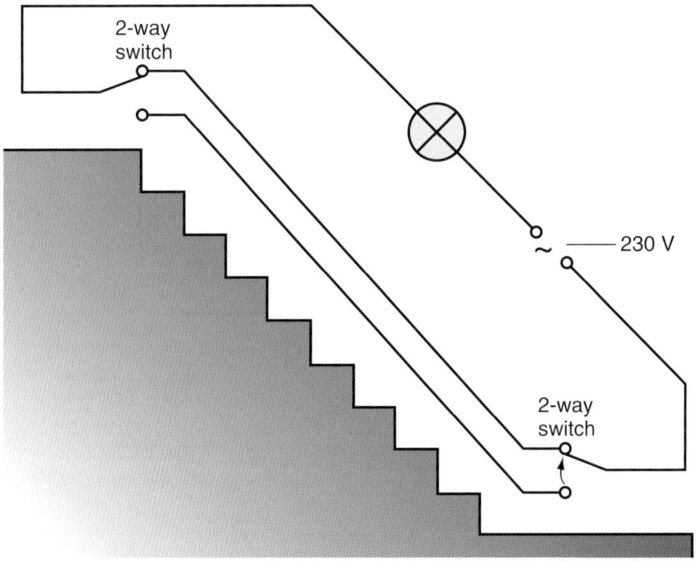

Figure 32a Going to bed at night, when both switches are up, the circuit is complete and a current flows through the bulb

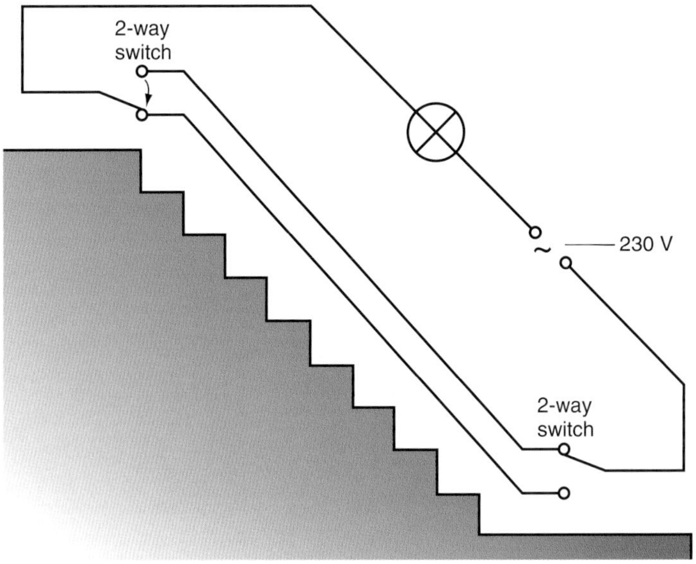

Figure 43b At the top of the stairs one of the switches is pressed down, the circuit is broken. You should verify for yourself what happens when the person comes downstairs. The effect is that each switch reverses the effect of the other one

Electrical safety

Voltages of 50 V and currents as low as 50 mA may be fatal so electrical safety is vitally important.

The three pin plug

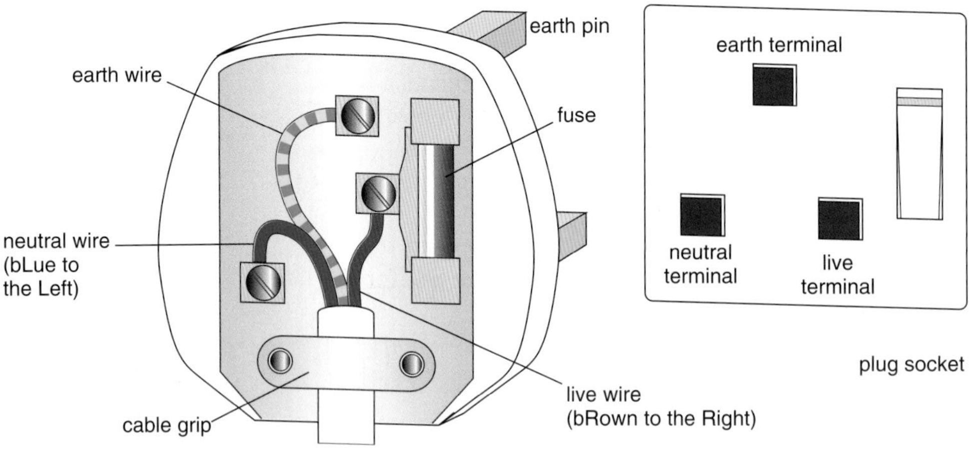

Figure 44 A correctly wired three pin plug

Wiring a three pin plug

- Hold the 3-core cable tightly with the cord grip.
- The wire with the blue insulation is the neutral wire, connect this to the left hand pin.
- The brown insulated wire is the live wire, connect this to the right hand pin. This pin has a fuse attached because it is connected to the live wire.
- The wire with the yellow and green insulation is the earth wire, connect this to the top pin.
- Each of these wires should be wrapped around its securing screw so that it is tightened as the screw tightens.

Each pin in the plug fits into a corresponding hole in the socket. The earth pin is longer than the others so that it goes into the socket first and pushes aside safety covers which cover the rear of the neutral and live holes in the socket.

If an appliance becomes live, a current flows through the earth wire, and from the socket earth connection to the earth via a water pipe. During the process the fuse in the plug will blow. Before it is replaced, the appliance should be checked by a qualified electrician.

Fuses

A fuse is a device which is meant to prevent damage to an appliance. The fuse used is either a 3 A (red) for appliances up to 720 W or 13 A (brown) for appliances between 720 W to 3 kW. If a larger than usual current flows, the fuse will melt and so break the circuit.

Figure 45 Fuses

How to select a fuse

Each appliance has a power rating.

How much current the appliance will use is found using the power formula:

$$\begin{aligned} \text{Power} &= \text{voltage} \times \text{current} \\ 460 &= 230 \times \text{current} \\ \therefore \quad \text{current} &= \frac{260}{230} \\ &= 2\ \text{A} \end{aligned}$$

Figure 46 The power rating label on the side of an electric jig-saw

This is the normal current the device uses, any large current can destroy it. A 3 A fuse would allow a normal working current to flow and protect the appliance from larger currents. A 13 A would allow a dangerously high current to flow and still not 'blow'. So it is important to use the correct size of fuse. It is important to remember that a fuse does not protect the person using the appliance. It can take 1 to 2 seconds for a fuse to melt – enough time for the user to receive a fatal electric shock.

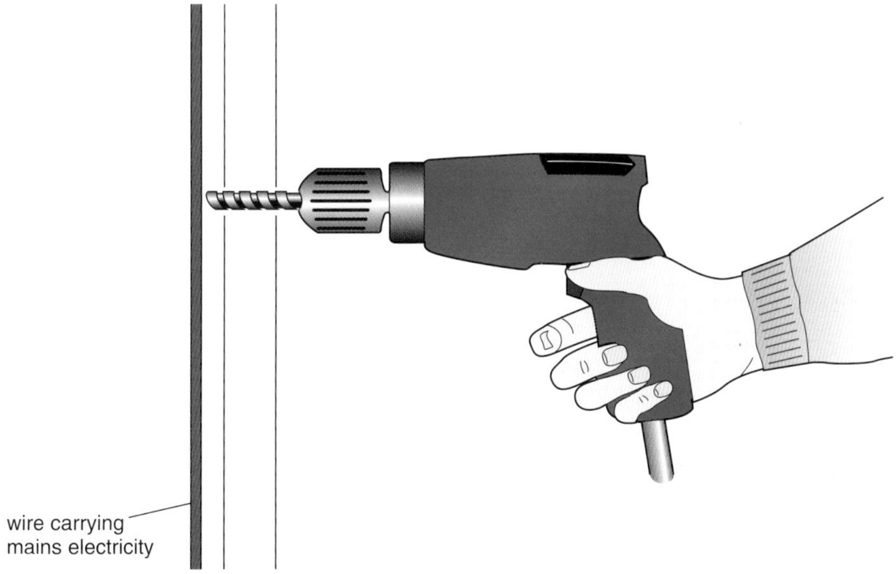

Figure 47 If there is no earth wire connected to the casing of the drill the current will flow through the person

The earth wire

An earth prevents damage to the user. Suppose a fault develops in an electric fire and the element is in contact with the casing of the fire. The casing will be live and if someone were to touch it they would get a possibly fatal electric shock as the current rushes through their bodies to the earth. The earth wire prevents this. It offers a low resistance route of escape, enabling the current to go to earth by a wire rather than through a human body. After a few seconds the large current will blow the fuse. Any appliance with a metal casing could become live if a fault developed.

Double insulation

Appliances such as vacuum cleaners and hair dryers are usually double insulated. The appliance is encased in an insulating plastic case and is connected to the supply by a two core insulated cable containing only a live and a neutral wire. Any metal attachments which the user might touch are fitted into the plastic case so that they do not make a direct connection with the motor or other internal electrical parts. The symbol for double insulated appliances is:

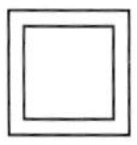

Paying for electricity

Electricity companies bill customers for electrical energy in special units known as **kilowatt hours** (kWh). Sometimes referred to as the 'unit' of electricity. One kilowatt hour is the amount of energy transferred when 1000 W is delivered for one hour. You should prove for yourself that

$$1\text{ kWh} = 3\,600\,000\text{ Joules.}$$

There are two important numbers on an electricity bill:

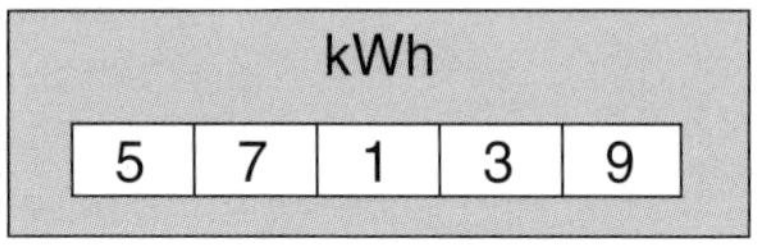

Present meter reading

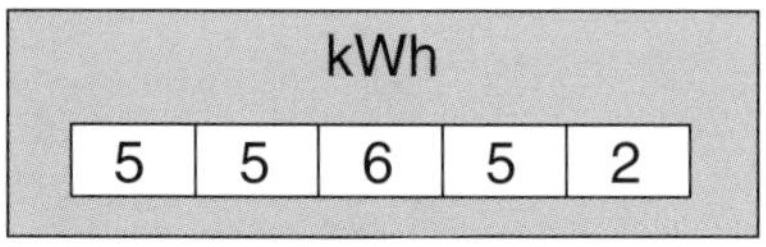

Previous meter reading

Northern Electricity Board Customer account no: 3427 364

Present meter reading	Previous meter reading	Units used	Cost per unit (incl. VAT)	£
57139	55652	1487	11.0p	163.57

The difference between the present and previous readings is the number of units used. In this particular example

$$57139 - 55652 = 1487\text{ units (kWh)}$$

1487 units have been used. If the cost of a unit is known, then the cost of the electricity used may be determined.

Different appliances have different power ratings and the following two formulae are very useful in calculating the cost of using a particular appliance for a given amount of time.

$$\text{Number of units used} = \text{Power rating (in kilowatts)} \times \text{Time (in hours)}$$
$$\text{Total cost} = \text{Number of units used} \times \text{Cost per unit}$$

Example

1 Calculate the cost of using 100 W study lamp for 8 hours (assume that the price of a unit is 9p).

power = 100 W = 0.1 kW

time = 8 hours

Substituting – no. of units used = 0.1 × 8 = 0.8 units

cost = 0.8 × 9

= 7.2p

2 Calculate the cost of using 3000 W immersion heater for 8 hours.

power = 3000 W = 3.0 kW

time = 8 hours

Substituting – no. of units used = 3.0 × 8 = 24 units

cost = 24 × 9

= £2.16

Clearly, studying is much cheaper than having a bath!

Questions

36 a) What are the colours of (i) the live, (ii) the neutral and (iii) the earth wire?

b) The earth wire comes loose in a convection heater and a wire from the heating element touches the metal case.

(i) What will happen to a person who touches the case when the heater is turned on?

(ii) If the earth wire had remained in its correct position how would it and the fuse (in the plug) have worked together to make the heater safe?

37 Explain what is meant by (i) a direct current and (ii) an alternating current. Draw sketch graphs to illustrate your answer.

38 Circuit breakers are often used nowadays instead of fuses, especially with appliances that require a large current to make them work. Why are circuit breakers better than fuses in these cases?

39 Cartridge fuses are normally available as 3 A, 5 A, or 13 A.

a) What would probably happen if you used a 3 A fuse in the plug for a 3 kW electric fire?

b) Why is it bad practice to use a 13 A fuse in a plug for a 60 W study lamp?

c) What size of fuse would you use for a hair dryer labelled, 240 V, 800 W? Explain how you worked out your answer.

40 What is the greatest number of 60 W bulbs that can be run off the mains, if you are not going to overload a 5 A fuse?

41 Calculate how many units of electrical energy, in kWh, are used for

a) 100 W lamp for 12 hours?

b) 250 W TV for 4 hours?

c) a 2400 W kettle for 5 minutes?

42 If the price for 1 unit is 9p, what is the running cost of each item in question 41?

43 An electric shower is rated at 230 V, 15 A .

a) Calculate the electrical power used by the shower heater.

b) Calculate the cost of a 10 minute shower if 1 kWh costs 11p.

Websites

Use your favourite search engine (such as **www.google.com** or **www.excite.com**) and search using the keywords:

Lightning	Current electricity	Diodes
Static electricity	Thermistors	Domestic electricity

www.eskimo.com~billb/ele-edu.html
http://sln.fi.edu/franklin/scientist/electric.html
http://library.thinkguest.org/2763/
www.school-for-champions.com/science/staticexpl.html
www.library.thinkquest.org/28032/
www.vvm.com/~radioray/html/e101-22html

Exam questions

1 a) Large amounts of electric charge can collect on clouds. What danger can this cause for tall buildings beneath the clouds? *(2 marks)*

b) (i) Explain how a balloon can become positively charged when it is rubbed with a cloth. *(3 marks)*

(ii) A second balloon is rubbed with another cloth and is hung up beside the first. The diagram below shows how the two balloons hang side by side.

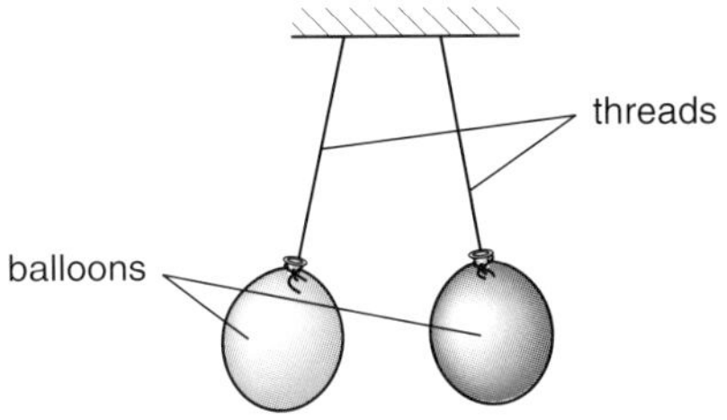

1) What can you tell about the charges on the balloons? *(1 mark)*

2) Explain your answer. *(3 marks)*

c) (i) Draw an electric circuit diagram in which two bulbs are in parallel and controlled by a single switch. *(3 marks)*

(ii) The light bulbs get dimmer. What can you tell about the current flowing in the bulbs? *(1 mark)*

d) (i) Show that the total resistance between R and T in the circuit below is 10 Ω.

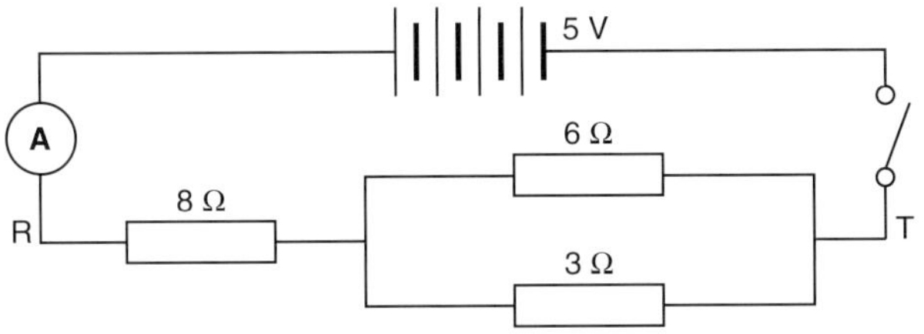

(4 marks)

(ii) Calculate the reading on the ammeter when the switch is closed. Show clearly how you get your answer. *(3 marks)*

(iii) Calculate the voltage across the 8 Ω resistor. Show clearly how you get your answer. *(3 marks)*

(iv) Calculate the power in the 8 Ω resistor. Show clearly how you get your answer. *(4 marks)*

(v) What is the voltage across the 6 Ω resistor? Show clearly how you get your answer. *(2 marks)*

(vi) What is the voltage across the 3 Ω resistor? *(1 mark)*

2 a) Two identical lamps are to be connected in parallel to a battery.

(i) Draw the circuit diagram to show how the lamps would be connected. *(2 marks)*

(ii) The resistance of one lamp is 0.6 Ω and the resistance of the other is 0.3 Ω. What is the total resistance of the lamps in parallel? Show clearly how you get your answer. *(3 marks)*

(iii) Both lamps are shining brightly. Then one lamp blows and goes out. Would the brightness of the other lamp increase, decrease or stay the same? Give a reason for your answer. *(2 marks)*

b) A student is investigating how the current passing through a resistance wire depends on the voltage across its ends. The circuit diagram below shows part of the circuit which she set up.

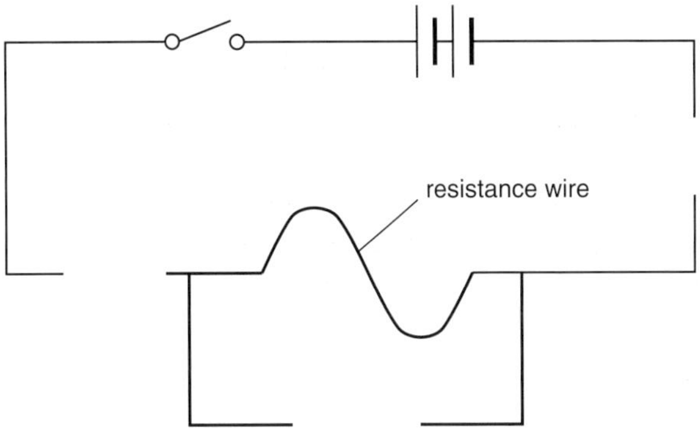

(i) Copy the diagram and in the correct space, draw the correct symbol for the apparatus she would use:

to measure the current in the circuit

to measure the voltage across the wire

to change the current flowing in the resistance wire.

(3 marks)

The student obtains the following set of results:

Voltage in V	0	0.2	0.4	0.6	0.8	1.0
Current in mA	0	25	50	70	100	125

(ii) Copy the grid and plot a graph of voltage against current and draw the best fit line.

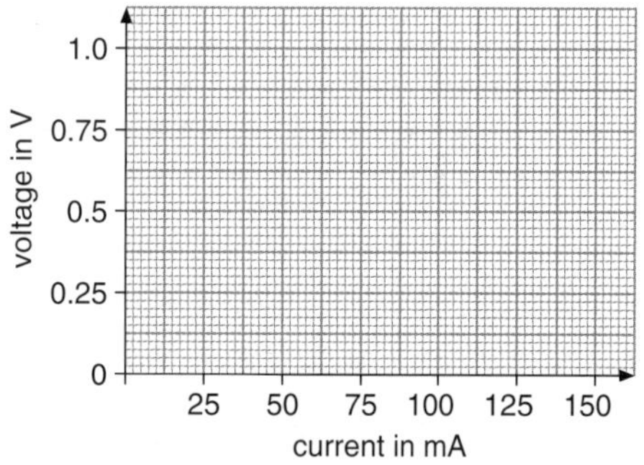

(4 marks)

(iii) From the table above, which current was recorded incorrectly by the student.

(1 mark)

(iv) Calculate the resistance of this wire when the current flowing in it is 50 mA. *(4 marks)*

(v) Is the resistance of this wire constant for currents up to 50 mA? Give a reason for your answer.

(2 marks)

(vi) Before reading the meter the student switched the apparatus off for a few minutes. Then she switched the apparatus on again and read the ammeter and voltmeter. Give a reason, not concerned with cost or safety, why she might have done this.

(1 mark)

3 a) The diagram below shows a 1.5 V cell connected to two *identical* bulbs and a switch. When the switch is closed, both bulbs light.

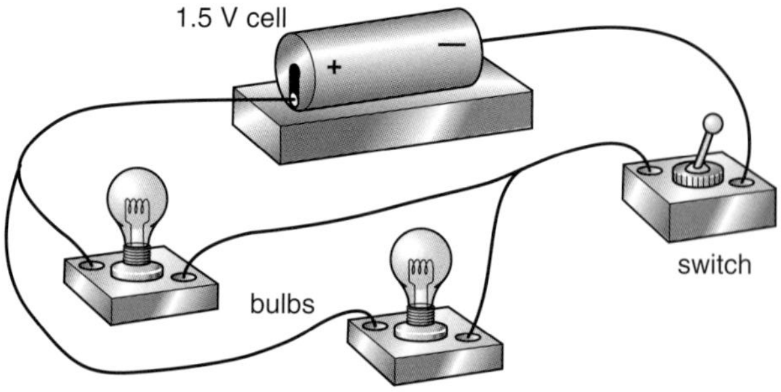

(i) Draw the circuit diagram for this arrangement using standard symbols. *(4 marks)*

(ii) What name is given to this type of circuit? *(1 mark)*

(iii) Describe and explain what you would observe if one of the bulbs were removed and the switch closed. *(2 marks)*

When both bulbs are lit the current passing through one of them is 0.3 A.

(iv) Calculate the resistance of this bulb. Show clearly how you get your answer. *(4 marks)*

b) Another circuit is made using one of the bulbs and two 1.5 V cells as shown below.

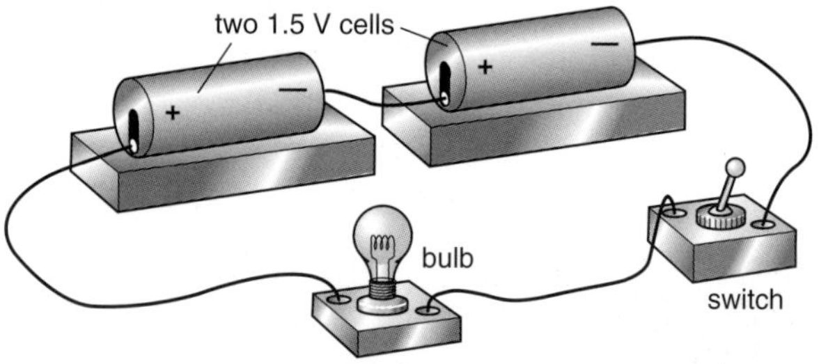

(i) What is the voltage across the bulb? *(2 marks)*

(ii) Calculate the current that passes through this circuit when the switch is closed. Show clearly how you get your answer. *(4 marks)*

(iii) Using your answers to part b)(ii) and the current passing through the bulb in part a) comment on the brightness of the bulb in the circuit above. *(2 marks)*

c) The diagram below shows the main parts of the fuel gauge of a car. The slider completes the circuit so that the ammeter shows a current. As the level of fuel falls the float also falls and the slider moves to the left keeping contact with the resistance wire.

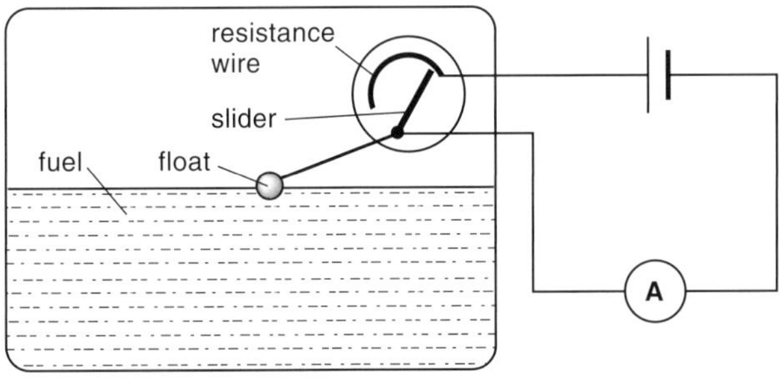

(i) As the slider moves to the left (anticlockwise) how does the resistance of the circuit change? Explain your answer.

(2 marks)

(ii) How does the current in the ammeter change as the fuel level falls? Explain your answer.

(2 marks)

4 a) Mary needs to measure the electrical resistance of a filament light bulb.

(i) Draw a diagram of the circuit that she would use to get a series of voltage and current readings from which to find a series of values of the bulb's resistance.

Below is a table of readings which she obtained in her experiment.

Current in A	0	0.10	0.20	0.30	0.40	0.50
Voltage in V	0	0.5	1.0	1.8	3.2	5.0

(ii) Calculate the resistance of the filament of the bulb when the current has a value of 0.1 A and when the current has a value of 0.4 A.

(iii) Plot a graph of voltage (y-axis) against current (x-axis).

(iv) Explain the shape of the graph.

b) An electric fire is connected to the mains supply by means of a three-pin plug.

(i) An electric fire has a rating of 2000 W when used on a 240 V mains supply. Calculate the rating of the fuse suitable for use with this fire. The available fuse ratings are 1 A, 3 A, 5 A and 13 A.

(ii) Describe the size of the current in the live, neutral and earth wires when the fire is switched on and working properly.

(iii) The live wire becomes loose and comes in contact with the metal body of the electric fire. Describe the danger that could arise when the electric fire is switched on.

(iv) How should the earth wire be connected so as to remove this danger?

(v) How should the fuse be connected so as to remove this danger?

(vi) Explain how the action of the earth wire and the fuse remove this danger.

5 a) Mrs Johnston's electricity meter was read at one month intervals.

Reading at 1 April 2000 11 897 kWh
Reading at 1 May 2000 12 107 kWh

(i) How many units of electricity were used in the Johnston home during April?

(1 mark)

(ii) If one unit of electricity costs 10p calculate the cost of electricity to Mrs Johnston during April. Show clearly how you get your answer.

(2 marks)

b) An electric fire is wired using a three-pin plug as shown in the diagram below.

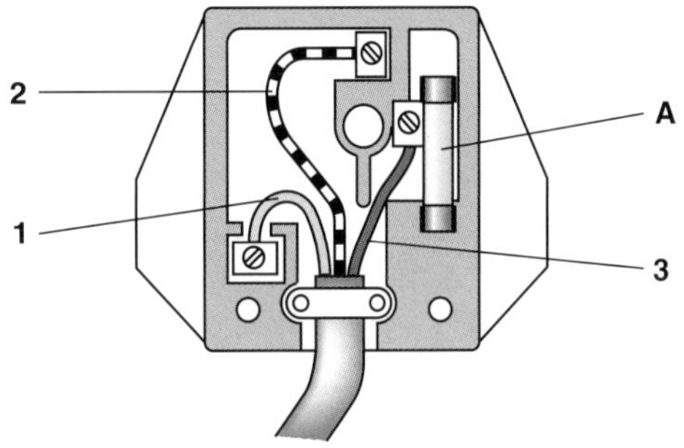

(i) Name the part labelled A. (*1 mark*)

(ii) Which of the wires 1, 2 or 3 should be connected to the metal casing of the fire? (*1 mark*)

(iii) State the colours of the insulation on wires 1 and 2. (*2 marks*)

c) (i) Two copper wires have the same length but different thickness. How does the resistance of a wire change as its thickness increases? (*2 marks*)

(ii) Two copper wires have the same thickness but different lengths. How does the resistance of a wire change as its length increases? (*2 marks*)

d) (i) Copy the circuit diagram below and complete the two-way switches A and B so that the bulb lights.

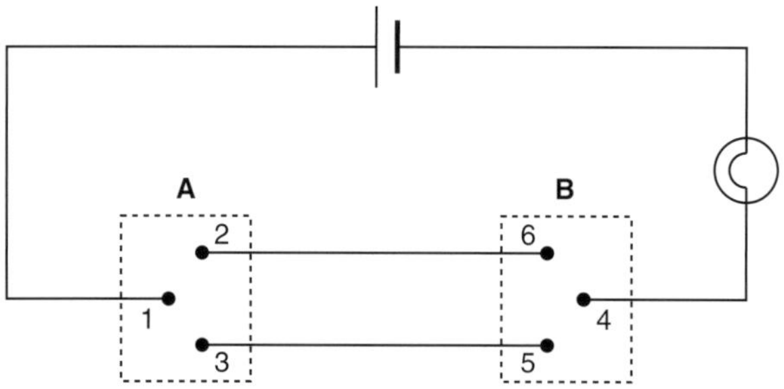

(*2 marks*)

(ii) Now that you have completed the switches, describe the path of the current from the positive terminal of the battery to the negative terminal, by copying and completing the following sentence.

The current flows from the positive terminal to 1 to ___ to ___ to ___ to the lamp and to the negative terminal. (*2 marks*)

e) Kevin set up the circuit shown below using two identical resistors.

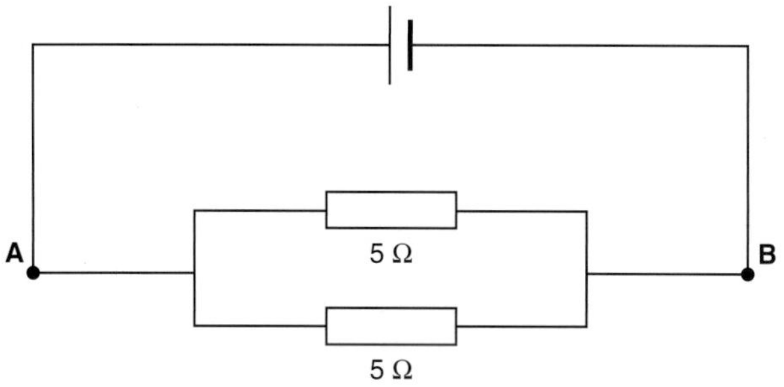

(i) How are the resistors said to be connected? (*1 mark*)

(ii) What is the total resistance between A and B? (*2 marks*)

(iii) Copy the circuit diagram and mark with an X, the position where an ammeter should be connected to measure the current through one resistor only. (*1 mark*)

6 a) A colour television is marked 240 V, 80 W.

(i) Explain carefully what these numbers mean. (*2 marks*)

(ii) Calculate the current that passes through this appliance when it is on. Show clearly how you get your answer. (*3 marks*)

(iii) Select a fuse that should be fitted to this appliance from the list below. Explain your choice.

1 A, 3 A, 5 A, 13 A (*2 marks*)

(iv) Calculate the resistance of the television set. Show clearly how you get your answer. (*3 marks*)

(v) The flex that connects this television to the mains has only two wires inside it. The diagram below shows the inside of a three-pin plug. Copy the diagram and complete it to show how the plug should be wired. Label each wire with its name and colour.

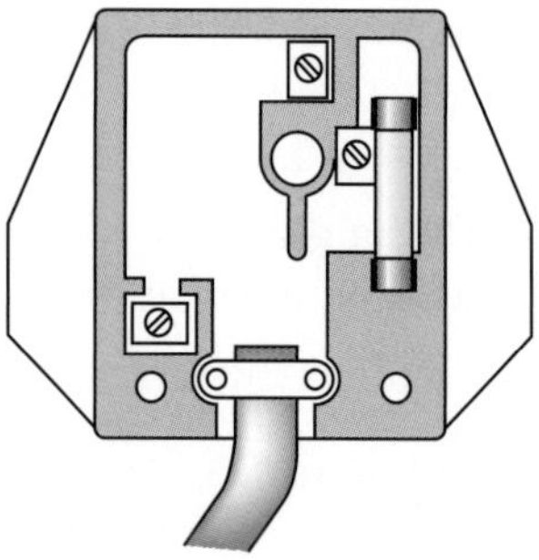

(*3 marks*)

(vi) To which of these wires should the switch on the television be connected?

(1 mark)

(vii) Apart from allowing the user to switch the television on and off this is done for another reason. What is this other reason?

(1 mark)

(viii) Explain how the owner of this television is protected from possible electric shock.

(3 marks)

b) The oven of an electric cooker is rated at 8 kW.

(i) Calculate the cost of using the oven to cook for 2 hours. The cost of electricity is 11p per unit. Show clearly how you get your answer.

(3 marks)

The copper cable used to connect the cooker to the mains supply is 15 m long and has an area of cross section of 6 mm^2. The resistivity of copper is $1.8 \times 10^{-8}\ \Omega$ m.

(ii) Calculate the resistance of the cable. Show clearly how you get your answer.

(6 marks)

When the oven is on, the same current passes through the cable as the heating elements.

(iii) Explain why the cable does not heat up.

(2 marks)

Chapter 6

Electromagnetism

Learning objectives

By the end of this chapter you should know:

- How to make a simple electromagnet and recall, qualitatively, how the strength of the electromagnet is affected by the number of turns, the current and the material used for the core
- How to describe the shape and direction of the magnetic field pattern produced by the current in a solenoid and relate the current direction to the polarity
- How electromagnetic relays, electric bells and circuit breakers work
- That a current-carrying conductor in a magnetic field experiences a force perpendicular to both the current and magnetic field directions, and that reversing the current direction reverses the direction of the force
- The two methods by which a current may be induced in a conductor
- That a.c. generators are used in the production of electricity
- How step-up and step-down transformers are used in the transmission of electricity
- How to describe the construction of a transformer, including the primary coil, secondary coil and core
- How to use the transformer equation, $V_p/N_p = V_s/N_s$

Currents, magnetism and circuit breakers

When an electrical current flows through a wire, not only does it heat up, but a magnetic field is created around the wire.

The field due to a current-carrying wire

In Figure 1, a long straight wire carrying an electrical current is placed vertically through a horizontal piece of cardboard. Iron filings have been sprinkled onto the cardboard to reveal the magnetic lines of force when the current is switch on and the cardboard lightly tapped. This experiment shows that:

- if the current is large, the lines of force are concentrated, which means that the magnetic field is strong
- the magnetic field gets weaker further away from the wire
- the direction of the magnetic field lines can be found using a plotting compass.

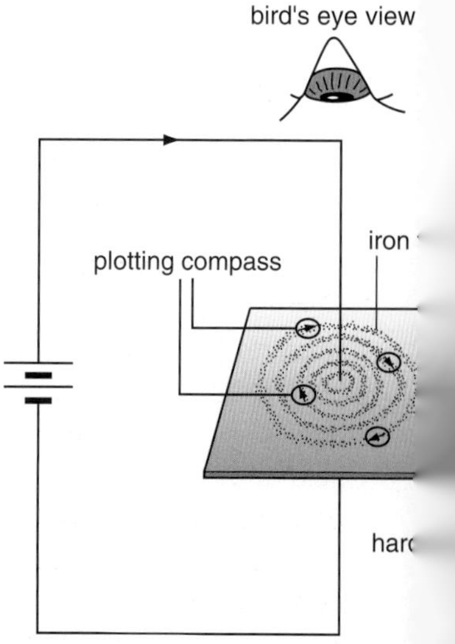

Figure 1 To show that there is magnetic field around a currer carrying wire

The field due to current-carrying coils

Figure 2 shows the magnetic field around a single loop of wire which is carrying a current. Near A, the field lines point anticlockwise as you look at them, and near B, the lines point clockwise. In the middle, the fields from each part of the loop combine to produce a magnetic field running from left to right. This loop of wire is like a very short bar magnet. Magnetic field lines come out of the left-hand side (north pole) and go back into the right-hand side (south pole).

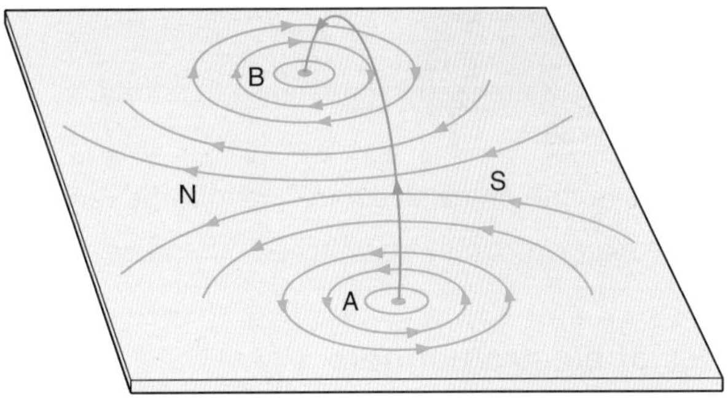

Figure 2 The magnetic field around a single loop of current-carrying wire

The strength of the magnetic field can be increased by increasing the number of turns of wire in the coil and also by increasing the current through the coil.

Making a simple electromagnet

A stronger magnetic field may be made by wrapping the wires in the form of a long coil, which is referred to as a **solenoid**.

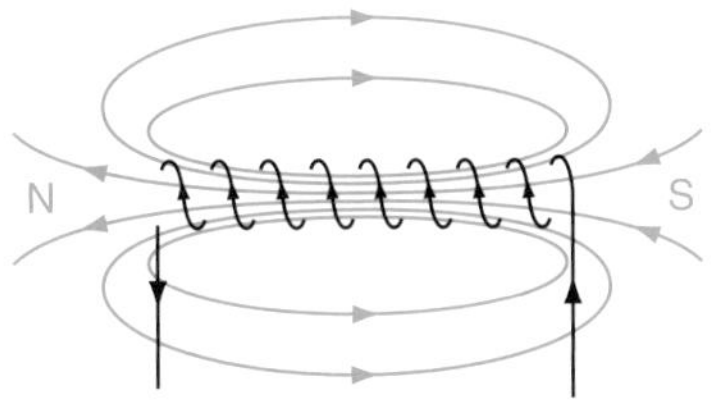

Figure 3 The pattern of magnetiic field around a solenoid

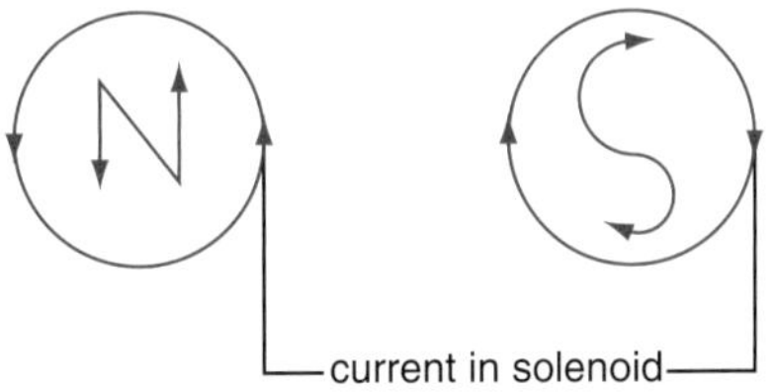

Figure 4 This is a good way of working out the polarity of the end of a solenoid

The strength of the magnetic field produced by a solenoid can be increased by:

- using a larger current
- using more turns of wire
- putting a soft iron rod into the middle of the solenoid.

With the soft iron rod inserted into the solenoid, we have made a simple **electromagnet**.

Unlike an ordinary magnet, an electromagnet can be switched on and off. In a simple electromagnet, a coil, consisting of several hundred turns of insulated copper wire, is wound round a core, usually made of iron. When a current flows through the coil, it produces a magnetic field. This magnetises the core, producing a magnetic field about a thousand times stronger than that produced by the coil alone. Soft iron is so called because it is easy to magnetise and demagnetise. By using soft iron as the core, the magnetism is only temporary, and is lost as soon as the current through the coil is switched off. Steel would not be suitable as a core because it would become permanently magnetised.

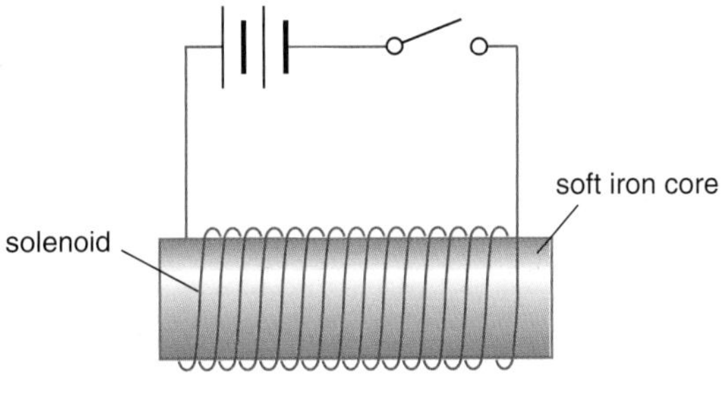

Figure 5 A simple elctromagnet

Advantages of electromagnets compared to magnets

Electromagnets are used in preference to normal magnets because:

- the strength of the electromagnet may be varied
- the magnetism may be switched off and on.

Figure 6 Large electromagnets are used in scrap yards to separate magnetic materials from non-magnetic materials

Uses of electromagnets

Electromagnets can be used:

- to separate metallic from non-metallic materials
- to lift magnetic materials like iron and steel in scrap yards
- in relay switches and bells.

The magnetic relay

A **magnetic relay** is a switch operated by an electromagnet. With a relay, a small switch with thin wires can be used to turn on a much larger current in a more powerful circuit, for example, one with a large electric motor in it.

When the switch S is closed, a small current flows through the electromagnet. This pulls the iron armature towards the soft iron core, which closes the contacts R. As a result, a very large current flows through the motor.

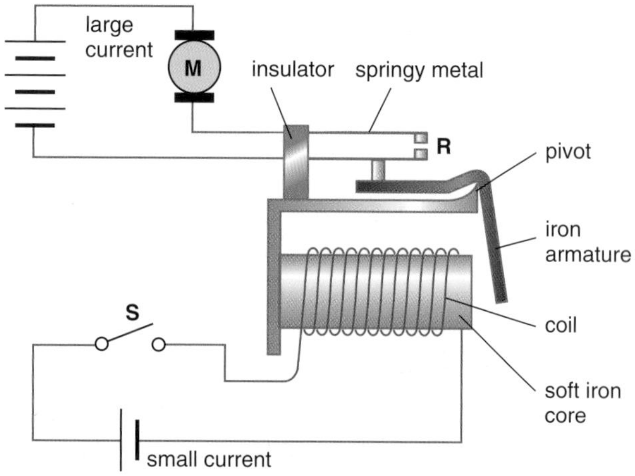

Figure 7 A magnetic relay

Uses of a relay

1. Relays are often used to interface computers to external devices, for example when the electrical output of a computer is used to control a printer.
2. External security lighting.
3. In circuits which control the starter motor in cars.

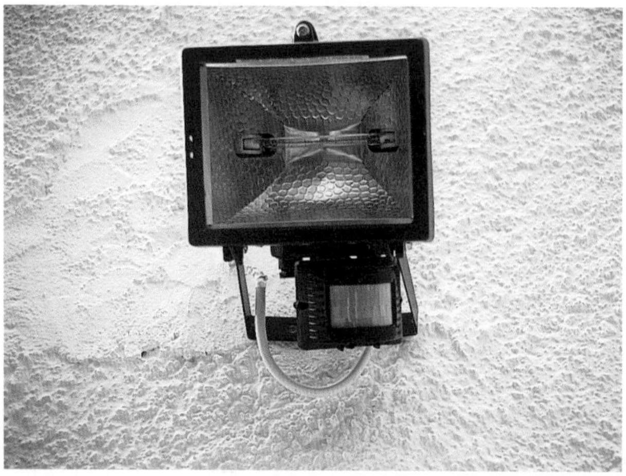

Figure 8 This security light contains a magnetic relay

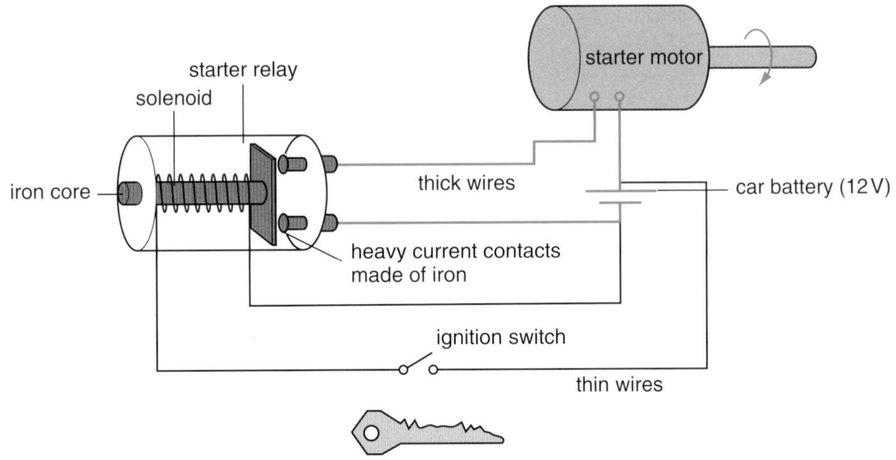

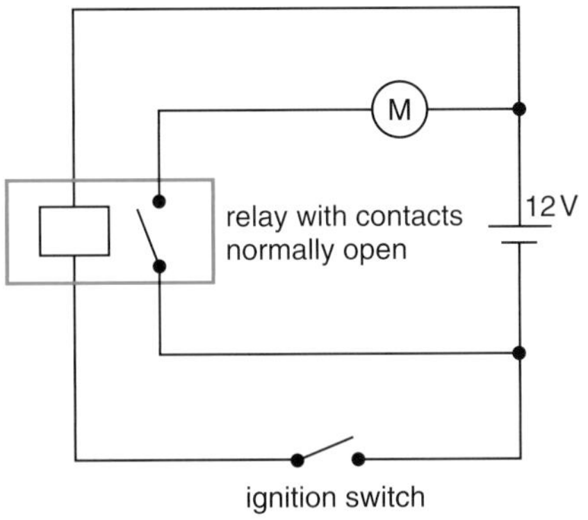

Figure 9a The relay for the starter motor in a car. **b** The circuit diagram for this relay circuit

The electric bell

An **electric bell** contains an electromagnet which switches itself off and on very rapidly, moving the bell hammer as it does so. The arrangement is called a 'make-and-break' circuit. When you press the switch, current flows through the electromagnet, which pulls the hammer across so that it strikes the gong. The movement separates the contacts X and switches off the current and hence the electromagnet. So the hammer springs back, the contacts close, the current flows again magnetising the electromagnet, which pulls the hammer across again, and so on. This continues as long as the bell switch is pressed.

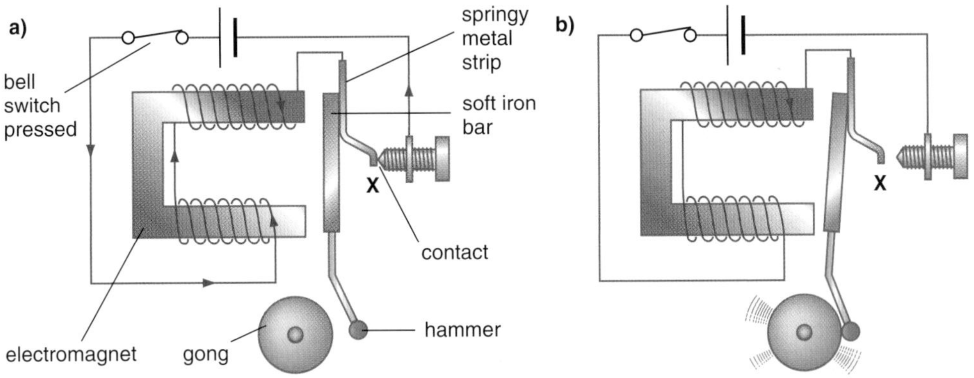

Figure 10 A simple 'make-and-break' circuit in an electric bell

Circuit breakers

Another use for electromagnets is in circuit breakers, of which there are two types: trip switches and residual current devices.

Trip switches

These may be used in place of fuses to protect electrical equipment. As its name suggests, a circuit 'trips' (or breaks) when the current flowing becomes too large and exceeds a certain value. Figure 11 shows the construction and operation of such a trip switch.

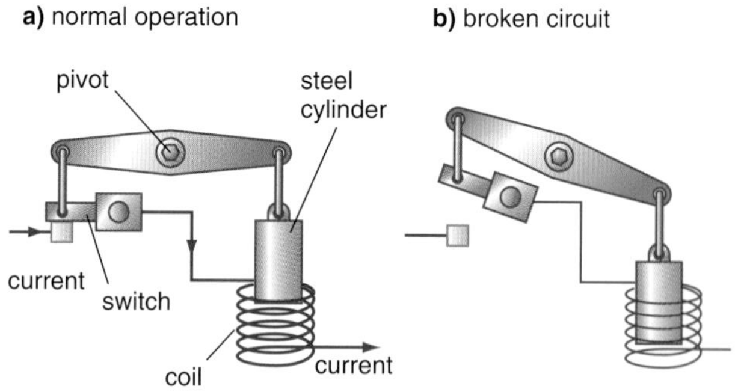

Figure 11 A trip switch

So how does it work? The current in the circuit flows through the switch and the coil. When the current is small, the electromagnet is not strong enough to pull the steel cylinder down. When the current reaches the critical value allowed for the circuit, the electromagnet pulls strongly enough to attract the steel cylinder downwards and open the switch. The advantage of such a trip switch is that it is easily reset, unlike a fuse which has to be replaced. The major disadvantage is that the operating time for the switch is 1–2 seconds, so it is unsuitable for protecting the user. This problem is overcome in the second type of circuit breaker.

Residual current device (RCD)

As can be seen in Figure 12, the currents in the live and neutral wires are compared. If they are unequal due to a short circuit, the iron bar becomes unbalanced and the circuit is broken. It normally only takes around 40 milliseconds for the circuit to break – much faster than the fuse or the trip switch, and hence the RCD is more effective at preventing the user from receiving an electrical shock.

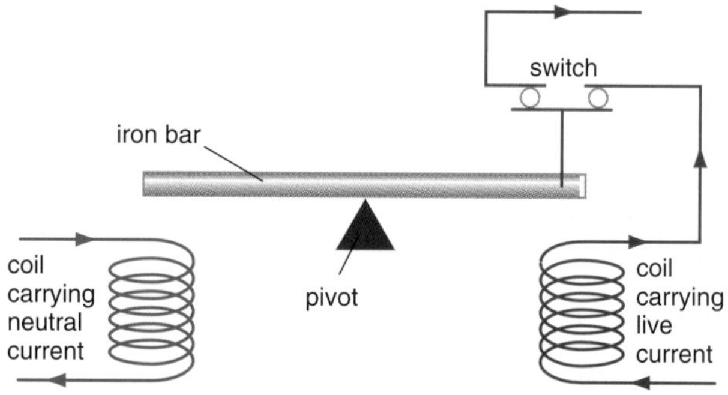

Figure 12 A residual current device

Magnetic force on a current-carrying wire – the motor effect

Figure 13 shows a length of copper wire that has been placed in a magnetic field. The copper wire is not magnetic so the wire itself is not affected by the magnet. However, with a current passing through it, there is a force on the wire. Where does this force come from?

The force arises because the current produces its own magnetic field which interacts with the field of the magnet. The resulting magnetic field is shown in Figure 14. Note how the originally circular field lines due to the current in the wire have become distorted. The field lines below the wire are concentrated while the field lines above the wire are not. The result is that the wire experiences a force as the field lines tend to straighten.

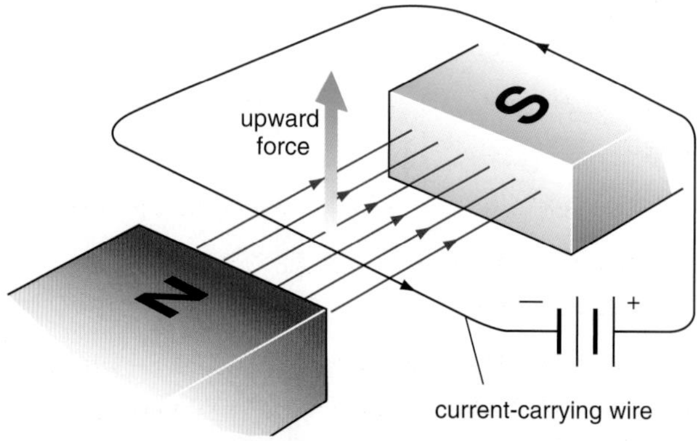

Figure 13 The movement of a current-carrying wire in a magnetic field

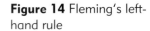

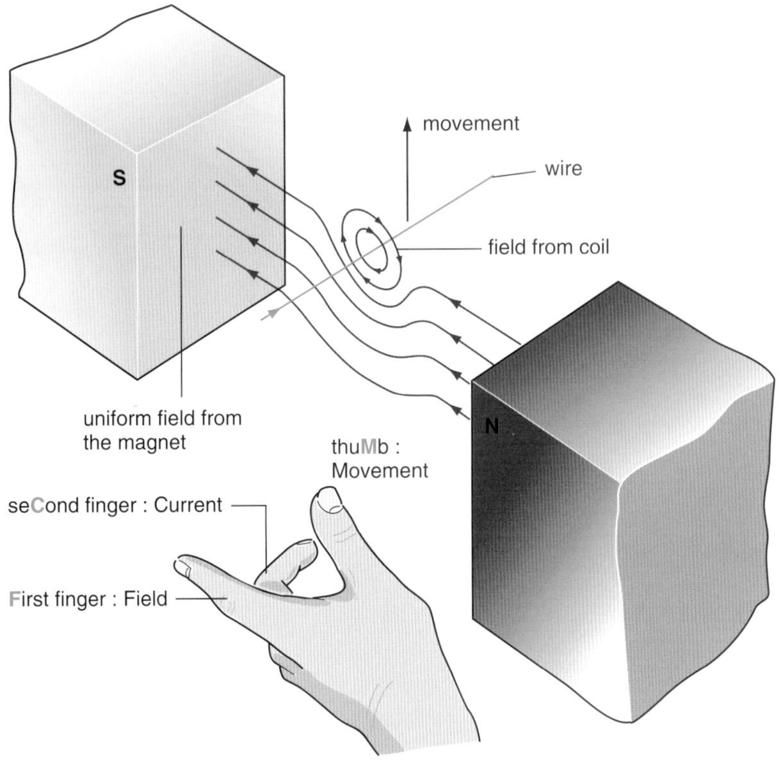

Figure 14 Fleming's left-hand rule

If either the current in the wire changes direction or the polarity of the magnet is reversed, then the direction of the force on the wire is reversed.

The force is increased if:

- the current in the wire is increased
- a stronger magnet is used
- the length of the wire exposed to the magnetic field is increased.

The relationship between the direction of motion, the current and the magnetic field when a current-carrying wire is in a magnetic field is predicted by **Fleming's Left-Hand Rule**. The rule states that if the thumb and first two fingers of the left hand are held at right angles to each other, then the thumb points in the direction of the force or motion, the first finger will be pointing in the direction of the field and the second finger will be pointing in the direction of the current.

When applying this rule it is important to remember how the field and current directions are defined:

- the field direction is from the N pole of a magnet to the S pole
- the current direction is from the positive (+) terminal of a battery round to the negative (−).

Fleming's Left-Hand Rule only applies if the current and field directions are at right angles to each other. If the current and fields are parallel, there is no force on the wire and it will not move.

Several devices use the fact that there is a force on a current-carrying conductor in a magnetic field. They include the loudspeaker and the electric motor.

The turning effect on a current-carrying coil in a magnetic field

The loop in Figure 15 lies between the poles of a magnet. The current flows in opposite directions along the two sides of the loop. If you apply Fleming's Left-Hand Rule, when a current is passed through the loop, one side of the loop is pushed up and the other side is pushed down. In other words there is a turning effect on the loop.

If the number of loops is increased to form a coil, the turning effect is greatly increased. This is the principle involved in electric motors.

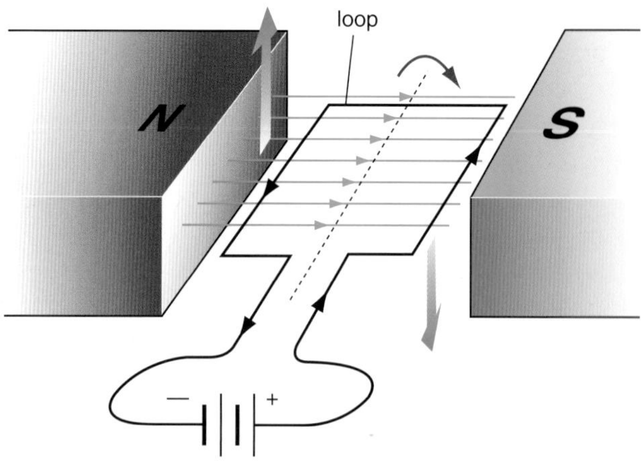

Figure 15 When a current is passed through the loop, it experiences a turning effect

The d.c. electric motor

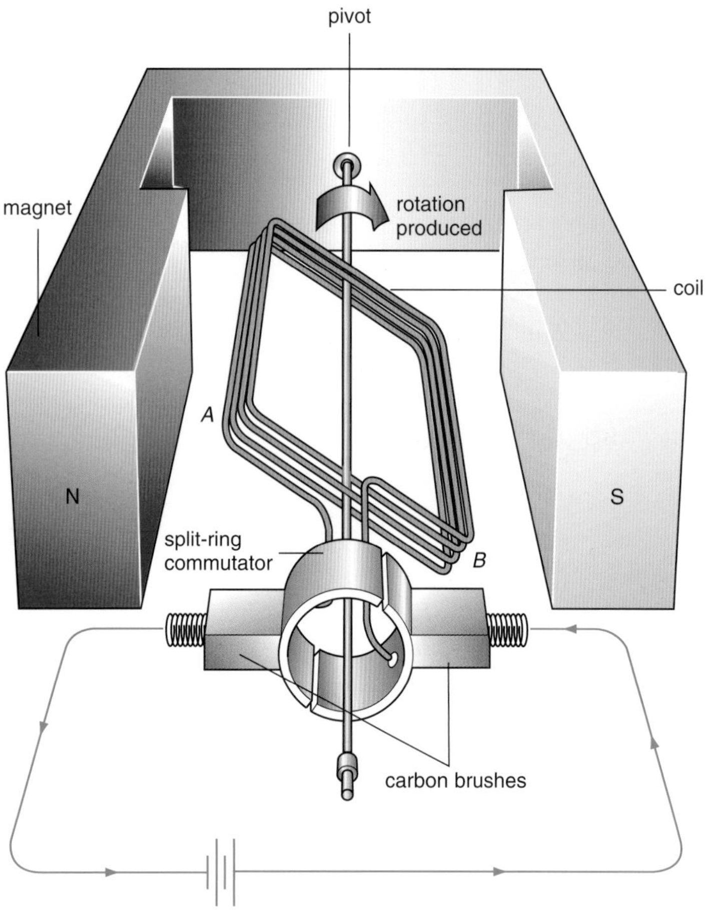

Figure 16 A simple electric motor

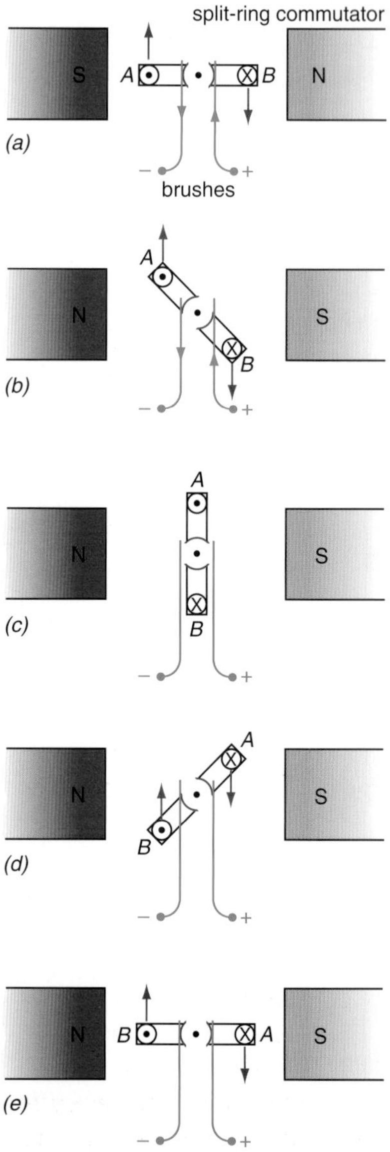

Figure 17 The turning action of the coil in the electric motor

Figure 16 shows a simple electric motor. It runs on direct current (d.c.), the unidirectional current that flows from a battery. The coil is made of insulated copper wire. The coil is free to rotate on an axle between the poles of a magnet. The commutator, or split-ring, is fixed to the coil and rotates with it. Figure 17 details this action. The brushes are two contacts which rub against the commutator and keep the coil connected to the battery. They are usually made of carbon.

When the coil is horizontal, the forces are furthest apart and have their maximum turning effect on the coil. With no change to the forces, the coil would eventually come to rest in the vertical position. However, as the coil overshoots the vertical, the commutator changes the direction of the current through it. So the forces change direction and push the coil further around until it is again vertical, and so on. In this way the coil keeps rotating clockwise, half a turn at a time. If either the battery or the poles of the magnet are reversed, the coil would rotate anticlockwise.

The turning effect on the coil can be increased by:

- increasing the current in the coil
- increasing the number of turns on the coil
- increasing the strength of the magnetic field
- increasing the area of the coil.

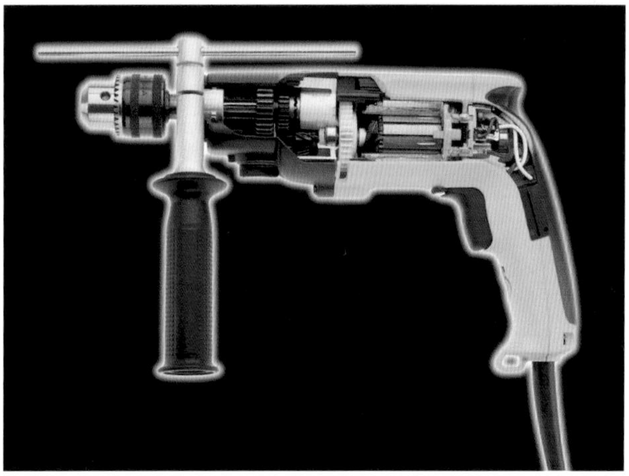

Figure 18 A cut-away view of a De Walt drill, showing the electric motor and gears inside

Questions

1 An electromagnet is a coil of wire through which a current can be passed.

a) State three ways in which the strength of the electromagnet may be increased.

b) An electromagnet may be switched on and off. Suggest one situation where this would be an advantage over the constant field permanent magnet.

2 The diagram shows the construction of an electric bell. Put the following sentences in the correct order to explain how the bell works.

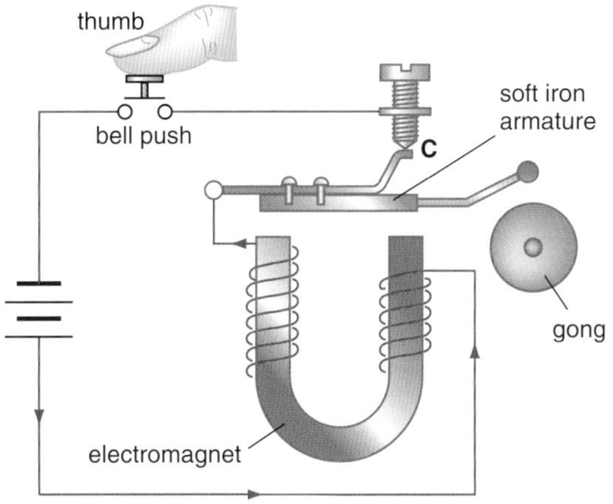

The springy metal pulls the hammer back.
A current flows through the electromagnet.
At the same time, the circuit is broken at point C.
Tom presses the bell push.
The electromagnet attracts the iron armature.
At C, the circuit is complete again.
The hammer strikes the gong.

3 The motor effect may be demonstrated using the apparatus shown in the diagram. When a current is passed through the moveable brass rod, it rolls along the fixed brass rails.

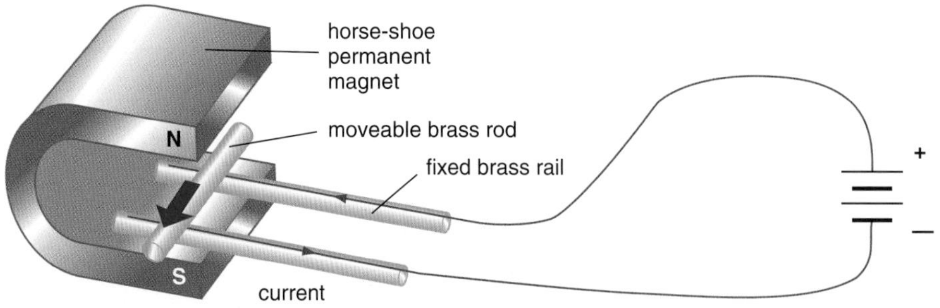

a) State the direction of the magnetic lines of force between the poles of the magnet.
b) In which direction will the rod roll?
c) The rod is placed back in its original position. What will happen to the rod if the poles of the magnet are reversed?
d) The rod is placed back in its original position. What will happen to the rod if the poles of the battery are reversed?

4 Below is a simplified diagram of a d.c. motor. The loop of wire is horizontal in a horizontal magnetic field.

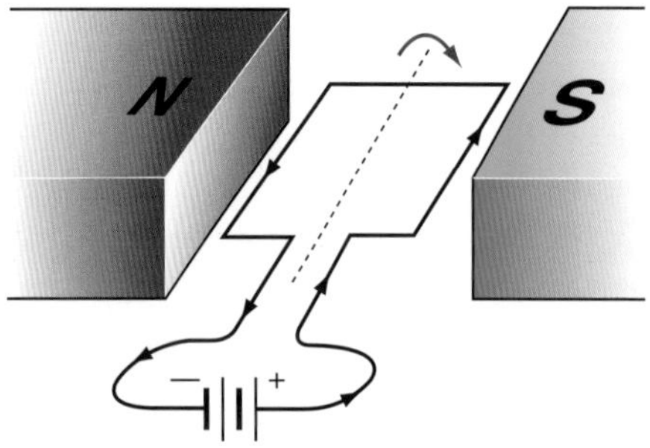

a) What does 'd.c.' mean?
b) In which direction is the force on side AB of the wire loop?
c) In which direction is the force on side CD of the wire loop?
d) Explain how these forces cause the loop to rotate.
e) What can you say about the force on side BC of the loop?

Electromagnetic induction

In the electric motor, electricity is put into the coil producing motion. It was Faraday who suggested that the process could be reversed, i.e. electricity can be produced by moving a conductor through a magnetic field. This process is called **electromagnetic induction**.

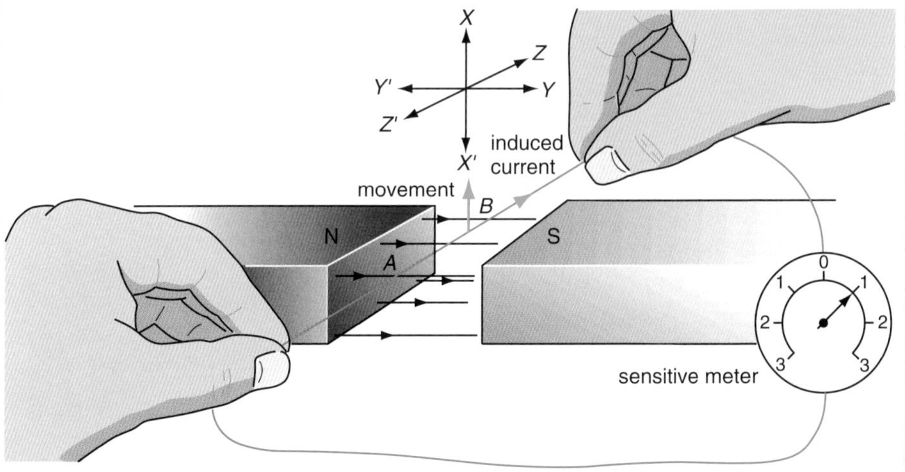

Figure 19 To demonstrate electromagnetic induction

Figure 19 shows an experiment to find out what affects the making of a current. It is found that there are two main factors:

1 Direction of movement. To generate a current, the wire must cross lines of magnetic field. A current is produced if the wire is moved up and down along the direction XX′. But there is no current if the wire moves along ZZ′ or YY′. Reversing the direction of movement reverses the current. So, if moving the wire up makes the meter move to the right, then moving the wire down makes it go to the left.

2 Size of current. The current flow can be increased in the following ways:
- moving the wire more quickly
- using stronger magnets
- looping the wire so that several turns of wire pass through the poles.

It is also possible to induce a current by keeping the wire stationary but moving the magnetic field.

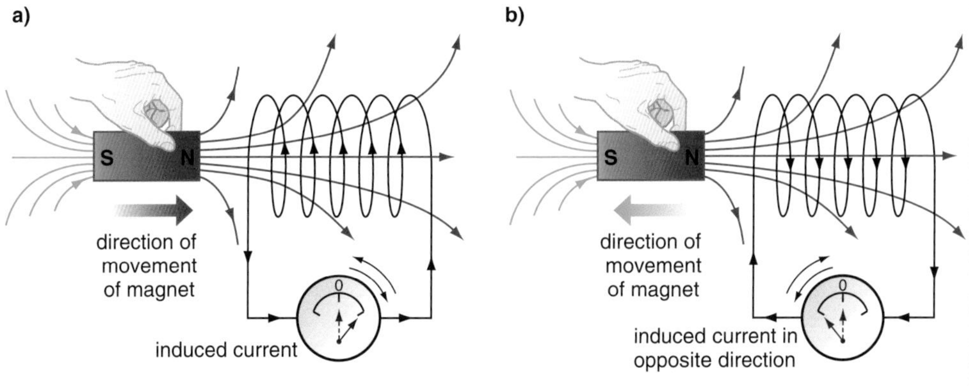

Figure 20 Inducing a current by moving the magnetic field

In Figure 20a, a current is generated by moving a magnet into a solenoid. When the current flows, a compass needle is attracted towards end Y. So end Y is behaving as a south pole and end X as a north pole. So as the magnet moves towards the solenoid, there is a magnetic force which repels it, so you have to do some work to push the magnet into the solenoid. The work done in pushing the magnet generates the electrical energy.

In Figure 20b the magnet is being pulled out of the solenoid. The direction of the current is reversed and so there is now an attractive force acting on the magnet. The hand pulling the magnet is still doing work to produce electrical energy.

Figure 21 Airport security barriers are used to make sure passengers aren't carrying guns or bombs. Metal objects cause changes in an electromagnetic field when they pass through the barrier. A circuit detects these changes and an alarm is set off

When a current is produced by electromagnetic induction, energy is always used to create the electrical energy. In the example described in Figure 20 the energy originally came from the muscles working the hand holding the magnet. So electromagnetic induction is just a way of converting energy from mechanical energy to electrical energy. This is the principle behind electricity generation and transformers.

Application of electromagnetic induction

A major application of electromagnetic induction is the **a.c. generator (alternator)**.

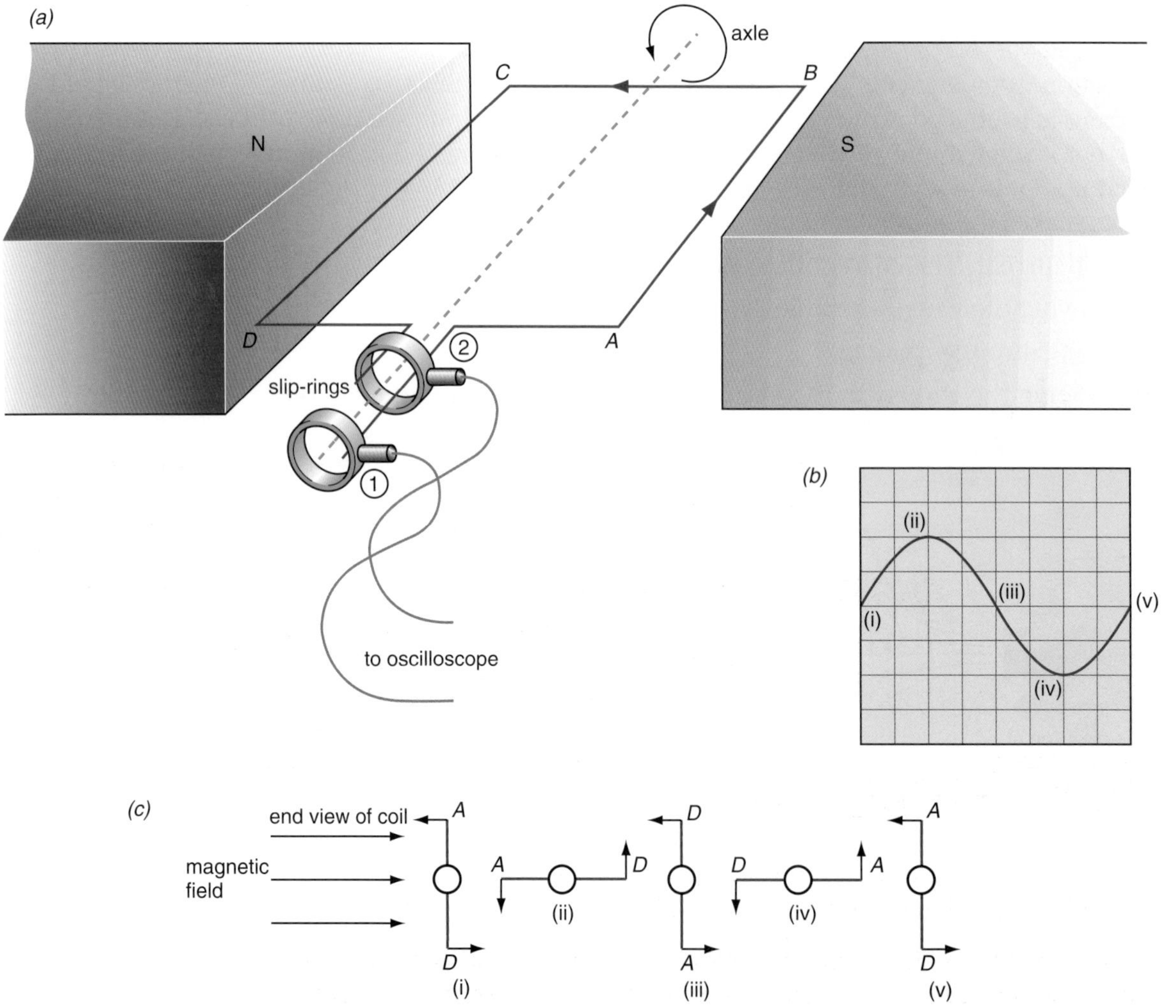

Figure 22a An a.c. generator. **b** How the voltage waveform produced by the generator appears on an oscilloscope screen. **c** The position of the coil

Figure 22 shows the design of a very simple alternating current (a.c.) generator. When the axle is turned, a coil of wire moves through a magnetic field. This induces a voltage between the ends of the coil. Figure 22b shows how the voltage waveform produced by the generator looks on an oscilloscope screen.

Questions

5 Julie holds one loop of insulated copper wire in a magnetic field, as shown in the diagram. She moves the wire downwards through the magnetic field.

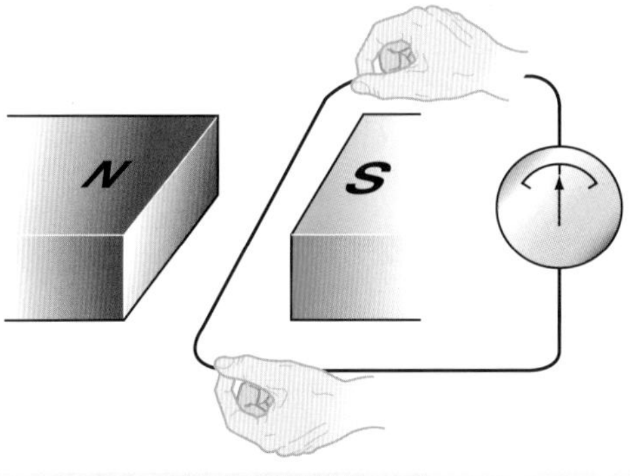

a) Explain why a current is induced in the loop of wire.
b) What will happen to the current if the loop of wire is moved upwards?
c) How should Julie move the wire to produce a bigger current?
d) Julie then moves the loop of wire from side to side. Will a current be induced? Explain your answer.

Electricity generation and transmission

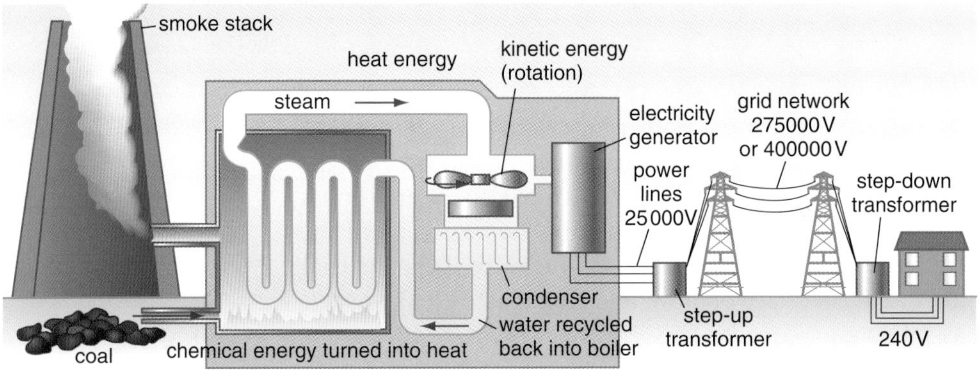

Figure 23 How power is transmitted from a power station, through the national grid, to your home

Power for the mains electricity supply is generated in power stations, transmitted through long-distance cables and then distributed to consumers.

Ballylumford Power Station contains four a.c. generators, each producing a current of 20 000 amps at a voltage of 33 000 volts. The current from each generator is fed to a huge step-up transformer (see page 153) which transfers power to overhead cables at a greatly increased voltage of 275 000 volts. The cables feed power to a nationwide supply network called the **grid**. Power from the grid is distributed by a series of **substations**. These contain step-down transformers (see page 153) which reduce the voltage in stages to the level needed by consumers. In the UK, for example, this is 230 V for domestic consumers, although industry usually takes its power at a higher voltage.

Electricity transmission

Electrical power is distributed around the country from power stations through a grid of high-voltage power lines.

Figure 24 shows the national grid for the UK. There are loops which ensure that when a local power station is switched off, electricity can still reach all the consumers in the area. The national grid in the UK is connected to the Northern Ireland grid and to the French grid. Southern Scotland sells excess electricity to Northern Ireland. France produces more electricity than it needs and sells large quantities to neighbouring countries.

The electricity in overhead power lines is transmitted to our homes and industry at 275 kV or 400 kV.

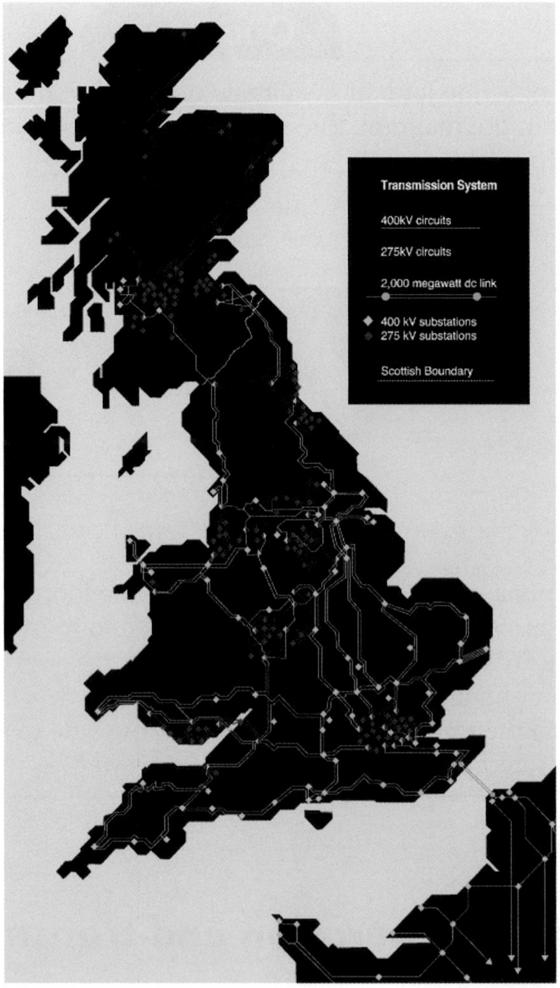

Figure 24 The national grid for the UK

Why use high voltages?

The high voltages used to transmit electrical power around a country are extremely dangerous. That is why the cables that carry the power are supported high above people, traffic and buildings on tall pylons. Sometimes the cables are buried underground, but this is much more expensive, and the cables must be safely insulated. High voltages are used because it means that the current flowing in the cables is relatively low, and this wastes less energy. This can be explained as follows.

When a current flows in a wire or cable, some of the energy it is carrying is lost because of the cable's resistance – i.e. the cables get hot. A small current wastes less energy than a high current. Consider the following two methods of transmitting electricity:

Method I

Let the resistance of the cable be 10 Ω, while carrying a current of 1000 A. Then

$$R = 10\ \Omega$$
$$I = 1000\ \text{A}$$

$$\text{Power wasted in cables} = I^2R = 1000^2 \times 10 = \mathbf{10\ MW}$$

Method II

Let the resistance of the cable be 10 Ω, while carrying a current of 100 A. Then

$$R = 10\ \Omega$$
$$I = 100\ \text{A}$$

$$\text{Power wasted in cables} = I^2R = 100^2 \times 10 = \mathbf{0.1\ MW}$$

Clearly transmitting the smaller current reduces dramatically the heat lost in the cables.

Transformers

Power stations typically generate electricity at 30 kV. This has to be converted to the grid voltage, usually 300 kV, using **transformers**. For these voltages we say that the voltage is stepped up by a factor of 10.

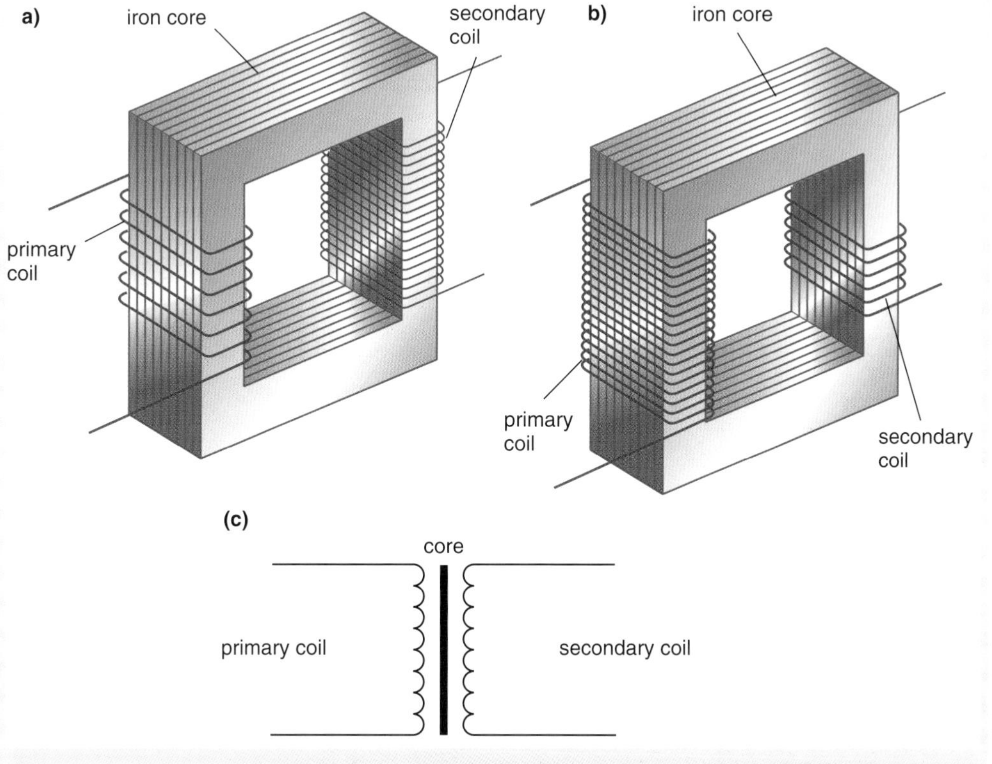

Figure 25a This is a step-up transformer because there are more turns in the secondary coil than in the primary.
b This is a step-down transformer, as there are fewer turns in the secondary coil than in the primary.
c A circuit symbol for a transformer

Figure 25a shows the construction of a suitable transformer. It consists of two coils of wire wrapped round a laminated iron core. Figure 25b shows the construction of a step-down transformer. Figure 25c shows the circuit symbol for a transformer.

All transformers have three parts:

1 Primary coil – the incoming voltage V_p (voltage across primary coil) is connected across this coil.
2 Secondary coil – this provides the output voltage V_s (voltage across the secondary coil) to the external circuit.
3 Laminated iron core – this links the two coils magnetically.

Figure 26 This transformer delivers power to the national grid

There is no electrical connection between the two coils, which are constructed using insulated wire.

To step up the voltage by a factor of 10, there must be 10 times as many turns on the secondary coil as on the primary. The **turns ratio** tells us the factor by which the voltage will be changed.

A step-up transformer increases the voltage – there are more turns on the secondary coil than on the primary.

A step-down transformer decreases the voltage – there are fewer turns on the secondary coil than on the primary.

(Note: according to the Principle of Conservation of Energy, if the voltage is stepped up, then the current must be stepped down and vice versa. The energy per second going into the transformer must equal the energy per second leaving the transformer.)

There is an important equation, known as the **transformer equation**, relating the two voltages V_p and V_s to the number of turns on each coil, N_p and N_s:

$$\frac{\text{Voltage across the primary coil}}{\text{Number of turns on the primary coil}} = \frac{\text{Voltage across the secondary coil}}{\text{Number of turns on the secondary coil}}$$

$$\frac{V_p}{N_p} = \frac{V_s}{N_s}$$

Where V_p = primary voltage
V_s = secondary voltage
N_p = Number of turns on primary coil
N_s = Number of turns on secondary coil.

Example

A transformer is needed to step down mains voltage at 240 V to supply 20 V. If the primary coil has 4800 turns, how many turns must the secondary coil have?

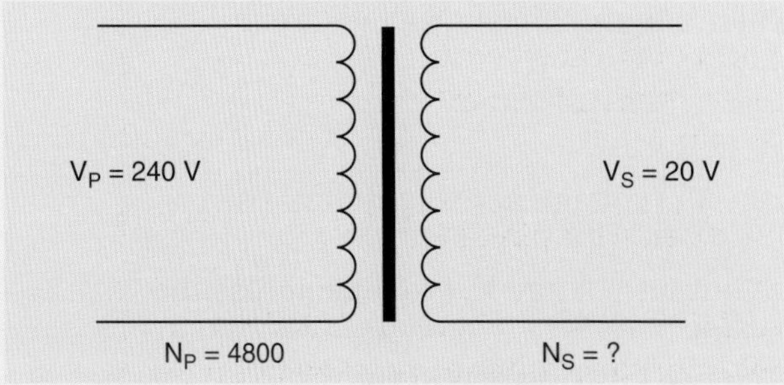

$V_p = 240\text{ V}$
$V_s = 20\text{ V}$
$N_p = 4800$
$N_s = ?$

$$\frac{V_p}{N_p} = \frac{V_s}{N_s}$$

Substituting

$$\frac{240\text{ V}}{4800} = \frac{20\text{ V}}{N_s}$$

Rearranging and solving for N_s

$$N_s = \frac{4800 \times 20\text{ V}}{240\text{ V}}$$

$$= \textbf{400 turns}$$

How a transformer works

The alternating current in the primary coil converts the coil into an electromagnet which produces an alternating magnetic field. The core transports this alternating field to the secondary coil. Now the secondary coil is a conductor in a changing magnetic field. A current is therefore induced in the secondary coil. This type of electromagnetic induction is referred to as mutual Induction.

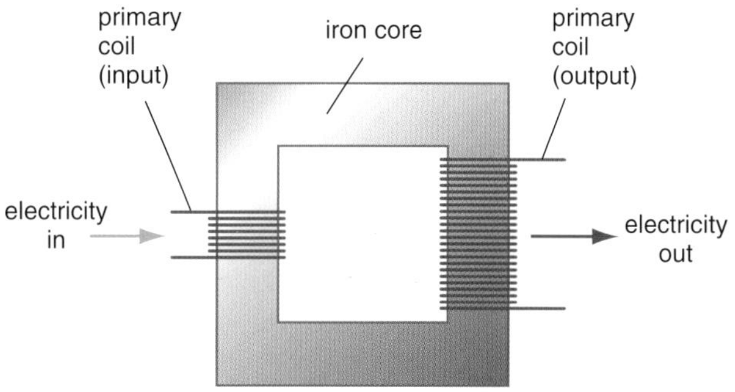

Figure 27 How a transformer works

It is important to realise that transformers convert alternating voltages from one form to another, but they do not work with d.c. If direct current is connected to a transformer, there is no output voltage. This is because the magnetic field produced by the primary coil is unchanging. With an unchanging field passing through the secondary coil, no voltage is induced.

Questions

6 Why is electrical power transmitted in the grid at high voltage?

7 a) What are the three essential parts of a transformer?
b) What is the purpose of the core of a transformer?
c) Why must the core be made of soft iron?

8 Explain why a transformer will not work with direct current.

9 A step-down transformer changes 240 V to 48 V. There are 2000 turns on the primary coil. Find the number of turns on the secondary coil.

10 The diagram represents a simple transformer with 20 turns on the primary coil and 80 turns on the secondary coil. If 4 V is supplied to the primary coil, what voltage would there be across the secondary?

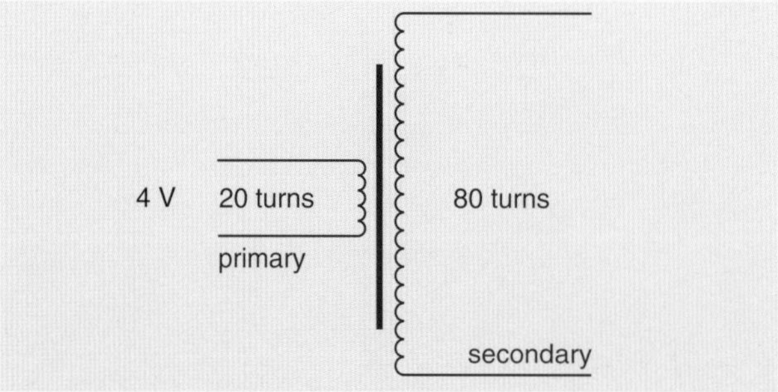

11 The voltage across the power lines supplying a house is 24 000 V.

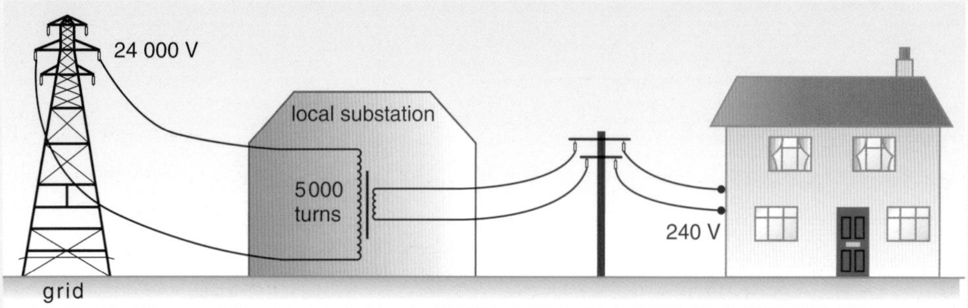

a) What type of transformer must be used?
b) Why is the supply not transmitted all the way at 240 V?
c) The 24 000 V supply cannot be used unchanged in the house – why?
d) How many turns are there in the secondary coil of the local transformer?

12 An oil-fired power station produces electricity at 25 000 V. This voltage is stepped up to 400 000 V by a transformer.

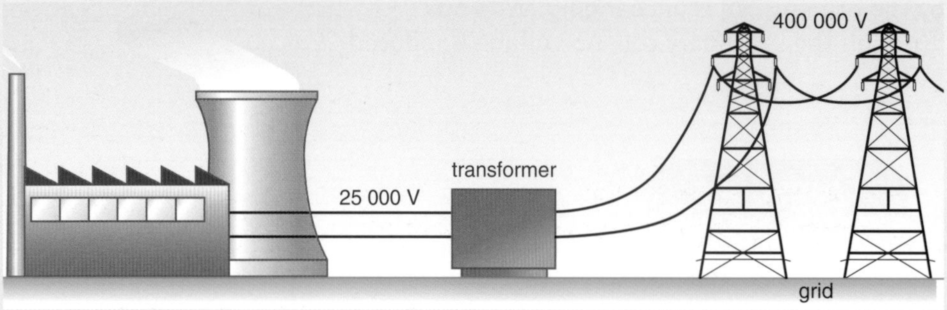

a) What type of transformer is used between the power station and the national grid?
b) The number of turns in the primary coil of the transformer is 10 000. Calculate the number of turns in the secondary coil.
c) Why is a voltage as high as 400 000 V used in the transmission of electrical energy?

Websites

Use your favourite search engine (such as **www.google.com** or **www.excite.com**) and search using the keywords.

Electromagnet
Electromagnetic relay
Circuit breakers
Electric motors
a.c. generator
Electricity generation

www.school-for-champions.com/science/magnetism.html

www.sciencetech.nmstc.ca/english/schoolzone/info_Magnets.cfm

www.duboismarketing.com/magnetism.html

Exam questions

1 a) The diagram below shows an electromagnetic relay.

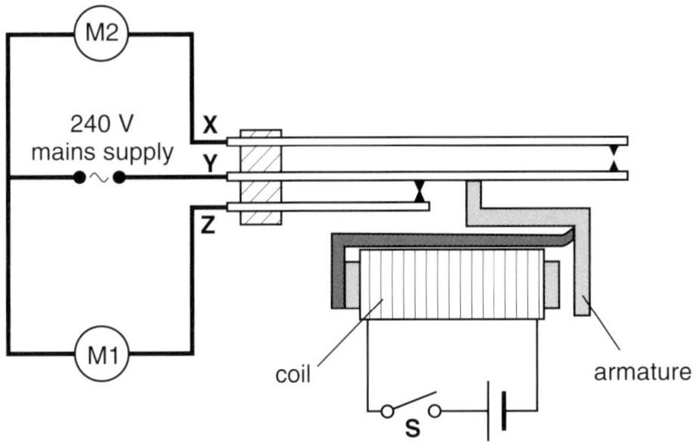

(i) What would you see happening to the armature when the switch S is closed? *(2 marks)*

(ii) Explain your answer to part b)(i). *(2 marks)*

(iii) What, if anything, happens to the motors Ml and M2 when the switch S is closed? *(2 marks)*

(iv) Explain why the wires at X, Y and Z are thicker than those at the coil. *(2 marks)*

b) Jo makes a model generator using the apparatus shown in the diagram below. Jo pulls down the bar magnet and then lets go. The magnet oscillates into and out of the coil.

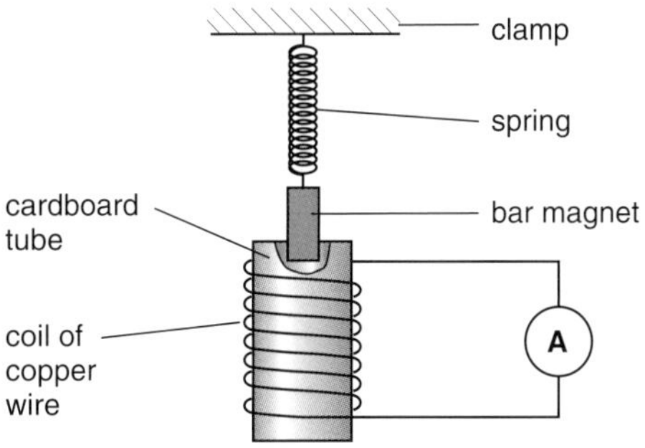

(i) Explain why a current flows in the coil. *(2 marks)*

(ii) Is the current in the coil alternating or direct? Give a reason for your answer. *(2 marks)*

(iii) Copy the axes below and sketch the graph of current against time for the model generator above.

(2 marks)

2 a) The diagram shows a simple transformer. The primary coil is connected to an a.c. supply.

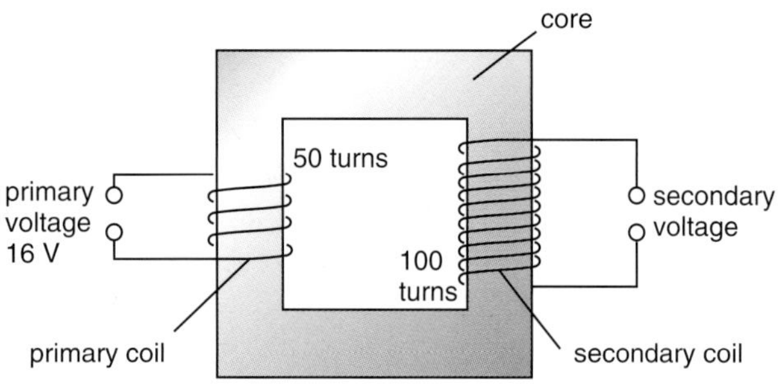

(i) What do the letters a.c. stand for? How is a.c. different from d.c.? *(3 marks)*

(ii) The primary and secondary coils are both wound on the same core. What is this core made of? *(1 mark)*

(iii) Using the information shown on the diagram calculate the secondary voltage. Show clearly how you get your answer. *(4 marks)*

b) The diagram below shows the layout of a power pack which contains a transformer. The moveable switch can be turned so that it touches the contacts A to K.

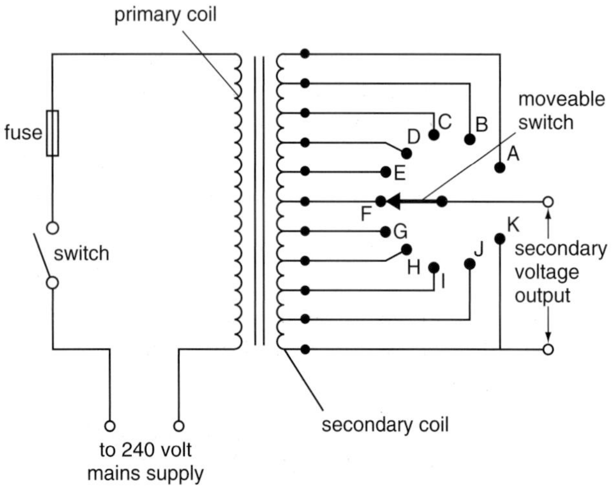

This allows the value of the secondary voltage to be varied. There are 50 turns of wire between consecutive pairs of terminals A to K, i.e. between A and B there are 50 turns and between B and C there are 50 turns and so on.

(i) The maximum secondary voltage output of the power pack is 20 V. In what voltage steps can the secondary voltage output be varied? Show clearly how you get your answer. *(3 marks)*

(ii) Calculate the total number of turns on the secondary coil. *(1 mark)*

(iii) Calculate how many turns of wire there must be on the 240 V primary coil of this transformer. Show clearly how you get your answer. *(3 marks)*

(iv) Explain the function of the fuse. *(2 marks)*

c) The diagram below shows the main parts of a nuclear power station. Inside the nuclear reactor, nuclei undergo fission.

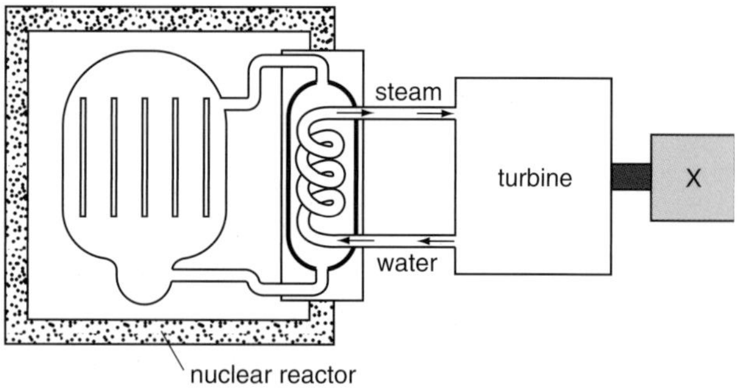

(i) What type of energy is produced by nuclei undergoing fission? *(2 marks)*

(ii) Name the part marked X and state what it does. *(2 marks)*

d) The diagram below shows how electricity from the power station is distributed to homes.

(i) Copy the diagram and write the names of the types of transformer in the appropriate boxes.

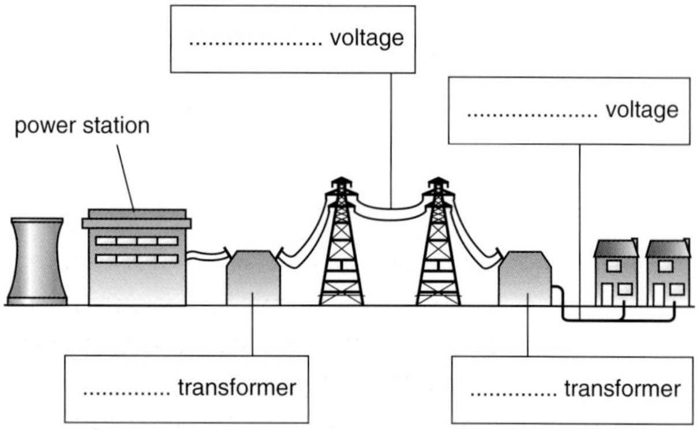

(2 marks)

(ii) In the appropriate boxes on your diagram, label those parts of the distribution system where the voltage is high and those points where it is low. *(2 marks)*

(iii) Why are high voltages used in the distribution of electricity? *(2 marks)*

3 a) The diagram below shows the structure of a simple make-and-break electric bell.

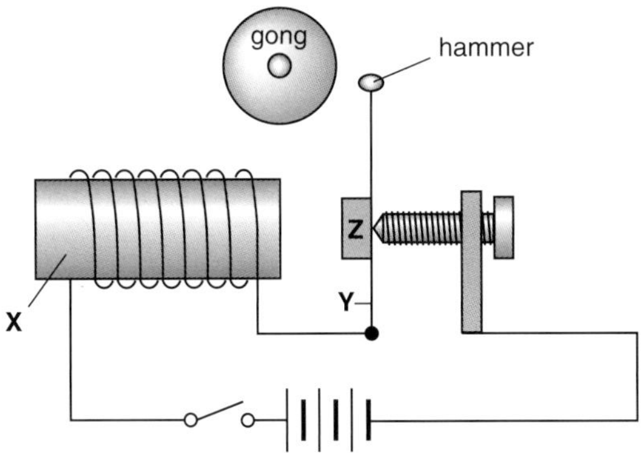

(i) Name the materials from which the parts labelled X and Y are made. *(2 marks)*

(ii) Describe fully how the bell works, giving reasons for the choice of materials for the parts labelled X and Y. *(6 marks)*

b) A coil carrying a current has two magnetic poles.

(i) Copy the diagram below and mark the magnetic poles produced. *(2 marks)*

(ii) On your diagram, draw the magnetic field produced.

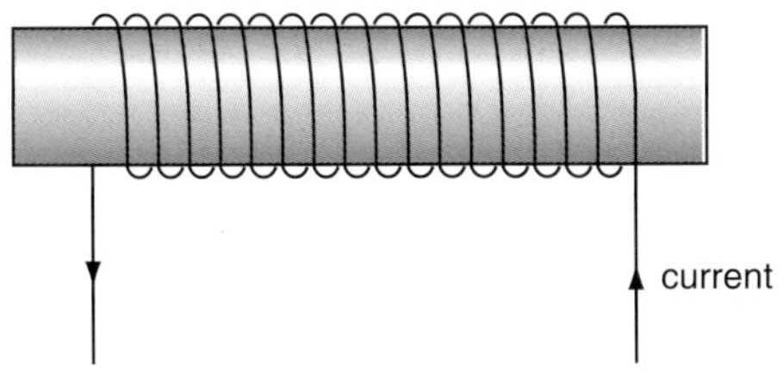

(4 marks)

c) (i) Draw a clearly-labelled diagram to show the construction of a step-up transformer. Indicate clearly where the input voltage is applied and where output voltage is produced. *(7 marks)*

(ii) Which of the following can be stepped up by a transformer?

a.c. voltages
d.c. voltages

(1 mark)

(iii) When 6 V is applied to the primary coil of a transformer, 12 V is produced at the secondary coil. If the primary coil has 200 turns, calculate the number of turns on the secondary coil. Show clearly how you get your answer. *(4 marks)*

d) Explain fully why the output of a power station is connected to a step-up transformer. *(4 marks)*

4 a) At a power station the main transformer is supplied from a 25 kV generator.

(i) How much energy is tranferred from the generator for each coulomb of charge? *(1 mark)*

(ii) The main transformer steps up the voltage to 275 kV before sending it out to the grid. Describe fully the purpose of stepping up the voltage. *(2 marks)*

(iii) In what other part of the electricity transmission system must transformers be used? *(1 mark)*

(iv) Why must these other transformers be used? *(1 mark)*

b) An electric shower has a power rating of 8000 W. It is switched on for 15 minutes.

(i) How much energy, in kilowatt-hours, does the shower use? Show clearly how you obtain your answer. *(4 marks)*

(ii) If one unit of electricity costs 10p, calculate the cost of heating the water. Show clearly how you obtain your answer. *(1 mark)*

c) Two coils are placed beside one another.

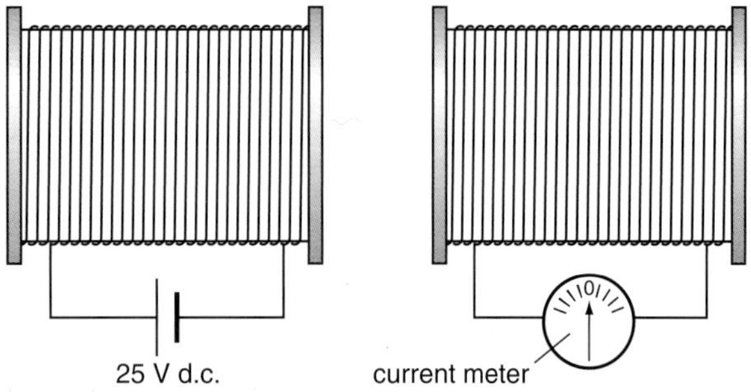

A current meter is connected to one coil as shown in the diagram.

(i) The first coil has been connected to a 25 V d.c. supply.

Describe what happens to the meter reading,

1) when the first coil moves away from the second coil.

(1 mark)

2) when the first coil moves back towards the second coil.

(2 marks)

(ii) The 25 V d.c. supply is now replaced with a 25 V a.c. 1 Hz supply connected to the first coil.

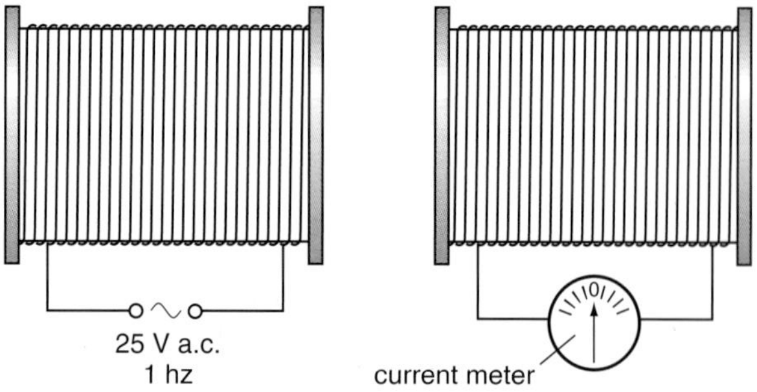

Describe fully what (if anything) happens to the meter reading if the first coil remains stationary.

(2 marks)

Chapter 7

Radioactivity

Learning objectives

By the end of this chapter you should know:

- The structure of the atom in terms of protons, neutrons and electrons
- The meaning of the terms mass number, atomic number and isotope
- How to represent a nucleus using its chemical symbol, mass number and atomic number
- The properties of alpha particles, beta particles and gamma radiation
- Some uses of radioactivity in industry, agriculture and medicine
- What radioactive decay means
- What changes occur in the nucleus of an atom when it undergoes radioactive decay
- How to represent nuclear processes in terms of nuclear equations
- The meaning of half-life and the unit used for radioactivity
- How to carry out calculations on half-life
- The meaning of background activity and how to account for it in experiments
- How to measure the range of nuclear radiations in suitable absorbers
- The dangers associated with radioactivity and how to minimise them
- How to describe fission and fusion in simple terms

Atomic structure and radioactivity

The structure of atoms

We take it for granted today that all matter is made up of **atoms**, but what are atoms made of? Experiments carried out by J.J. Thomson and Lord Rutherford led physicists in the early part of the twentieth century to believe that atoms themselves had a structure.

Evidence for the existence of electrons

When a current goes through a metal wire, the wire gets hot. If the wire is hot enough, it emits negatively-charged particles. If the wire itself is connected to the negative terminal of a battery, these negatively-charged particles are repelled from the wire, called the **cathode**, and can be collected by a positive plate, the **anode**. The wire and plate must be set in a vacuum if the negatively-charged particles are not to be deflected by collisions with gas atoms.

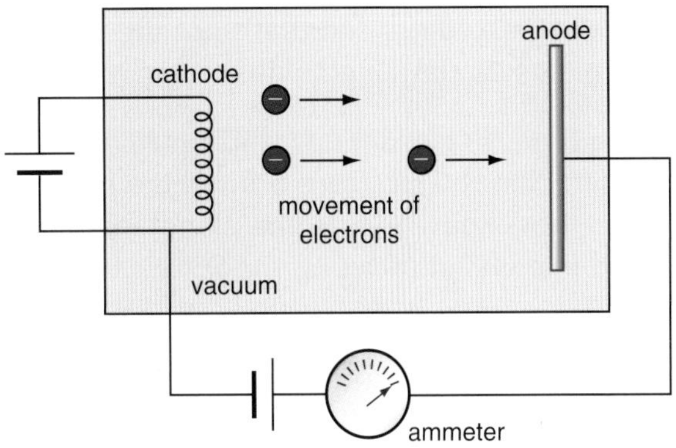

Figure 1 Demonstrating the existence of electrons

The process is called **thermionic emission**. Early in the twentieth century, physicists were able to show that these particles came from the atoms of the metal filament. Thomson called them **electrons**. Their attraction to the positive plate showed clearly that they were negatively charged.

Since these electrons were so easily deflected by a magnet, Thomson knew that they were very, very light compared to the atoms that emitted them. He also realised that since atoms themselves are electrically neutral, there had to be some part of the atom that had a positive charge.

How were the electrons arranged in atoms? One of the earliest models was the 'plum pudding' or 'currant bun' model in which electrons were dotted throughout the atom like currants in a bun. The positive charge was thought to spread throughout the volume like the dough of the bun.

Evidence for the existence of nuclei

Partly to test Thomson's theory, Rutherford suggested that the recently discovered positively-charged α-particles (see page 165) might be fired at a thin gold foil. Most of the α-particles went straight through the foil with little or no deflection. But what really shocked the Rutherford team was that some α-particles were deflected through very large angles and a few even came straight back at them. Rutherford then realised that there had to be something 'hard' inside the atom to cause this strange 'back scattering'. He called it the atomic nucleus.

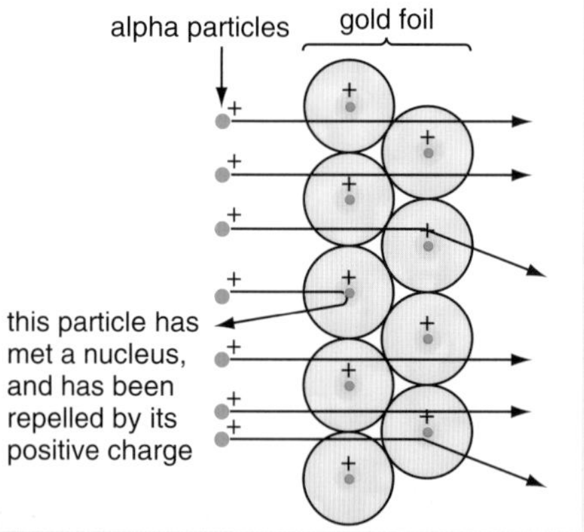
alpha particles
gold foil
this particle has met a nucleus, and has been repelled by its positive charge

Figure 2 Most of the alpha particles pass straight through the gold foil or are slightly deflected. A very few make a 'direct hit' on the nucleus and bounce back

Rutherford argued that since most of the α-particles missed the nucleus it had to be very small. Since it appeared to repel the positively-charged α-particles, the nucleus had to be positively charged. Why did most of the α-particles pass straight through the atom? Rutherford correctly argued that most of the atom was really just empty space.

Finally, Rutherford realised that since the electron was so light, most of the atom's mass was contained within the nucleus itself

Later, in order to explain how certain elements gave out light, Rutherford was to suggest that the electrons orbited the nucleus in circular paths. So the plum pudding model gave way to the planetary model, with the orbiting electrons pictured like planets orbiting the Sun.

Rutherford's gold foil experiment took place around 1909–10. It was not until 1933 that convincing evidence was presented by James Chadwick that there were two different types of particle in the nucleus – uncharged neutrons as well as positively-charged protons.

Did you know?

The nucleus of almost every atom contains protons and neutrons. At one time it was thought that protons and neutrons had no structure, but we now know that both are made of mysterious particles called **quarks**.

The planetary model of the atom

The relative masses and charges of the particles that make up the atom are given in Table 1 below.

Table 1

Particle	Location	Relative mass*	Relative charge*
Proton	Within the nucleus	1	+l
Neutron	Within the nucleus	1	0
Electron	Orbiting the nucleus	1/1840	−l

* Mass and charge are measured in comparison with the proton.

A neutral atom must have the same number of protons as orbiting electrons. Figure 3 shows a helium atom. Since there are two orbiting electrons, there must also be two protons in the nucleus. Note that the diagram is not to scale: the diameter of the atom (about 1×10^{-10} m) is about 100 000 times greater than that of the nucleus (about 1×10^{-15} m).

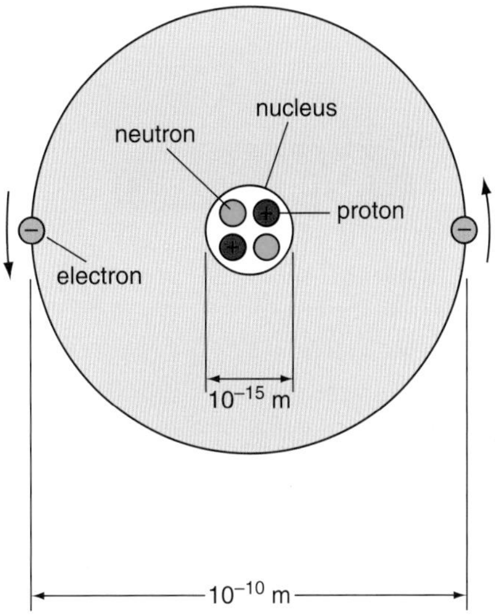

Figure 3 A helium atom

Atomic number and mass number

The number of protons in the nucleus of an atom determines what the atom is. All hydrogen nuclei have one proton, all helium nuclei have two protons, all lithium nuclei have three protons and so on. The number of protons is called the **atomic number** and is given the symbol Z.

As the masss of the electrons is negligible, the total number of particles in the nucleus determines the total mass of an atom. Particles in the nucleus are called **nucleons**, so the **mass number** (or nucleon number) is the sum of the number of protons and the number of neutrons. Mass number is given the symbol A.

> Atomic number, Z = number of protons
> Mass number, A = number of protons + number of neutrons = number of nucleons

Every nucleus can therefore be written in the form: ${}^{A}_{Z}X$

where X is the chemical symbol, A is the mass number and Z is the atomic number.

For example, uranium is given the chemical symbol U. All uranium nuclei have 92 protons in the nucleus. One form of uranium, called uranium-235, has a mass number of 235. This means it has 92 protons and 143 neutrons (235 − 92 = 143). A uranium nucleus is given the symbol:

$${}^{235}_{92}U$$

It is important to realise that this is the symbol for the *nucleus* of the atom. Orbiting electrons are completely ignored.

You will notice that the top number gives the mass of the nucleus and the bottom number gives the charge. This same system can also be used to describe protons, neutrons and electrons.

Proton $^{1}_{1}p$ Neutron $^{1}_{0}n$ Electron $^{0}_{-1}e$

Isotopes

Not all the atoms of the same element have the same mass. For example, one form of helium (helium-3) has three nucleons and another form (helium-4) has four nucleons. But all helium nuclei have two protons. So, helium-3 has two protons and one neutron helium-4 has two protons and two neutrons

Physicists call atoms with the same number of protons but a different number of neutrons **isotopes**. The main isotopes of helium are therefore:

$^{3}_{2}He$ and $^{4}_{2}He$

Questions

1 How many protons, neutrons and electrons are in the nucleus of carbon-14 if its symbol is $^{14}_{6}C$

2 The element sodium has the chemical symbol Na. In a particular sodium isotope there are 12 neutrons. In a neutral sodium atom there are 11 orbiting electrons. Write down the symbol for the nucleus of this isotope

3 In what way are the nuclei of isotopes the same? In what way are they different?

Radioactivity

In 1896, the French scientist Henri Becquerel discovered that certain rocks containing uranium gave out strange radiation that could penetrate paper and fog photographic film. He called the effect **radioactivity**. His students, Pierre and Marie Curie, were later to identify three separate types of radiation. Unsure of a suitable name, the Curies called them alpha (α), beta (β) and gamma (γ) radiation afler the first three letters of the Greek alphabet. For their work on radioactivity, the Curies and Henri Becquerel were jointly awarded the Nobel Prize for Physics in 1903

Radioactive material is found naturally all around us and inside our bodies. A small number of carbon atoms are radioactive carbon-14 isotopes. They are found in the carbon dioxide in the air and in the cells of all living organisms. Traces of radioactive elements, for example potassium, can be found in our food. Certain rocks contain uranium, all the isotopes of which are radioactive, and this decays giving radon, a radioactive gas. There is also radiation reaching Earth from outer space. All these natural sources are known together as **background radiation**.

Did you know?

The only Irishman to have won a Nobel Prize for Physics was E.T.S. Walton. His award was for building and using one of the earliest accelerators or 'atom-smashers'. Until recently, his daughter was teaching Physics in Belfast.

Ionising radiation

The nuclei of some atoms are unstable and emit radiation. This is known as **ionising radiation** because as it passes through matter, it causes some of the atoms to become ions.

Figure 4 An unstable nucleus emitting a particle and a ray

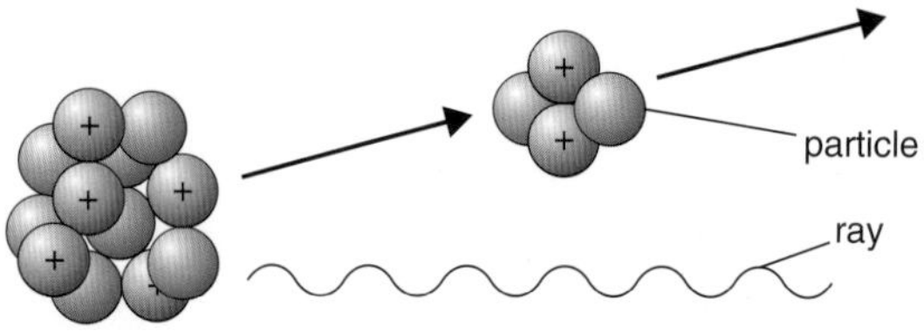

Types of radiation

Alpha (α) radiation

- Alpha radiation is made up of a stream of alpha particles emitted from large nuclei.
- An alpha particle is a helium nucleus with two protons and two neutrons, and so has a relative atomic mass of 4.
- Alpha particles are positively charged and so will be deflected in a magnetic field.
- Alpha particles have poor powers of penetration and can only travel through a few centimetres of air. They can easily be stopped by a sheet of paper.
- Alpha radiation has the strongest ionising power.

Beta (β) radiation

- Beta radiation is made up of a stream of beta particles emitted from nuclei where the number of neutrons is much larger than the number of protons.
- A beta particle is a fast electron which has been formed in the nucleus and thus it has relative atomic mass of about $^{1}/_{1840}$.
- As beta particles are negatively charged, they will be deflected in a magnetic field. This deflection will be greater than that of alpha particles, as the beta particles have much smaller mass.
- Beta particles move much faster than alpha particles and so have a greater penetrating power.
- Beta particles can travel several metres in air, but will be stopped by 5 mm thick aluminium foil.
- Beta radiation has an ionising power between that of alpha and gamma radiation.

Gamma (γ) radiation

- Unlike the other types of radiation, gamma radiation does not consist of particles but of high-energy waves.
- Like alpha and beta radiation, gamma radiation comes from a disintegrating unstable nucleus.
- As there are no particles, gamma radiation has no mass.
- As there are no charged particles, a magnetic field has no effect on gamma radiation.
- Gamma radiation has great penetrating power, travelling several metres in air.
- A thick block of lead or concrete is used to greatly reduce the effects of gamma radiation, but is not able to stop it completely.
- Gamma radiation has the weakest ionising power.

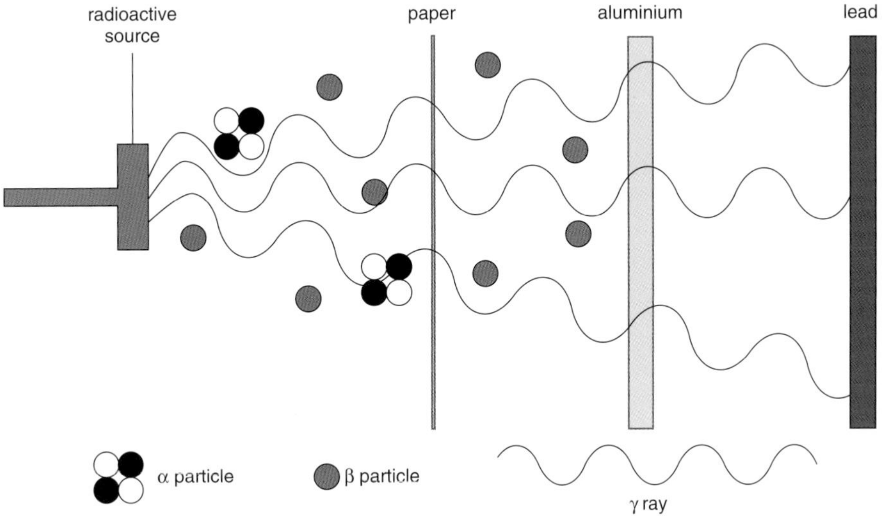

Figure 5 Selective absorption of radioactive emissions

Uses of radiation

1 Carbon dating of organic material. All living organisms contain some carbon-14. When the organism is alive, the ratio of carbon-12 to carbon-14 remains constant. Once the organism dies, the amount of carbon-14 decreases as the radioactive isotope decays. Comparing the amount of carbon-14 present in a sample with the amount in a living organism allows calculation of the age of the sample. Fortunately carbon-14 has a long half-life (see page 168) and so decays slowly. This method was used to date the Dead Sea Scrolls.

2 Gamma radiation from the cobalt-60 isotope can be used to treat tumours.

3 Gamma radiation can be used to treat fresh food. By killing bacteria on the food, the radiation helps the food to keep for longer. The use is controversial, however, as many people are worried about the long-term effects on the human body of eating irradiated food.

4 Surgical instruments and hospital dressings can be sterilised by exposure to gamma radiation.

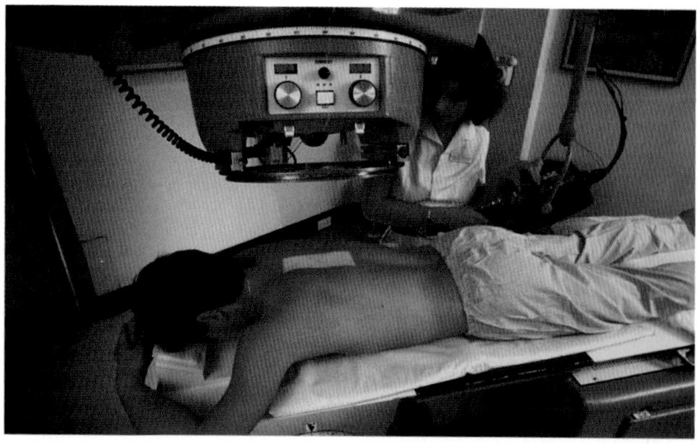

Figure 6 Radiotherapy involves the use of radioactive materials to treat cancers

Figure 7 Operating equipment is sterilised by gamma rays

Figure 8 Using a beta source to control the thickness of an aluminium sheet

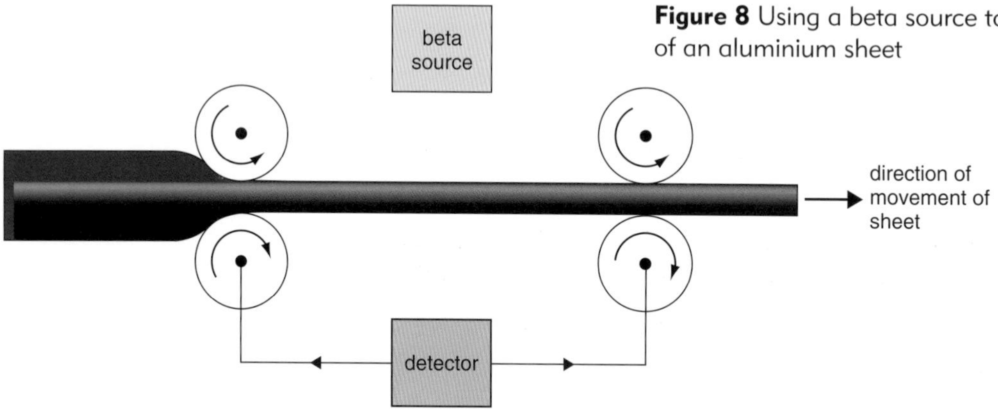

5 Beta radiation can be used to monitor the thickness of a sheet of paper or aluminium. An emitter is placed on one side of the sheet and a detector on the other. As the sheet moves past, the activity detected will be the same as long as the thickness remains unchanged.

6 A suitable radioactive isotope can be used to provide information about fluid movement and mixing to monitor, for example, leaks in underground pipes.

Figure 9 Radioactive tracers can be used to locate a leak in a pipe

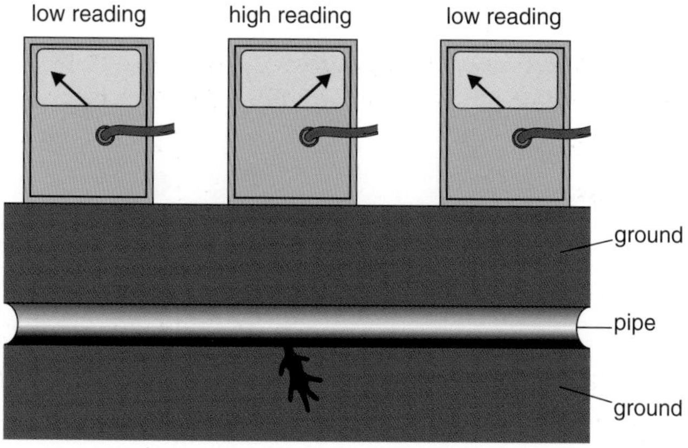

7 Iodine-131 is used in investigations of the thyroid gland.

Great care must be taken when using radioactive isotopes because the radiation can damage living cells by altering the structure of the cell's chemicals. Protective clothing must be worn and the amount of time that the worker is exposed to the radiation must be strictly controlled. Radioactive isotopes that are taken internally are usually not alpha emitters, as they are such powerful ionisers, and they must have a short half-life so that they do not remain for too long in the tissues.

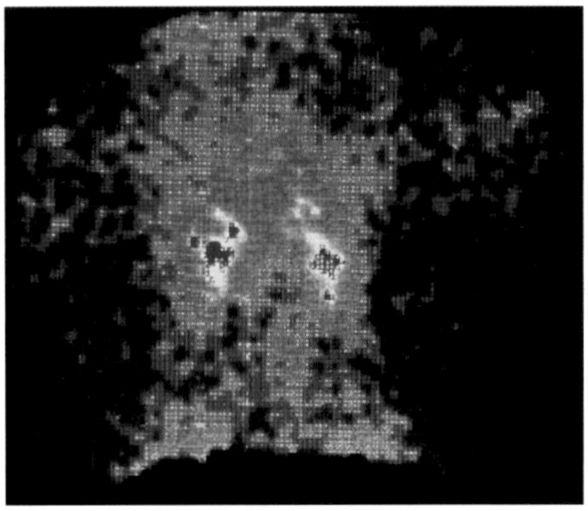

Figure 10 This scan shows radioactive iodine-131 localised in the thyroid gland

Nuclear equations

Symbol equations can be written to represent alpha and beta decay. The alpha particle can be written as ${}^{4}_{2}\alpha$ or ${}^{4}_{2}\mathrm{He}$ and the beta particle as ${}^{0}_{-1}\beta$ or ${}^{0}_{-1}\mathrm{e}$.

Examples

1 Alpha decay of uranium-238

$${}^{238}_{92}\mathrm{U} \rightarrow {}^{234}_{90}\mathrm{Th} + {}^{4}_{2}\mathrm{He}\ (\text{or } \alpha)$$

2 Beta decay of carbon-14

$${}^{14}_{6}\mathrm{C} \rightarrow {}^{14}_{7}\mathrm{N} + {}^{0}_{-1}\mathrm{e}\ (\text{or } \beta)$$

When writing symbol equations it is important to remember the following:

- the total mass number on the left-hand side must equal the total mass number on the right-hand side
- the total atomic number on one side must equal the total atomic number on the other side.

If you know the original isotope and that formed by the decay, it is possible to determine the type of decay by working out the type of particle emitted.

If you know the original isotope and the type of decay, you can work out the isotope that is formed by the decay.

Example

Radium-226 decays to polonium-222. Radium (Ra) has atomic number 86 and polonium (Po) has atomic number 84. Which type of decay occurs?

$${}^{226}_{86}\mathrm{Ra} \rightarrow {}^{222}_{84}\mathrm{Po} + {}^{a}_{b}\mathrm{X}$$

mass number: $226 = 222 + a$

$a = 226 - 222 = 4$

atomic number: $86 = 84 + b$

$b = 86 - 84 = 2$

The particle with a mass number of 4 and an atomic number of 2 is helium and so X is an alpha particle. The type of decay is alpha decay.

Questions

4 Work out the type of decay in each of the following examples:
a) Bismuth-213 to polonium-213.
b) Radium-226 to radon-222.
c) Francium-221 to actinium-217.

5 Work out the name and mass number of the isotope formed in each of the following examples:
a) Alpha decay of polonium-214.
b) Beta decay of lead-212.
c) Beta decay of thallium-210.

6 a) How does the value of the mass number change in alpha decay?
b) How does the value of the atomic number change in alpha decay?
c) How does the value of the mass number change in beta decay?
d) How does the value of the atomic number change in beta decay?

Half-life

As a radioactive isotope decays, the activity of the sample decreases.

The half-life of an isotope is defined as the time taken for the radioactivity to fall by half.

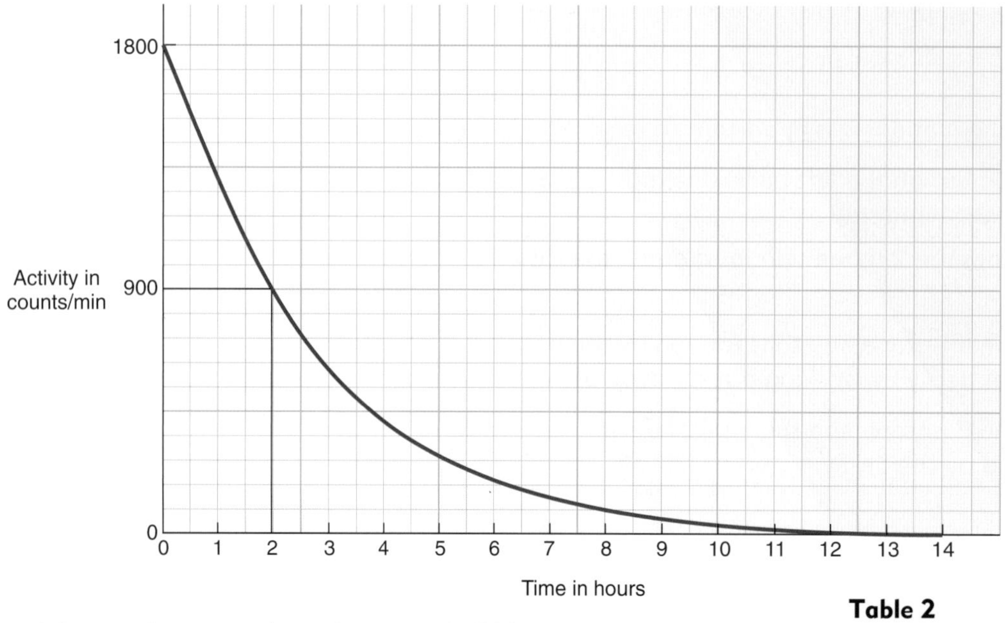

Figure 11 The radioactive decay curve for a substance with a half-life of 2 hours

Each isotope has a specific and constant half-life. Some half-lives are very short – a matter of seconds or even a fraction of a second – and others can be thousands of years. Table 2 gives the half-lives of some common radioactive isotopes.

Table 2

Isotope	Half-life
Uranium-238	4 500 000 000 years
Carbon-14	5730 years
Phosphorus-30	2.5 minutes
Oxygen-15	2.06 minutes
Barium-144	11.4 seconds
Polonium-216	0.145 seconds

The unit of radioactivity

Radioactivity only occurs when unstable nuclei decay. The greater the number of disintegrations taking place every second, the greater is the radioactivity. The unit for radioactivity is the **Becquerel** (Bq).
1 Bq = 1 disintegration per second.

Examples of half-life calculations

1 What mass of nitrogen-13 would remain if 80 g were allowed to decay for 30 minutes? Nitrogen-13 has a half-life of 10 minutes.

Mass of nitrogen-13 remaining	Time in half-lives	Time in minutes
80 g	0	0
40 g	1	10
20 g	2	20
10 g	3	30

Answer: 10 g would remain after 30 minutes.

2 How long would it take for 20 g of cobalt-60 to decay to 5 g? The half-life of cobalt-60 is 5.26 years.
20 g to 10 g takes 5.26 years
10 g to 5 g takes another 5.26 years

Answer: total time taken is 10.52 years.

3 Strontium-93 takes 32 minutes to decay to 6.25% of its original mass. Calculate the value of its half-life.

% of strontium-93 remaining	Time in half-lives	Time in minutes
100	0	
50	1	
25	2	
12.5	3	
6.25	4	32

So 4 half-lives take 32 minutes. Each half-life $= \frac{32}{4}$ minutes $= 8$ minutes.

Answer: The half-life of strontium-93 is 8 minutes.

4 When a radioactive material of half-life 24 hours arrives in a hospital its activity is 1000 Bq. Calculate its activity 24 hours before and 72 hours after its arrival.

Activity in Bq	Time in half-lives	Time in hours
2000	−1	−24
1000 (start from here)	0	0
500	1	24
250	2	48
125	3	72

Answer: Activity 24 hours before arrival is 2000 Bq.
Activity 72 hours after arrival is 125 Bq.

5 Plot the graph of activity (y-axis) against time (x-axis) using the data in Question 4. Start the graph from time = 0 and activity = 1000 Bq. Use the graph to find the activity 36 hours after the material arrives at the hospital.

Answer: From graph, about 355 Bq.

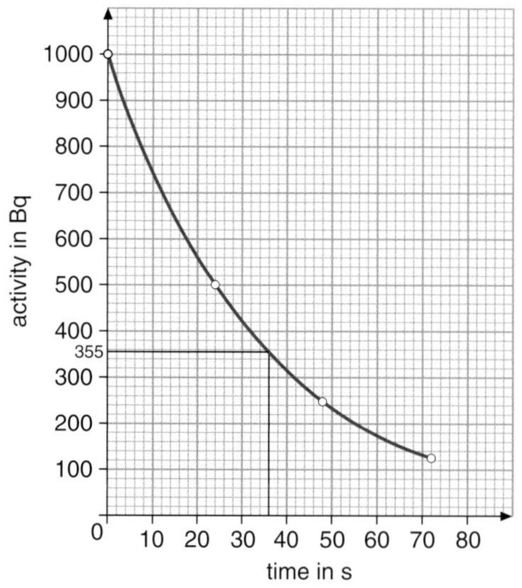

Practical work with radioactive materials

Students under the age of 16 are advised that they are expressly forbidden to handle radioactive sources.

The most common type of radiation detector is the **Geiger-Müller tube** (GM-tube) connected to a counter or ratemeter.

When alpha, beta or gamma radiation enters the GM tube, it causes some of the argon gas inside to ionise and give an electrical discharge. This discharge is detected and counted by the counter. If the counter is connected to its internal speaker, you can hear the click when radiation enters the tube.

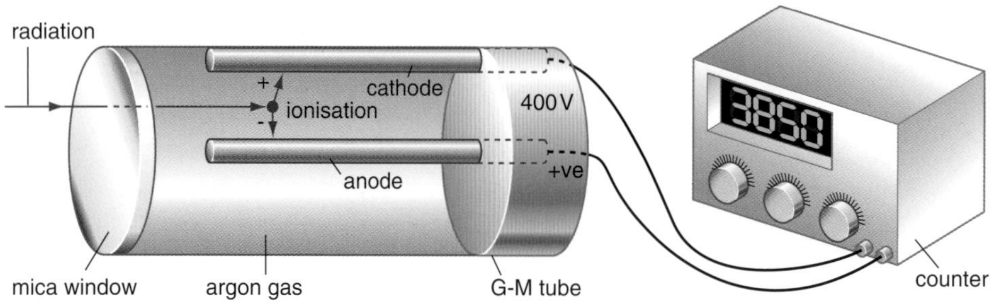

Figure 12 Section through a GM tube

It is not necessary to know how a GM tube works, but it is important to know how it could be used to do practical work on radiation.

To measure the background radiation

First remove known sources of radiation from the laboratory, then set the GM counter to zero. Switch on the counter and start a stopwatch. After 30 minutes read the count on the counter. Divide the count by 30 to obtain the background count rate in counts per minute. A typical figure is around 15 counts per minute. Fortunately, the background count in Northern Ireland does not present a serious health risk.

The background count must always be subtracted from any other count when measuring the activity from a specific source.

Precautions when using closed radioactive sources in schools

- Always store the sources in a lead-lined box, under lock and key, when not required for experimental use.
- Always handle sources using tongs, holding the source at arm's length and pointing it away from any bystander.
- Always work quickly and methodically with sources to minimise the dose to the user.

Measuring the approximate range of radiation

Alpha

- Place a GM tube on a wooden cradle and connect it to a ratemeter.
- Hold an alpha source directly in front of the window of the tube and slowly increase the distance between the source and the tube. At about 3 cm (depending on the source used) the ratemeter reading falls dramatically to that of background radiation.
- Place a thin piece of paper in contact with the window of the GM tube. Bring the alpha source up to the paper so that the casing of the source touches it. The reading on the ratemeter is no greater than the background count showing that the alpha particles are unable to penetrate the paper.

Beta

- Place a 1 mm thick piece of aluminium in contact with the window of the GM tube.
- Bring the beta source up to the aluminium so that the casing of the source touches it.
- The reading on the ratemeter is observed to be significantly above the background count, showing that some beta particles have penetrated the aluminium.
- Repeat the process with 2 mm, 3 mm, etc. thick pieces of aluminium. At about 5 mm there is a significant reduction in the count rate on the ratemeter, indicating the approximate range of beta particles in aluminium.

Gamma

If the beta particle experiment is repeated with a gamma source, there is practically no reduction in the count rate for a 5 mm thick piece of aluminium . If the aluminium sheets are replaced with lead, it will be found that even school sources will give gamma radiation that can easily penetrate several centimetres of lead.

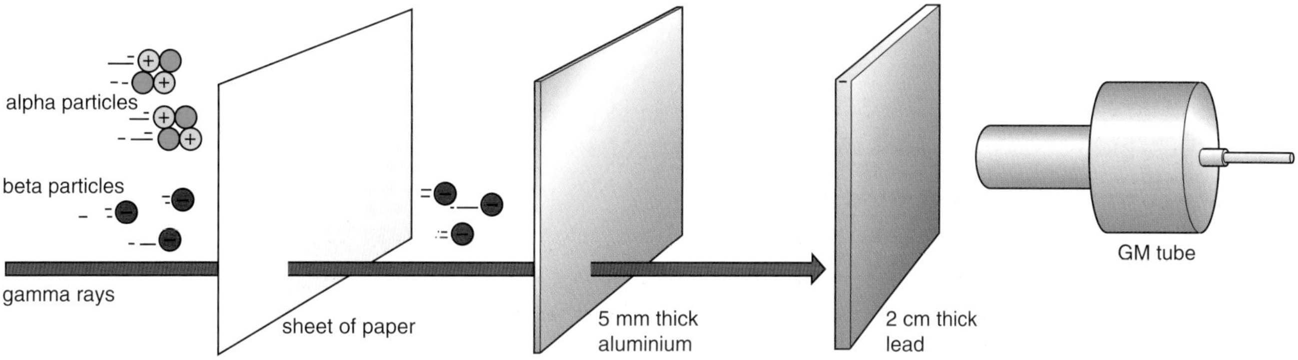

Figure 13 The penetrative range of the three types of radiation

Nuclear fission and nuclear fusion

Nuclear fission

Radioactivity involves the random disintegration of an unstable nucleus. But some heavy nuclei, like those of uranium, can actually be forced to split into two lighter nuclei. The process is called **nuclear fission**. This usually comes about as a result of the heavy nucleus being struck by a slow neutron. The heavy nucleus splits and the fragments move apart at very high speed, carrying with them a vast amount of energy. At the same time, two or three fast neutrons are also emitted. These are the fission neutrons. The fission neutrons go on to produce further fission and so create a chain reaction.

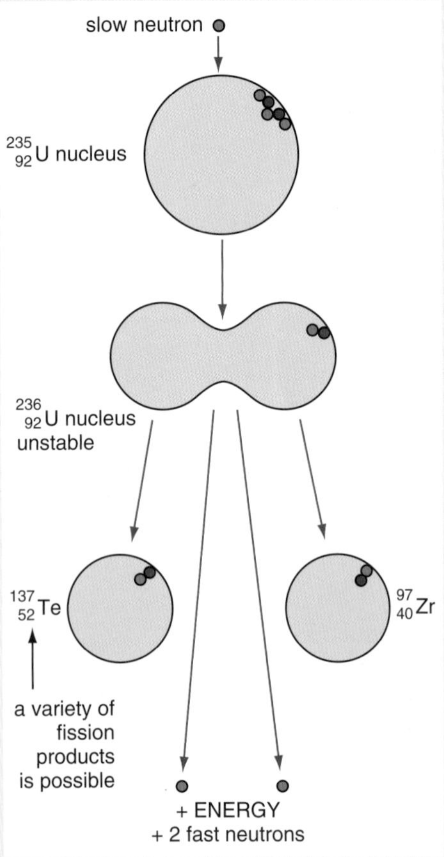

Figure 14a The fission of a uranium-235 nucleus

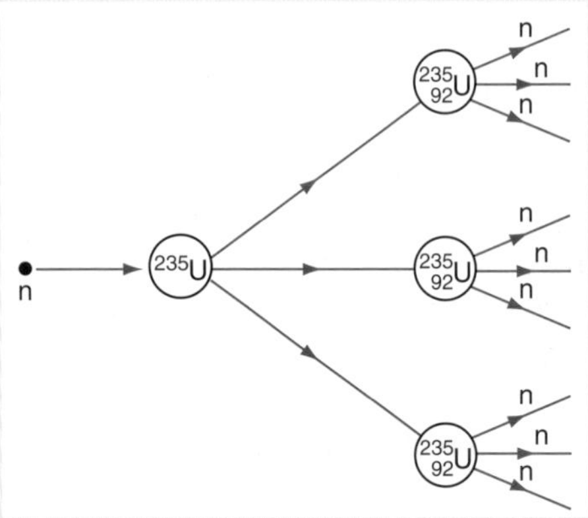

b A chain reaction in uranium-235

Just how much energy is emitted in fission? The fission of a single uranium nucleus produces about 40 000 times more energy than would be produced by a single carbon atom (in coal) reacting with oxygen to produce carbon dioxide. Physicists did not take long to realise the huge potential for energy production using nuclear fission.

In a nuclear power station, steps are taken to ensure that, on average, just one of the fission neutrons goes on to produce further fission. This is **controlled nuclear fission**. The heat produced in the reaction is used to turn water into steam and drive a turbine to generate electricity. In a nuclear bomb there is no attempt to control the fission process.

Did you know?

Some waste materials from nuclear power stations will remain radioactive for tens of thousands of years. The best way to deal with the storage of these materials remains a challenge for physicists and engineers.

A major disadvantage of all fission processes is that the fission fragments are almost always highly radioactive. This type of radioactive waste is extremely dangerous and expensive measures must be taken to store it until the level of activity is sufficiently small. In some cases this means the waste must be stored deep underground, in a vitrified (glass-like) state, for tens of thousands of years. The danger is that over time, the containers may leak and cause underground water pollution. A further danger comes from earthquakes. Earthquakes can rupture containers of radioactive waste buried underground, causing the radioactive material to leak into the soil and water sources. Even in Britain there are over 200 earthquakes every year, many so weak that they are barely recorded. But as recently as September 2002, there was an earthquake in Britain of magnitude 4.8, strong enough to be felt by people asleep in their beds in the city of Birmingham.

Nuclear fusion

This is the process which goes on in stars like our Sun. At the centre of the Sun the temperature is about 15 000 000°C. At this temperature, the nuclei of atoms are all stripped of their orbiting electrons and they are moving at a tremendous speed. Being positively charged, the nuclei would normally repel each other, but if they are moving fast enough, they can join (or fuse) to form a new nucleus.

In the Sun, hydrogen isotopes known as tritium (or hydrogen-3) and deuterium (hydrogen-2) collide and fuse to create a new nucleus, helium-4. This causes the release of a vast amount of energy, some of which eventually reaches Earth as electromagnetic radiation.

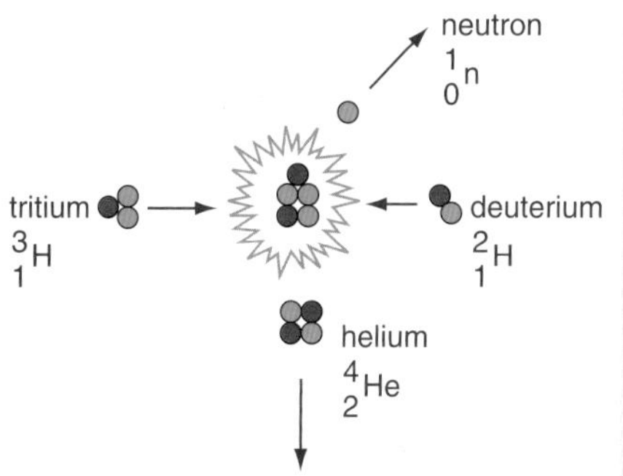

Figure 15 The fusion of deuterium and tritium

There are many attempts to obtain controlled nuclear fusion on Earth. One research centre is at Culham in Oxfordshire. But so far, physicists have faced major difficulties. One is the problem of how to contain the reacting plasma at a high enough temperature and for a sufficiently long time for the reaction to take place. If we learn how to control nuclear fusion here on Earth, the rewards will be enormous. We will have an almost unlimited source of energy (from the hydrogen in sea water) with harmless waste products (inert helium nuclei).

Websites

Use your favourite search engine (such as **www.google.com** or **www.excite.com**) and search using the keywords:

atomic + nucleus	radioactivity
proton	nuclear + fission
neutron	nuclear + fusion
electron	half-life

http://www.environment.detr.gov.uk/radioactivity/physics/index.htm

http://www.astro.soton.ac.uk/~ajb/fission.html

Exam questions

1 a) The table below shows the particles that make up a neutral carbon atom. Copy and complete the table showing the mass, charge, number and location of the particles. Some information has already been added to the table

Particle	Mass	Charge	Number	Location
Electron		−1		
Neutron	1		6	In the nucleus
Proton			6	

(7 marks)

b) Radon is a naturally-occurring radioactive gas.

(i) Explain what is meant by radioactive. *(2 marks)*

(ii) Explain the danger of breathing radon gas into the lungs. *(2 marks)*

(iii) Explain, in terms of the particles that make up the nucleus, the meaning of isotope. *(2 marks)*

c) A student investigates the decay of a radioactive substance. She measures the corrected count rate of the substance every 20 minutes.

(i) At the start the count rate was 800 counts per minute. Copy the graph below and plot this point and four more points that she found. The half-life of the radioactive substance is 20 minutes. *(5 marks)*

(ii) Draw a smooth curve through the plotted points. *(1 mark)*

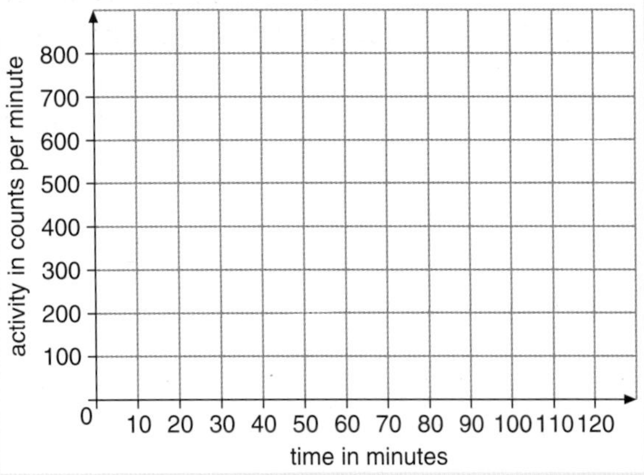

d) (i) The range of beta radiation in aluminium is several millimetres. Explain what this means. *(1 mark)*

(ii) Draw a neat and well-labelled diagram of the assembled apparatus that could be used to measure the range of beta particles in aluminium. *(3 marks)*

(iii) What measurements would be taken during this experiment? *(3 marks)*

(iv) How would you use these measurements to find the range of beta particles in aluminium? *(2 marks)*

(v) Sketch the graph that you would expect to obtain from these measurements and mark on it the range of the beta radiation. Label each axis. *(2 marks)*

2 a) The isotope $^{14}C_6$ changes into an isotope of nitrogen when it emits a beta particle. The chemical symbol for nitrogen is N. Write down an equation involving atomic numbers and mass numbers to describe this reaction. *(4 marks)*

b) A radioactive isotope of gold emits gamma rays. It is injected into a patient's bloodstream and used to study the working of the patient's heart. The gamma radiation emitted by the gold is detected outside the patient's body by a device called a gamma camera.

(i) Why would a radioactive isotope that emits alpha radiation be unsuitable for this purpose? *(2 marks)*

To check the half-life of this isotope of gold, a radiographer measured the activity of a sample of the isotope every 10 s. He then corrected for the background activity. His measurements are shown in the table below.

Corrected activity in counts per second	400	320	250	198	160	100	80
Time in seconds	0	10	20	30	40	60	70

(ii) What causes background activity and how did the radiographer correct his measurements?

(2 marks)

(iii) Using the measurements above plot a graph of corrected activity (y-axis) against time (x-axis).

(5 marks)

(iv) Use the graph to find the half-life of gold. Show clearly how you use the graph to obtain the best value of this half-life.

(2 marks)

3 A radioactive decay series can be represented on a graph of mass number, A, against atomic number, Z. Part of a table for such a series is given below:

Element (symbol)	Atomic number	Mass number	Decays by emitting	Leaving element
U	92	238	α	Th
Th	90	234	β	Pa
Pa	91	234	β	U
U	92 90	234 230	α	 Ra
Ra	88	226		Rn
Rn	86			Po
Po		222	β	At
At			α	Bi

a) In what ways do mass number and atomic number change in (i) α-decay and (ii) β-decay?

(4 marks)

b) Copy and complete the table above.

(3 marks)

c) Plot the points on a graph of mass number (y-axis) against atomic number (x-axis) to show the decay of each element. Join the points with arrows to show the decay.

(5 marks)

d) Explain why the emission of a gamma wave cannot be shown on such a graph.

(1 mark)

e) Identify two pairs of isotopes using the table.

(2 marks)

4 A sample containing 100 grams of a uranium isotope arrives at a factory. The table below shows how the mass of the isotope changes over time.

Mass of isotope in grams	Time in days
100	0
72	10
52	20
37	30
27	40

a) Explain the meaning of the following words: (i) half-life and (ii) isotope

(2 marks)

b) Plot the graph of mass of isotope (y-axis) against time (x-axis).

(4 marks)

c) From the graph calculate as accurately as possible the half-life of this isotope.

(2 marks)

d) Estimate the mass of the uranium present in the sample three weeks *before* it arrived in the factory.

(2 marks)

5 A certain material has a half-life of 12 minutes. What proportion of that material would you expect still to be present an hour later?

(3 marks)

6 A detector of radiation is placed close to a radioactive source of very long half-life. In four consecutive 10 second intervals, the following number of counts were recorded: 100, 107, 99, 102. Why were the four counts different?

(2 marks)

Chapter 8

Earth in space

Learning objectives

By the end of this chapter you should know:

- The position of the Sun and the planets within the Solar System
- The historical development of a heliocentric Solar System
- How to explain changes in day length and the seasons
- The effect of gravity on the movement of planets, comets and satellites
- The idea that gravitational force decreases with distance and increases with mass
- The idea that the Universe is made up of a very large number of galaxies and that our Solar System is called the Milky Way
- Why red shift is evidence for an expanding Universe
- The Big Bang and Steady State models for the creation of the Universe
- How stars are formed
- How to explain nuclear fusion in stars
- How to explain the concept of a light year
- What the search for extra-terrestrial intelligence involves

The Solar System

We now know that the Earth is one of nine **planets** which travel around the Sun. Each planet travels in an elliptical path and with the exception of Mercury and Venus, they all have at least one moon. Other objects also **orbit** the Sun. These are the **comets** and the **asteroids**. Table 1 below gives some data about the planets.

Table 1 Some data on the nine planets orbiting the Sun

Planet	Planet diameter compared with Earth	Average distance of planet from Sun compared with Earth	Time to orbit the Sun compared with Earth	Number of moons
Mercury	0.4	0.4	0.2	0
Venus	0.9	0.7	0.6	0
Earth	1.0	1.0	1.0	1
Mars	0.5	1.5	1.9	2
Jupiter	11.2	5.2	12.0	14
Saturn	9.4	9.5	29.0	24
Uranus	4.1	19.1	84.0	15
Neptune	3.9	30.1	165.0	3
Pluto	0.4	39.4	248.0	1

The orbits of the inner planets are almost circular with the Sun at the centre. The orbits of the other planets are much more elliptical (like a rugby ball). The orbit of Pluto is so elliptical that at times it is closer to the Sun than Neptune. Pluto's orbit is different from the other planets in another important respect. All the planets orbit the Sun in the same plane, except Pluto.

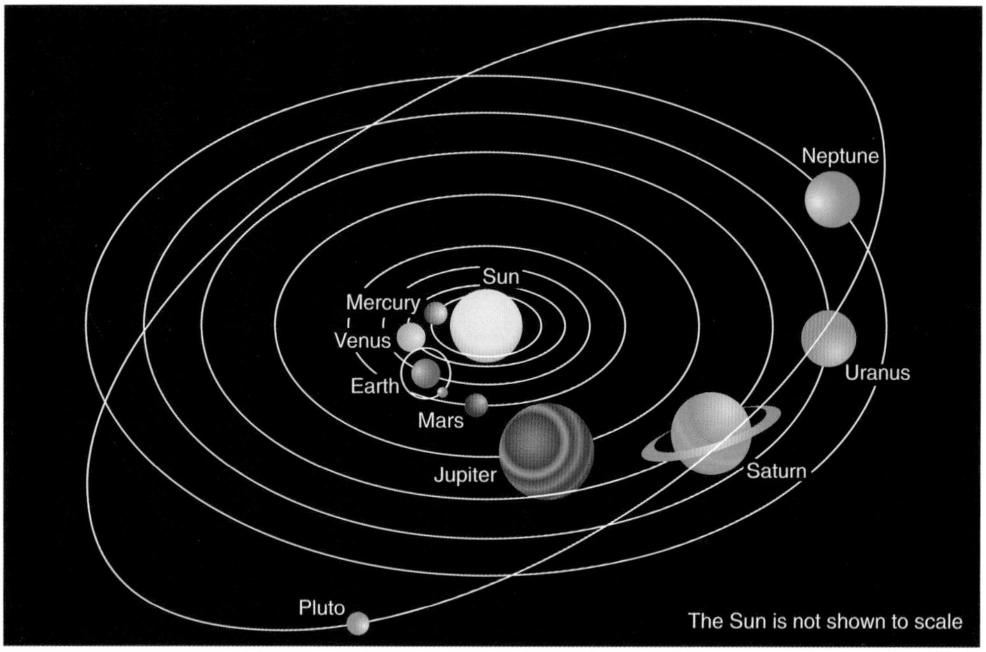

Figure 1 The Solar System

Heliocentric or geocentric

The model of the **Solar System** just described is called a **heliocentric** theory because it places the Sun at the centre of our Solar System. But the heliocentric theory is only one of many which man has used to explain the motion of the planets across the sky. Most early theories are **geocentric**, placing the Earth at the centre of the Universe.

About 500 BC the Greek mathematician Pythagoras proposed a geocentric theory. Pythagoras taught that the heavenly bodies orbited the Earth on crystal spheres: the inner spheres carried the Moon and the planets, the outer sphere, called the celestial sphere, carried the stars. He believed that the closer the sphere was to the Earth, the slower it rotated. This model allowed Pythagoras to explain the motion of the Sun, the Moon and the planets as seen from Earth. Unfortunately, the model was unable to explain why some planets, like Jupiter, appear to make strange loops as they travel across the sky.

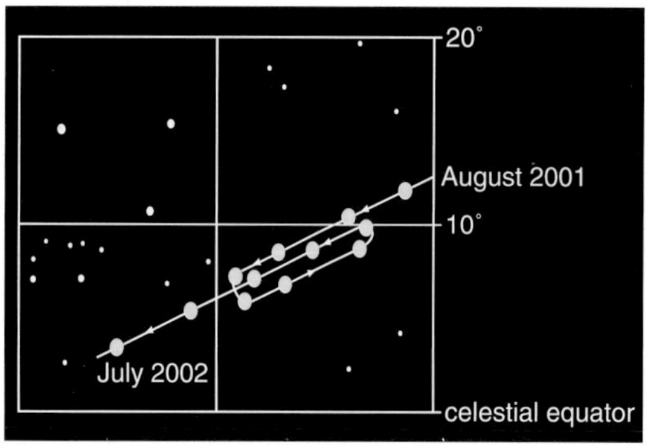

Figure 2 This simulation shows Jupiter's retrograde loop during 2001 and 2002. The position of Jupiter is marked at one-month intervals

Around AD 120, the Egyptian astronomer Ptolemy put forward an idea to explain why some planets show their strange motion across the sky. Like Pythagoras, Ptolemy believed that the Earth was at the centre of the Universe. Ptolemy also believed that the planets orbited the Earth in 'epicycles'. Figure 3 applies Ptolemy's idea to Jupiter.

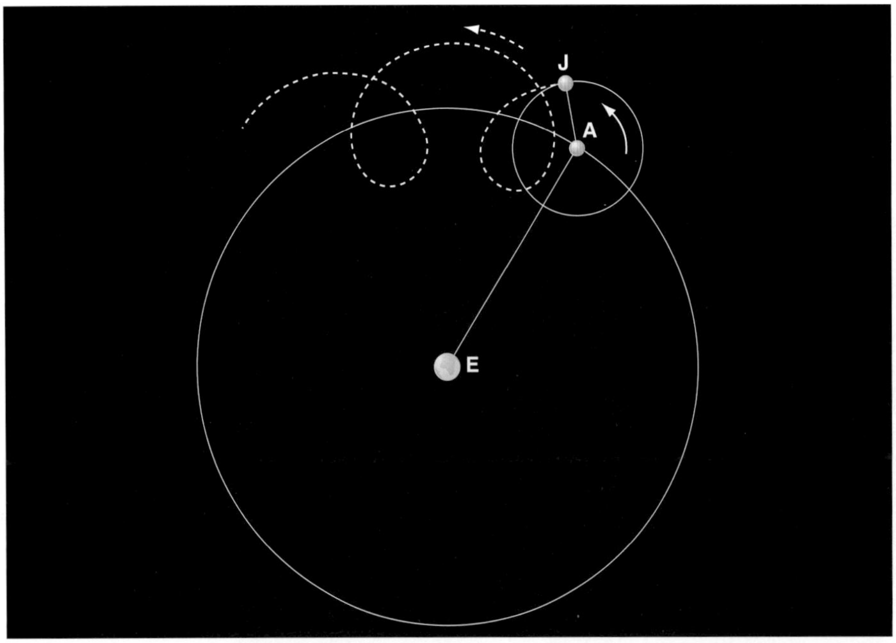

Figure 3 Ptolemy explained the loops of planets with this construction of 'epicycles'

Arm EA rotates around the Earth every 12 years, but at the same time arm AJ rotates around J once a year. The position of J (Jupiter) is the result of the combined movement of EA and AJ.

What is wrong with Ptolemy's theory? The main problem is that Ptolemy's system was not based on experimental evidence and observation, and the planetary motion it describes appears highly unlikely. In addition, there were so many other things that the theory could not explain. Why did the Moon show phases? Why was it that sometimes Venus was brighter than Mars and sometimes Mars was brighter than Venus?

All this changed when Nicholas Copernicus put forward a revolutionary idea in the early part of the sixteenth century. Copernicus' model placed the Sun at the centre of our Solar System, with the planets in orbit around it. Copernicus explained the different shapes (phases) of the Moon by saying that the Moon was in orbit around the Earth. After careful observation of the planets, Copernicus was able to prove convincingly that the order of the planets from the Sun was as they are listed today.

Copernicus was also able to:

- explain that the apparent 'looping' of planets was due to the combined motion of the Earth and the planet itself
- explain that at some times, Venus is closer to Earth than Mars, so it appears brighter, but at other times Venus is further away than Mars and appears less bright
- predict that Venus and Mercury should show phases, just as our Moon does.

Then in 1610, an Italian astronomer, Galileo Galilei, used a new invention, the telescope, to observe the planets. Just as Copernicus had predicted, Galileo observed the phases of Venus. When he turned his telescope to Jupiter, he saw what he first took to be new stars. But if they were stars, their motion was very strange indeed, for they appeared to change position over just a few hours. It did not take long for Galileo to realise that what he was looking at were some of Jupiter's many moons.

Galileo firmly believed in the heliocentric model put forward by Copernicus. But many opposed him and none was more powerful than the Pope. In the seventeenth century, the church taught that the Earth was the centre of God's creation and strongly disapproved of those who believed otherwise. Galileo was eventually imprisoned in his own home and forced not to teach his new ideas to anyone. Only after many years did the church change its position and admit that our Solar System is heliocentric and arranged as Galileo and Copernicus believed.

The four seasons

Every 24 hours the Earth spins once on its axis. When a person faces the Sun, it is day; when a person faces away from the Sun, it is night.

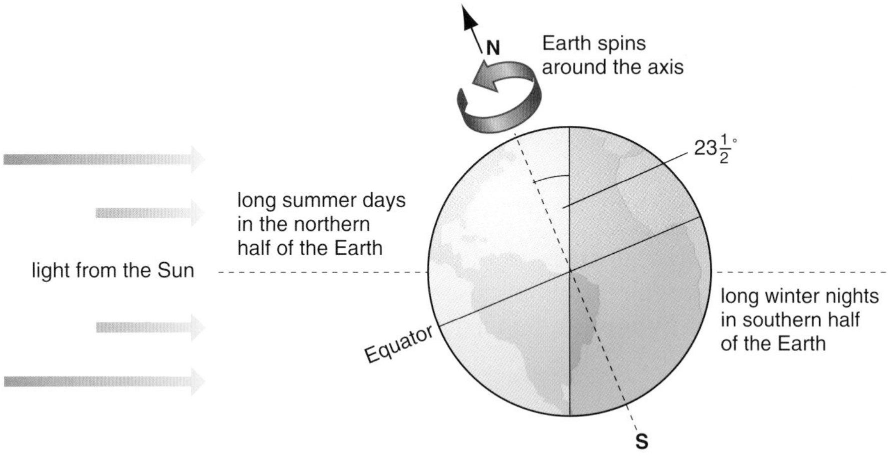

Figure 4 Why we have day and night

The Earth takes approximately $365\frac{1}{4}$ days to orbit the Sun. If there are 365 days in a 'normal' year, an extra day needs to be added every fourth year to make up for the four one-quarter days lost. This is called a **leap year**.

Figure 5 shows the yearly path of the Earth around the Sun.

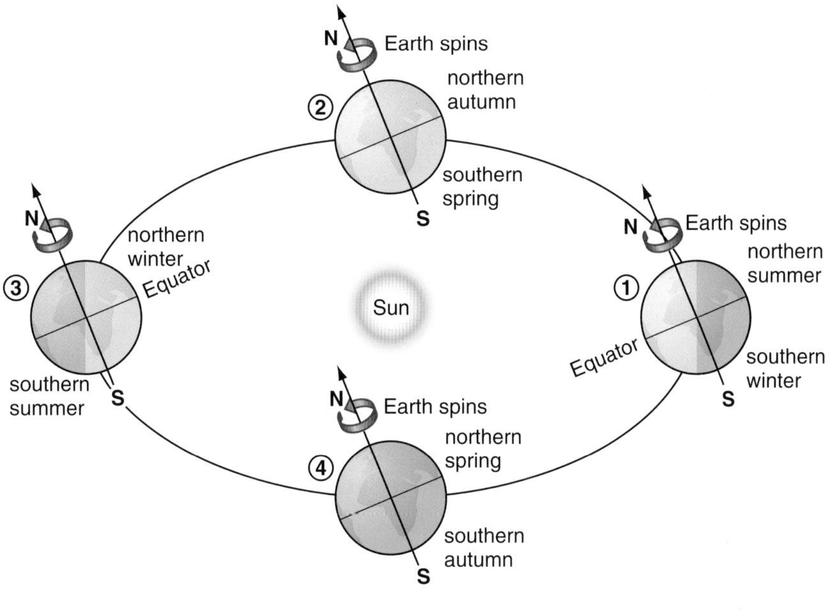

Figure 5 How the path of the Earth around the Sun explains the seasons

As the Earth goes round the Sun it spins on a tilted axis running between the North and South poles. This tilted axis is responsible for the **seasons** on Earth.

In the middle of Britain's summer, the axis in the northern hemisphere is tilted towards the Sun (position 1). At this time it is midwinter in the southern hemisphere. In the middle of Britain's winter, the northern axis tilts away from the Sun (position 3). At this time it is midsummer in the southern hemisphere.

Position 2 is midway between northern summer (position 1) and northern winter (position 3) so it represents northern autumn (or southern spring). Likewise, position 4 is midway between northern winter (position 3) and northern summer (position 1) so it represents northern spring (or southern autumn).

When drawing diagrams of this sort it is important that the axis of the Earth always points in the same direction. On looking at the diagram, all axes must appear parallel to each other.

Shadows

Suppose we measured the length of our shadow on different days in the year. To make the test fair, assume the length of the shadow is measured at the same time of day. There is no surprise in finding that the length of our shadow is longest in winter and shortest in summer. But why is this so?

The answer is that the Sun appears to be highest in the sky in summer and lowest in winter. Figure 6 shows the way in which the Sun appears to move across the sky at different times of the year. When the Sun is high in the sky (in summer), a person's shadow is short. When the Sun is low in the sky (in winter), their shadow is long.

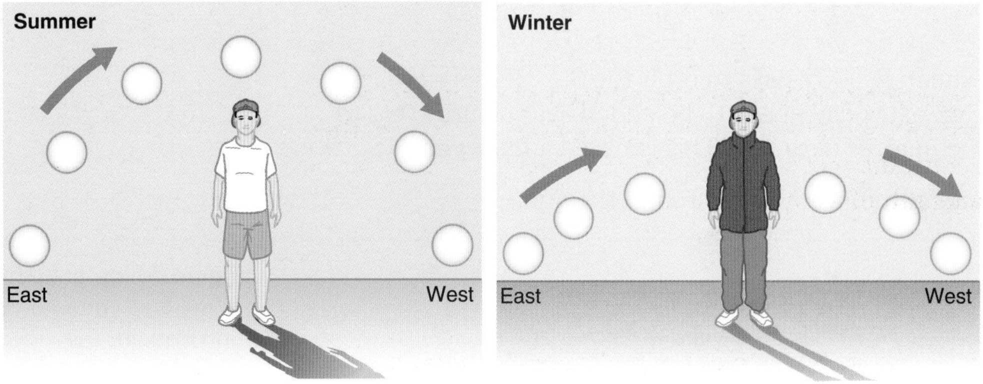

Figure 6 How the Sun appears to move at different times of the year

Gravitation

By the early seventeenth century scientists were convinced that the planets orbited the Sun. But why did they do so? It took Isaac Newton, in around 1665, to put forward a revolutionary idea that would change the way matter was looked at.

Newton's idea was that any two masses in the Universe attract each other, just like the opposite poles of a magnet do. This force between masses is the force of **gravity**. The size of the gravitational force increases with the mass of the objects and decreases the further they are apart. The direction of the gravitational force is between the centres of mass of the two objects.

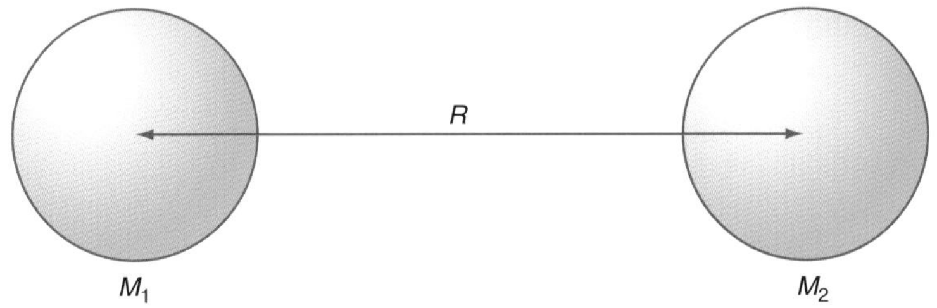

Figure 7

The gravitational force is too small to be noticed between an apple and a pear sitting on a bench. For the attractive force to be big enough to be noticed, at least one of the objects must be about the mass of a planet. That is why an apple falls to the ground. There is a strong attractive force, gravity, pulling the apple and the Earth together.

What is the size of the gravitational force on Earth? Experiments show that the Earth exerts an attractive force of about 10 N on every kilogram of mass at the surface. But as we move away from the Earth, that gravitational force decreases. At a height of about 6400 km above the surface, the force of the Earth's gravity is only about 2.4 N for every kilogram.

By the time we get as far away from the Earth as the Moon, the gravitational force towards the Earth is only about 0.003 N for every kilogram. That might appear to be a tiny force, but the Moon's mass is about 70 000 000 000 000 000 000 000 kg. So you can calculate for yourself, the size of the enormous force pulling them together. It is this gravitational force that keeps the Moon orbiting the Earth. In the same way, the gravitational force between the much more massive Sun and the planets keeps them in their orbits.

Why are the planets not slowing down? The planets are not moving through a gas. In space there are no frictional forces to oppose their motion, so they continue to move at a constant speed, like an object being whirled around in a circle at the end of a length of string.

The galaxies

The Sun is a very ordinary star with a surrounding planetary system. It is part of a system containing about 100 000 000 stars called a **galaxy**. This galaxy is called the **Milky Way**.

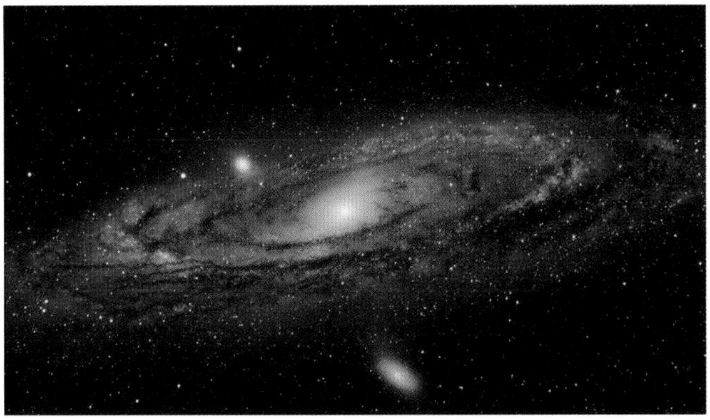

Figure 8 The Milky Way is not the only galaxy. This is another spiral galaxy called the Andromeda galaxy

The stars in the Milky Way are very far apart, usually many millions of times further apart than the planets in the Solar System. The Milky Way is a slowly-rotating, spiral-shaped galaxy and the Solar System is close to the ends of one of the arms of the spiral.

How big is the Milky Way? Best estimates are that it is enormous – from one side of the galaxy to the other is about 950 000 000 000 000 000 km.

But that is only the beginning. There are over a thousand million (a billion) galaxies in the Universe. And the galaxies themselves are very far apart. What is even more important, the galaxies appear to be getting further and further apart as time passes.

Where did the Universe come from?

There are two major scientific theories, the **Big Bang Theory** and the **Steady State Theory**. But whatever the theory, there are three important observations that must be explained: **red shift**, **Universe expansion** and the continuous **background radiation**.

Red shift and Universe expansion

Looking at the components of the light from different galaxies, they appear to have longer wavelengths than would be expected. Since red light has the longest wavelength in the visible spectrum, the effect is called red shift. The same sort of effect is obtained when a police car passes with its siren sounding. As the car approaches, the sound appears to have a higher pitch than we would expect. But as soon as the car passes, its pitch falls. A falling pitch means an increasing wavelength or a red shift. Red shift is evidence that the source is moving away from us.

It is significant that light from all the observable galaxies is red-shifted. It means that the galaxies are all moving away from the Earth. What is more, the further the galaxy is away from Earth, the greater is its red shift. This means that the most distant galaxies are moving away even faster than the nearer galaxies. The increasing separation of the galaxies is what people mean when they talk of Universe expansion.

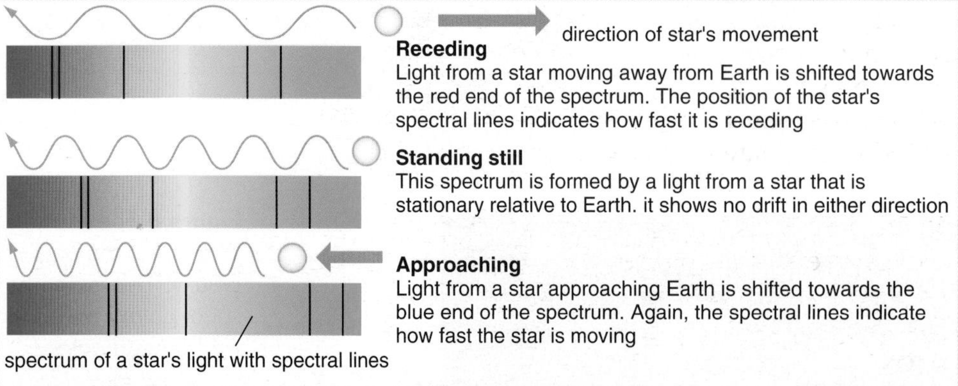

direction of star's movement
Receding
Light from a star moving away from Earth is shifted towards the red end of the spectrum. The position of the star's spectral lines indicates how fast it is receding
Standing still
This spectrum is formed by a light from a star that is stationary relative to Earth. it shows no drift in either direction
Approaching
Light from a star approaching Earth is shifted towards the blue end of the spectrum. Again, the spectral lines indicate how fast the star is moving
spectrum of a star's light with spectral lines

Figure 9

So what picture is envisaged when people talk of an expanding Universe? The best picture is that of a balloon being blown up. As the balloon inflates, points on its surface move further and further apart. Imagine that points on the balloon represent galaxies. As the balloon inflates, the 'galaxies' move away from each other.

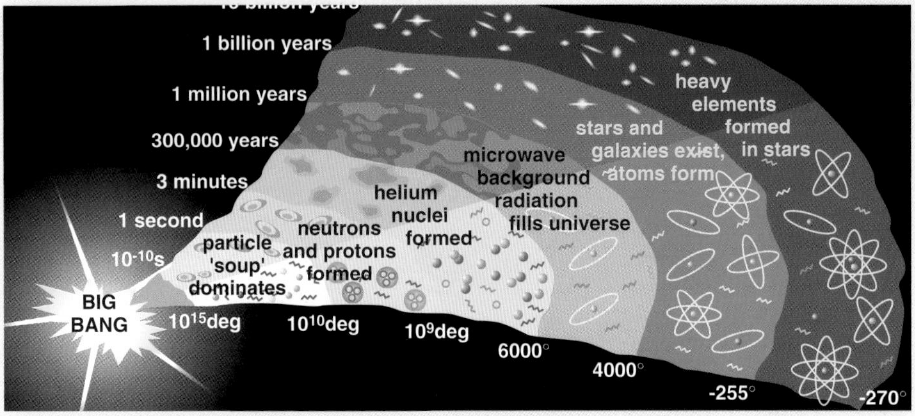

Figure 10

The background radiation

Between the galaxies there is very little matter; perhaps only a single atom every cubic centimetre. But if radio telescopes are directed at these areas of space, the atoms appear to give off microwave radiation. The wavelength of this radiation appears to be the same no matter where it occurs. What is astonishing is that such a wavelength corresponds to a temperature of about −270°C or 3 Kelvin. It is therefore called the 3 K continuous background radiation. But why is it there? To answer that question one must ask how the Universe came into being.

Steady State Theory

Most scientists today do not accept the Steady State Theory. It suggests that the Universe had no beginning and will have no end. In order to explain the expansion of the Universe, the theory suggests that matter is continually being created. Physicists are uncomfortable with this idea because it suggests that our thoughts about energy conservation might not be correct. In addition, the theory fails to explain why the Universe is expanding or why there is a 3 K continuous background radiation.

Big Bang Theory

Almost all physicists now accept the Big Bang Theory as the most likely explanation for the origin of the Universe. Since all the galaxies are currently travelling away from us at very great speed, then at some time in the distant past they must have been much closer together. Going back far enough in time, so it is argued, they must have been in the same place. This led to the idea that the Universe originated with an enormous cosmic explosion – the Big Bang.

According to most physicists, the Big Bang occurred about 15 000 million years ago. It certainly was not an explosion of the conventional type, since it was only then that matter, energy and time came into existence. What is confidently accepted is that the Big Bang came from a tiny point that physicists call a **singularity**.

Not long after the Big Bang, the Universe was made up of high-energy radiation and elementary particles like protons, neutrons and electrons. After millions of years gravity started pulling this matter together into larger clumps and galaxies started to form. This process continues today and astronomers can observe certain parts of the sky where new stars and galaxies are slowly being created.

How are new stars formed?

Stars form when clouds of hydrogen come together because of gravity. As these clouds become more and more dense, they start to spiral inwards and the temperature rises enormously. Gravity eventually compresses the hydrogen so much that the temperature reaches about 15 million °C. At this temperature, nuclear fusion reactions start and a star is born. The energy from the nuclear fusion is emitted as light and other radiation.

At the same time, other clouds of gas and dust come together, but may not have enough material for the temperature to reach 15 million °C. Such gas clouds are called **planetary nebulas** and eventually they become planets as a result of gravitational attraction. The process is called **accretion**. The presence of a massive star may cause them to become trapped in orbit. Since the gas and dust clouds originally spiralled in the same direction, so the planets would orbit the Sun in same sense.

Interestingly, all the planets except Pluto orbit the Sun in the same plane. Pluto's orbit intersects with the plane of the orbits of the other planets. This has led astronomers to believe that Pluto did not come into existence at the same time as the rest of the planets. The common view is that Pluto was a wandering planet, which drifted into the Solar System and became trapped in the gravitational field of the Sun.

So where does the 3 Kelvin background radiation come from? Today most physicists believe that it is the remnant of the Big Bang.

Nuclear fusion

Stars like the Sun are made up almost entirely of hydrogen nuclei. Being positively charged, these nuclei normally repel each other. But the temperature near the centre of the Sun is so high that the nuclei are colliding with each other at unbelievably high speeds. When they collide at such speeds they can form new, heavier nuclei such as helium-3 and helium-4. This process is called **nuclear fusion** and results in the production of vast quantities of heat and light energy.

Did you know?

The Sun is converting 4 000 000 tonnes of mass into energy every second and is expected to continue doing so for another 5 billion years or so.

The light year

On looking at the sky at night, it is important to remember just how very far away the stars are. The nearest star to Earth (after the Sun) is Alpha Proximi. But light reaching Earth from this star started its journey 4.2 years ago. Physicists say that the distance between Earth and Alpha Proximi is 4.2 light years.

What is a light year in metres? A light year is the distance travelled by a beam of light in one year. Since light travels at a speed of 300 000 000 (or 3×10^8) m/s, then:

- in 1 minute light travels $3 \times 10^8 \times 60 = 1.8 \times 10^{10}$ metres
- in 1 hour light travels $1.8 \times 10^{10} \times 60 = 1.08 \times 10^{12}$ metres
- in 1 day light travels $1.08 \times 10^{12} \times 24 = 2.592 \times 10^{13}$ metres
- in 1 year light travels $2.592 \times 10^{13} \times 365 = 9.46 \times 10^{15}$ metres.

So, a light year is 9 460 000 000 000 000 metres, and since Alpha Proximi is 4.2 light years away, the distance between Earth and the nearest star is $9.46 \times 10^{15} \times 4.2 = 3.97 \times 10^{16}$ metres or a staggering 39 700 000 000 000 000 metres.

Examples

1 The Sun is 150 000 000 km away from Earth. How long does it take the light from the Sun to reach Earth? The speed of light is 3×10^8 m/s.

150 000 000 km = 150 000 000 × 1000 metres = 1.5×10^{11} metres
Time = Distance/Speed = $1.5 \times 10^{11}/3 \times 10^8$ = 500 seconds

2 The Virgo cluster of galaxies lies 50 million light years away from us. How far is that in kilometres? The speed of light is 3×10^8 m/s.

Distance = Speed × Time
Distance = $(3 \times 10^8 \times 60 \times 60 \times 24 \times 365) \times 50\,000\,000$
⟵ one light year ⟶
Distance = 4.73×10^{23} metres = 4.73×10^{20} kilometres

The prospect of deep space exploration

In 1969 Neil Armstrong and Buzz Aldrin made history by being the first people to step on the Moon following a journey of about 400 000 km which took about four days. Although the Americans have made several manned space flights to the Moon since then, there has been no manned flights to any of the planets. The Americans have, however, announced that they hope to make a manned space flight to Mars before 2020. At the moment, the idea of humans travelling even to the outer planets like Jupiter or Saturn is only a dream. Beyond the planets remains, for now, strictly in the area of science fiction.

Figure 11 Buzz Aldrin standing on the Moon in 1969

The reasons why space exploration outside the Solar System is so difficult have to do with the huge distances involved. The nearest star is about 4×10^{16} metres away. With present technology a journey of that distance would take tens of thousands of years.

The problems facing such explorers include:

- Logistics – how to carry enough food, fuel, oxygen and water?
- Risks – those leaving would know that they would certainly die in space since the total journey time would last many generations.
- Cost – space tourism is a recent development. The Russians have placed people in Earth orbit for several hours for a price of about $14 million. What would be the cost of a flight to Alpha Proximi?

Example

Calculate how long it would take a spacecraft travelling at an average speed of 25 000 km per hour to reach a) Jupiter (about 650 million km from Earth) and b) the nearest star (about 4×10^{16} metres away from Earth).

The solution to the above problem should show that the spacecraft would take about three years to reach Jupiter and 180 000 years to reach the nearest star. The vast distances involved and the slow speed of existing spacecraft means there is no early prospect of making such journeys. For now the task is to produce spacecraft capable of much higher speeds.

Did you know?

The nuclear-powered spacecraft Cassini which was launched in 1997 is not expected to reach planet Saturn until 2004.

SETI

A person looking at the stars is looking into history. The light from the most distant stars in this galaxy may have started its journey 100 million years ago. The galaxy itself contains many billions of stars.

Until recently, it has not been possible to show that other stars had planetary systems. However, with the use of the Hubble telescope and other technologies, there is convincing evidence that at least some stars have orbiting planets. This has come about by close observation of stars whose light has been changed by the presence of an orbiting planet. Why the interest in planets? Well, life is much more likely to be present on a planet with a stable temperature and a suitable atmosphere.

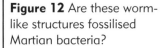

Did you know?

In 1984 a meteorite was discovered in Antarctica that scientists believe came from Mars. Inside the rock were microscopic, worm-like structures, which some believe are the fossilised remains of Martian bacteria.

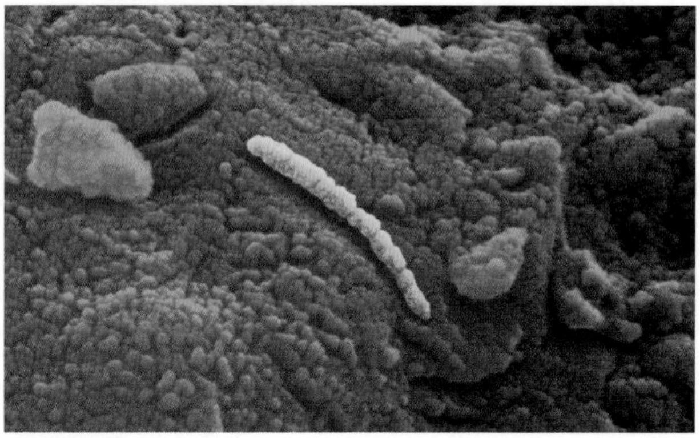

Figure 12 Are these worm-like structures fossilised Martian bacteria?

The discovery of other life forms would possibly be the most exciting discovery of all time. That is why many scientists are involved in **SETI**, the Search for Extra-Terrestrial Intelligence. Much of the work involves scanning the sky searching for meaningful radio signals. Others think it is more profitable to look at the data from planets in the Solar System. This last group has been rewarded by confirming the presence of water-ice on Mars. There is now speculation that perhaps some form of life exists beneath the surface of Mars, where it might be sufficiently warm. So far, however, there is no proof that there is any life anywhere in the Universe other than on Earth.

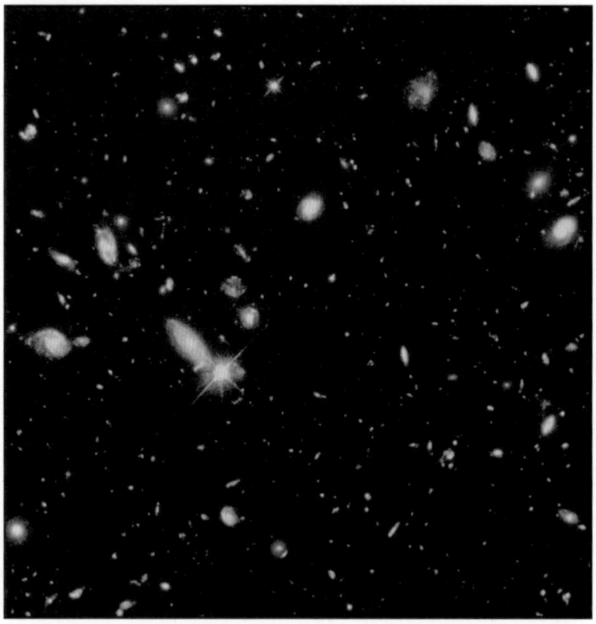

Figure 13 This photograph taken by the Hubble telescope shows stars over 100 million light years away

Questions

1 Write the following objects in order of increasing size: star, planet, asteroid, galaxy, Universe

2 a) What is red shift?
b) What does red shift tell us about neighbouring galaxies?

3 List the planets in order as you travel away from the Sun.

4 Why do people believe that the planets orbit the Sun?

5 What does the Big Bang theory have to say about the origin of the Universe?

6 Why is the Steady State theory unpopular at the moment?

7 Imagine an astronaut was in a stationary spaceship exactly half way between Jupiter and Mars. Which way would he move and why?

8 What is nuclear fusion and where does it occur in the Universe?

9 How did the planets come into existence?

10 According to current estimates, how old is the Universe?

Websites

Use your favourite search engine (such as **www.google.com** or **www.excite.com**) and search using the keywords:

Earth
Moon
Planets
Solar + System
Sun
Big + Bang
Hubble
Big + crunch
NASA

http://freespace.virginnet.co.uk/solar.system/index.html

http://www.eia.brad.ac.uk.uk/btl/

http://www.bbc.co.uk/planets/solarguide.shtml

http://www.zebu.uoregon/edu/galaxy.html

http://www.nasa.gov/

http://www.deepspace.ucsb/edu/ia/index.htm

Exam questions

1 Photographs. from the Hubble telescope show distant objects in the Universe. Some of them are spinning gas clouds.

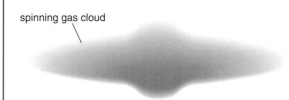

a) (i) Give another name for a gas cloud. *(1 mark)*

(ii) What does the spinning gas cloud consist of (apart from gas particles)? *(1 mark)*

(iii) What happens gradually to the material in the spinning gas cloud as time passes? *(1 mark)*

(iv) What will eventually be formed in the spinning gas cloud after millions of years? *(1 mark)*

b) (i) Name the nuclear process that powers a star. *(1 mark)*

(ii) Name one type of energy produced by this nuclear process. *(1 mark)*

c) The following diagram shows the four planets nearest the Sun.

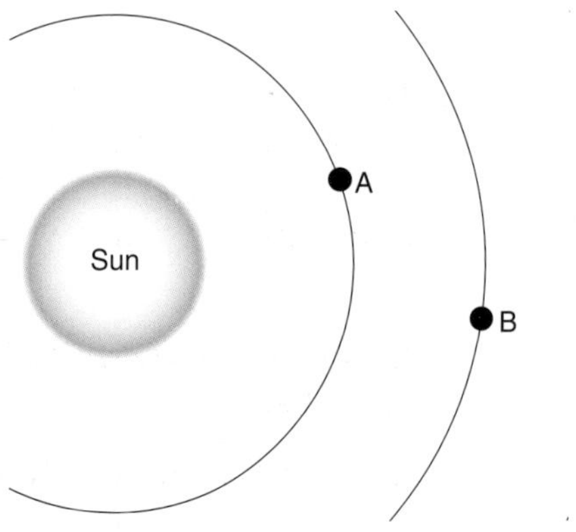

(i) The Earth is labelled. Name the other three planets. *(3 marks)*

(ii) The Earth orbits the Sun in the direction shown by the arrow on the Earth's orbit. Copy the diagram and indicate the directions of the orbits of planets B and C by drawing arrows on their orbits. *(2 marks)*

(iii) The Earth's orbital time is one Earth year. Copy and complete the following table to compare the orbital times of the planets A, B and C with the Earth's orbital time. Tick (✓) the correct boxes.

Planet	Orbital time less than 1 Earth year	Orbital time equal to 1 Earth year	Orbital time greater than 1 Earth year
A			
B			
C			

(3 marks)

2 a) The following diagram shows the Earth's orbit round the Sun.

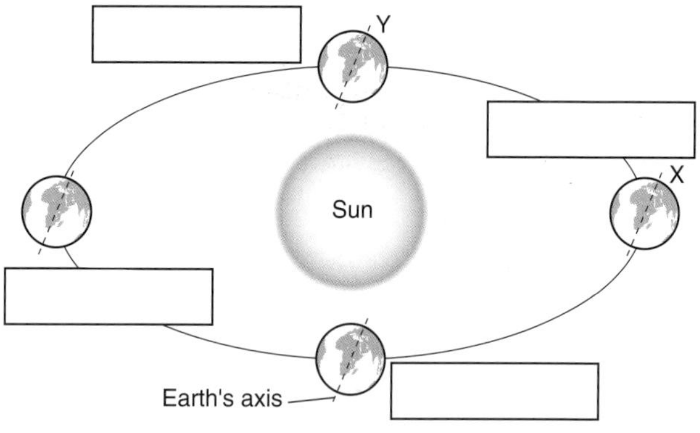

(i) Copy the diagram and name the seasons for the northern hemisphere in the boxes. *(2 marks)*

(ii) How long does it take the Earth to move from position X to position Y?

1 day 7 days 1 month 3 months 12 months

(1 mark)

b) The solar system contains nine planets. Complete the list of planets.

Name of planet	Distance from Sun in millions of kilometres
Earth	150
	778
Mercury	58
	108
	5990
Uranus	2870
Neptune	4497
Saturn	142
	228

(4 marks)

3 The Solar System forms part of a galaxy. The galaxy is part of a larger system.

a) What is the name of the larger system?

(1 mark)

b) The following diagram shows the nine planets which orbit the Sun.

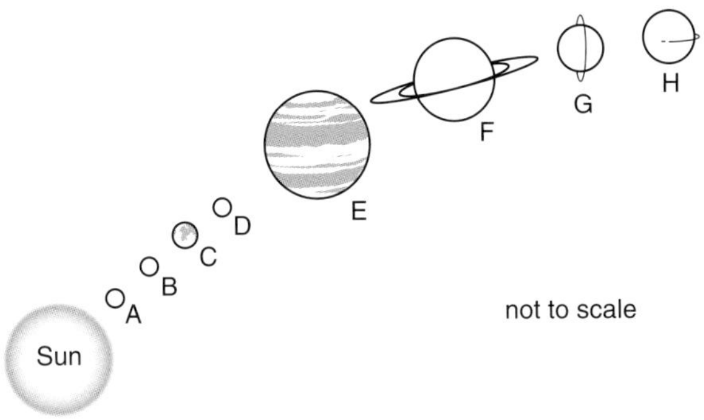

(i) Name the planet which is furthest from the Sun.

(1 mark)

Use the letters A to I to answer the following questions.

(ii) Which planet is the Earth?

(1 mark)

(iii) Which planet takes the shortest time to orbit the Sun?

(1 mark)

c) Name the four giant planets, E, F, G and H.

(2 marks)

d) The following diagram shows two planets orbiting the Sun.

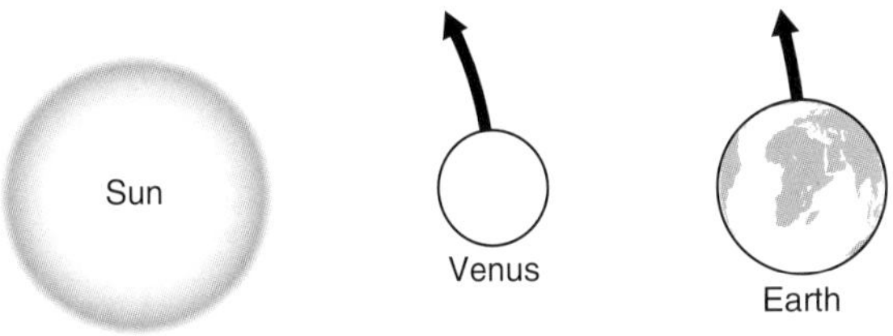

The masses of Venus and Earth are roughly equal.

(i) On which planet does the Sun exert the greatest gravitational force? *(1 mark)*

(ii) State the reason for your choice.

(1 mark)

(iii) Copy the diagram above and draw the path of planet Venus if the gravitational force exerted by the Sun suddenly disappears.

(1 mark)

e) The Sun emits radiation. What nuclear process takes place in the Sun to enable it to emit radiation? *(1 mark)*

f) Man has visited the Moon on several occasions. Explain fully why he has not visited Mars which is much further away.

(2 marks)

g) There are two scientific theories describing the formation of the Universe. One is the Big Bang Theory. Name the other theory.

(1 mark)

h) How does the Big Bang Theory describe:

(ii) the beginning of the Universe?

(2 marks)

(ii) the Universe at present?

(1 mark)

4 The diagrams below show the paths the Sun takes aross the sky on two days in the northern hemisphere. The days are approximately six months apart.

a) (i) Which diagram shows the path of the Sun in winter.

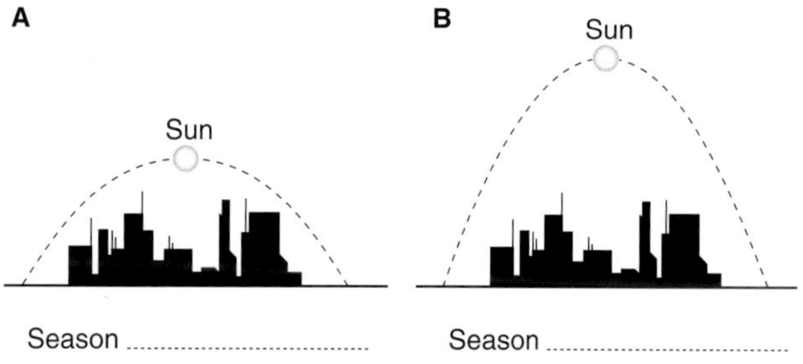

(1 mark)

(ii) The diagram below shows the Earth at two points on its orbit around the Sun. Each one corresponds to one of the days mentioned above. Copy the diagram and on each of the circles that represent the Earth, mark the axis of the Earth's rotation and below each state the season, for the northern hemisphere, that it shows.

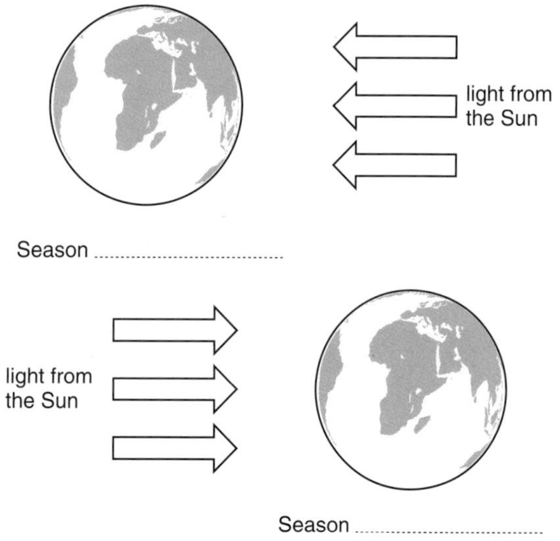

(2 marks)

b) The diagram below shows the model of the Solar System used over 2000 years ago by the Ancient Greeks. Their model had five planets, the Moon and the Sun all orbiting the Earth.

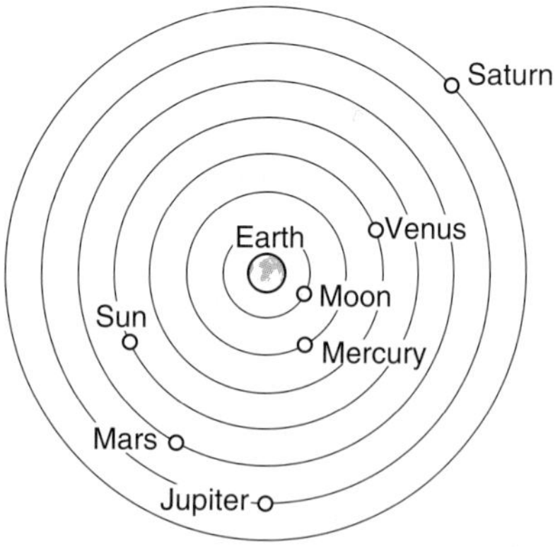

(i) State two differences between our present model of the Solar System and the model used by the Ancient Greeks.

(2 marks)

(ii) The nebular or gas cloud model is often used to describe how our Solar System was formed. Describe the main stages that took place during the formation of the Solar System according to this model.

(2 marks)

c) The diagram below shows the path of a comet as it approaches the Sun.

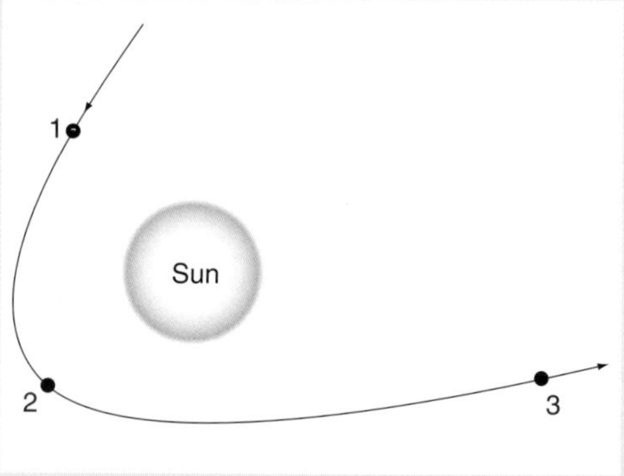

(i) Copy the diagram and draw an arrow to show the direction of the force acting on the comet at positions 1, 2 and 3.

(3 marks)

(ii) What causes this force?

(1 mark)

(iii) What can you say about the size of this force at position 1 compared to position 2? Explain your answer.

(2 marks)

(iv) As it moves along the path shown, the comet has gravitational potential energy. What other type of energy does it possess?

(1 mark)

(v) What happens to the gravitational potential energy of the comet as it moves from position 1 to position 2.

increases stays the same decreases

(1 mark)

(vi) At position 2 the comet is moving faster than at position 1. Explain in terms of energy why this is so.

(2 marks)

d) The light from the stars in galaxies other than our own is observed to be red shifted.

(i) What is meant by red shift?

(1 mark)

(ii) What does red shift tell us about the motion of these galaxies?

(2 marks)

Index

A

B

C

D

E

F

G

H

I

J

K

L

M

N

O

P

Q

R